THE OFFICIAL RED BOOK OF UNITED STATES
COINS

—————————— *1979* ——————————

A GUIDE BOOK
of
UNITED STATES COINS

By R. S. YEOMAN

32nd Revised Edition

Fully Illustrated
Catalog and Valuation List — 1616 to Date

Edited by Kenneth Bressett

A BRIEF HISTORY OF AMERICAN COINAGE
EARLY AMERICAN COINS AND TOKENS
EARLY MINT ISSUES • REGULAR MINT ISSUES
PRIVATE, STATE AND TERRITORIAL GOLD
SILVER AND GOLD COMMEMORATIVE ISSUES
PROOFS

Whitman Coin Products

Copyright © MCMLXXVIII by
WESTERN PUBLISHING COMPANY, INC.
RACINE, WISCONSIN 53404

Library of Congress Catalog Card No.: 76-9533

THE SPANISH MILLED DOLLAR
The Coin of Our Nation's Founders

The Spanish milled dollar valued at 8 *reales,* otherwise known as the "pillar dollar" or "piece of eight," has been given a place in romantic fiction unequaled by any other coin.

This time-honored piece and its fractional parts of ½ and 1 *real,* 2 and 4 *reales* were the principal coins of the American colonists, and were the forerunners of our own silver dollar and its fractional divisions.

The coin shown above bears the m̊ mint mark for Mexico City. Similar pieces with other mint marks were struck in Bolivia, Chile, Colombia, Guatemala and Peru. For details see listings in Whitman's *Coins of the World 1750-1850* by W. D. Craig and *Silver Dollars of North and South America* by Wayte Raymond. Average value for an 8 *reales* of common date and mint is about $80 in Very Fine condition. Dates range from 1732 to 1772.

Note: Many modern copies of the 8 *reales* exist. These are produced mostly as souvenirs and have little or no value.

THE PURPOSE OF THIS BOOK

Coin values listed in the Guide Book are averaged from data supplied by contributors several months before publication. The coin market is so active in some categories that values can easily change during this period. Prices are shown as a guide and are not intended to serve as a price-list for any dealer's stock.

Prices rise because: 1. The trend of our economy is inflationary. 2. The number of collectors is increasing rapidly, while coin supplies remain stationary. 3. Dealers can procure their stock of coins only from collectors or other dealers, who expect a profit over and above what they originally paid.

Prices decline because: 1. Speculators buy and sell in large quantities, drawing in thousands of unwary persons looking for quick profits. When the average collector stops buying, the prices drop. 2. Hoards of coins suddenly are released from estates of deceased collectors or Federal Reserve vaults (as in the case of silver dollars) and the like. Such conditions usually adjust themselves within months or a few years.

Those who edit, contribute to, and publish this book advocate the collecting of coins for pleasure and educational benefits. A secondary consideration is that of investment, the profits from which are realized over the long term based on intelligent purchases of the best grades of coins.

The *Handbook of United States Coins* by R. S. Yeoman, containing average prices dealers will pay for these coins, is obtainable at most hobby dealers. A companion book, *Buying and Selling U.S. Coins* by Ken Bressett (paperback edition), gives a capsule comparison of Guide Book and Handbook prices for coins in average grades.

Neither the publisher nor the editor of this book deals in coins; therefore, the values shown here are not offers to sell but are included only as general information.

CONTRIBUTORS TO THE THIRTY-SECOND EDITION

KENNETH E. BRESSETT, *Coordinating Editor*

Neil Shafer and Dick Thompsen, *Editorial Assistants*

Kamal M. Ahwash
Michael Aron
Robert F. Batchelder
Aubrey E. Bebee
Philip E. Benedetti, Sr.
George H. Blenker
Q. David Bowers
Walter Breen
Hy Brown
Mike G. Brownlee
Alan R. Cohen
Jerry Cohen
Ben M. Douglas
Ben Dreiske
Kurt Eckstein
Dennis Forgue
Harry J. Forman
Chuck Furjanic
Dorothy Gershenson
Ira Goldberg
Lawrence S. Goldberg
Kenneth M. Goldman
David Hall
James Halperin
Gene L. Henry

C. Edward Hipps
Jesse Iskowitz
Curtis Iversen
Steve Ivy
Robert H. Jacobs
Floyd O. Janney
Robert R. Johnson
A. M. Kagin
Donald Kagin
Paul Kagin
David W. Karp
Stanley Kesselman
Paul Koppenhaver
Mike Kliman
Abe Kosoff
Abner Kreisberg
Kenneth W. Lee
Julian Leidman
Ed Leventhal
John B. Love
Tom McAfee
Fred Malone
Raymond N. Merena
Lester Merkin
Bill Mertes

Roy A. Miller
Paul Nugget
Sylvia Novack
Jerome Nusbaum
V. H. Oswald
Walter R. Perschke
Joe Person
Richard Picker
Elmer B. Ray
Joel D. Rettew
Earl C. Schill
Robert R. Shaw
Norman Shultz
Mulford B. Simons, Jr.
Arthur J. Smith
Sam Smith
Benjamin Stack
Harvey G. Stack
Norman Stack
Leonard W. Stark
Maurice A. Storck, Sr.
Herbert Tobias
Russell P. Vaughn
R. E. Wallace
Gary L. Young

Special credit is due to the following for service and data in this book:

Herbert Bergen, Harry X Boosel, Q. David Bowers, Dan Brown, Malcolm O. E. Chell-Frost, Ted F. Clark, Mike Danish, Tom DeLorey, George Fuld, James A. Haxby, Robert W. Julian, Jerry Kimmell, Warren A. Lapp, Denis Loring, Raymond D. Munde, Eric P. Newman, Hubert L. Polzer, James F. Ruddy, Max M. Schwartz, Arlie Slabaugh, Sidney Smith, Philip Starr, Anthony Terranova, Jack H. Tod, Dolores Toll, Jenny Tomaszek, Stewart P. Witham, John Wright, and Leo A. Young.

Those now deceased, but whose contributions have been a part of this book since early editions, include:

David M. Bullowa, William L. Clark, Carl Curcio, Charles E. Green, Richard D. Kenney, Steve Kosoff, Franklyn H. Miller, Stuart Mosher, Ken Nichols, Al C. Overton, Earl Parker, Lewis M. Reagan, F. K. Saab, and Farran Zerbe.

CONDITION OF COINS
Essential elements of the A.N.A. grading system

PROOF — A specially made coin distinguished by sharpness of detail and usually with a brilliant mirrorlike surface. Proof refers to the method of manufacture and is not a condition, but normally the term implies perfect mint state unless otherwise noted. See pages 59 and 60 for details.

MINT STATE — The terms Mint State (MS) and Uncirculated (Unc.) are interchangeably used to describe coins showing no trace of wear. Such coins may vary to some degree because of blemishes, toning or slight imperfections as described in the following three subdivisions.

PERFECT UNCIRCULATED (MS-70) — Perfect new condition, showing no trace of wear. The finest quality possible, with no evidence of scratches, handling or contact with other coins. Very few regular issue coins are ever found in this condition.

CHOICE UNCIRCULATED (MS-65) — An above average Uncirculated coin which may be brilliant or lightly toned and has very few contact marks on the surface or rim.

UNCIRCULATED (MS-60) — Has no trace of wear but may show a moderate number of contact marks, and surface may be spotted or lack some luster.

CHOICE ABOUT UNCIRCULATED (AU-55) — Barest evidence of light wear on only the highest points of the design. Most of the mint luster remains.

ABOUT UNCIRCULATED (AU-50) — Has traces of light wear on many of the high points. At least half of the mint luster is still present.

CHOICE EXTREMELY FINE (EF-45) — Light overall wear shows on highest points. All design details are very sharp. Some of the mint luster is evident.

EXTREMELY FINE (EF-40) — Design is lightly worn throughout, but all features are sharp and well defined. Traces of mint luster show.

CHOICE VERY FINE (VF-30) — Light even wear on the surface and highest parts of the design. All lettering and major features are sharp.

VERY FINE (VF-20) — Shows moderate wear on high points of design. All major details are clear.

FINE (F-12) — Moderate to considerable even wear. Entire design is bold with overall pleasing appearance.

VERY GOOD (VF-8) — Well worn with main features clear and bold although rather flat.

GOOD (G-4) — Heavily worn with design visible but faint in areas. Many details are flat.

ABOUT GOOD (AG-3) — Very heavily worn with portions of lettering, date and legends worn smooth. The date may be barely readable.

IMPORTANT: Damaged coins, such as those which are bent, corroded, scratched, holed, nicked, stained, oxidized, or mutilated, are worth less than those without defects. *Flawless uncirculated coins are generally worth more than values quoted in this book.* Slightly worn coins which have been cleaned and conditioned to simulate uncirculated luster are worth considerably less than perfect pieces.

Manufacturing defects do not lessen value as much as other damage. Examples are: Colonial coins with planchet flaws and weakly struck designs; early silver and gold with weight adjustment "file marks" (parallel cuts made prior to striking); and proofs with "lint marks" (dust particles which mar the surface during striking).

Brief guides to grading are placed before each major coin type in this book. For those readers who desire more detailed descriptions of all coin grades, we recommend OFFICIAL A.N.A. GRADING STANDARDS FOR UNITED STATES COINS, by the American Numismatic Association.

AN INTRODUCTION TO UNITED STATES COINS

Money of the Early Americans

The story of American money, which occupies a period of over three centuries, began when the early settlers in New England carried on their fur trade with the Indians through the use of wampum, which had been fashioned from mussel shells in the form of "beads." Beaver skins, wampum, and in Virginia, tobacco, soon became the common accepted media of exchange for all other available commodities. The immigrants, in fact, had little use for coined money at first, but when traders arrived from foreign lands, coins were usually demanded in payment for goods. Any foreign coins were usually accepted, such as French louis, English guineas, German thalers, Dutch ducats, and various Spanish coins, including doubloons and particularly the Spanish milled dollar, or piece of eight. The coin last mentioned remained as a standard money unit throughout the entire colonial period. Even after the Revolutionary War, the Spanish dollar and its fractional parts continued to circulate in this country with official sanction until 1857. One *real* equaled 12½ cents and was known as a "bit." A quarter of the dollar thus became known as "two bits," a term still in common use.

England consistently ignored the plight of the colonists and made no effort to provide gold or silver coins, or a small-change currency for them. Although coins known as "Hogge Money" were provided for the Sommer Islands, now known as the Bermudas, about the year 1616, the first coins minted in America were minted by John Hull in the Massachusetts Bay Colony. The General Court of the colony granted him authority to begin coinage. Starting in 1652 the Boston mint provided the famous N.E., pine tree, and similar shillings, with their fractional parts, for the hardpressed colonists. Other colonies tried similar projects but failed.

As time went on coins and tokens of many types were introduced and employed by the colonists in their daily course of business. Lord Baltimore in Maryland was responsible for a series of silver pieces, which were probably struck in England in 1659. Mark Newby introduced a piece known as St. Patrick's Halfpence into the province of New Jersey in 1682. Coins dated 1722 to 1724, known as Rosa Americana and Hibernia coppers, were produced by William Wood in England and were widely circulated in America. The Carolina and New England Elephant tokens were current in the years following 1694. There were also a few issues of uncertain date and origin, such as the New Yorke Token, which circulated among the Dutch settlers and was probably sent over from Holland.

Enterprising American individuals were responsible for some of the copper pieces that circulated during the eighteenth century. The Gloucester Token, about which little is known, was one of these. John Higley of Granby, Connecticut, made an interesting series of threepence pieces during the period from 1737 to 1739. J. Chalmers, a goldsmith in Annapolis, Maryland, issued silver shillings, sixpence, and threepence pieces in 1783. In 1787 Ephraim Brasher, a New York goldsmith, struck a gold piece of the value of a doubloon (about $16.00). Standish Barry of Baltimore, Maryland, made a curious silver token threepence in 1790.

Still other tokens, struck in England, reached our shores in Revolutionary times and were for the most part speculative ventures. These much-needed, small-denomination coppers were readily circulated because of the great scarcity of fractional coins. Included in this category were the Nova Constellatio coppers and the Bar cent.

During the period of confederation following the War of Independence, still more English tokens were added to the great variety of coins and tokens employed in the new nation. In 1787 the Nova Eboracs, known as New York Coppers, the Georgius Triumpho, the Auctori Plebis, and later the Kentucky, Myddelton and Franklin Press tokens were introduced.

Another interesting series, important because of its close association with our first president, comprises those tokens bearing the portrait of Washington. Although most of these pieces are dated from 1783 to 1795, many of them were made in England around the turn of the century.

Coinage of the States

The Articles of Confederation, adopted March 1, 1781, provided that Congress should have the sole right to regulate the alloy and value of coin struck by its own authority or by that of the respective states.

Each state, therefore, had the right to coin money, but Congress served as a regulating authority. New Hampshire was the first state to consider coinage, but few if any coins were placed in circulation. The only specimens known bear the date 1776.

Vermont, Connecticut, and New Jersey granted coining privileges to companies or individuals. Massachusetts erected its own mint in which copper coins were produced. A number of interesting varieties of these state issues, most of which were struck in fairly large quantities, can still be easily acquired, and form the basis for many present day collections of early American coins.

The Beginnings of United States Coinage

Throughout the Colonial years, Americans had become accustomed to the use of the Spanish dollar and its fractional parts, the *real,* the medio (half-*real*), etc. It was only natural, therefore, that when a national coinage was under consideration the dollar was mentioned most frequently. In earlier years currency statutes in many of the colonies had given first consideration to the Spanish dollar. Connecticut, Massachusetts, and Virginia, particularly, passed laws making Spanish coins a legal tender. The first issue of Continental paper money May 10, 1775, offers further evidence that the dollar was to be our basic money unit, for it provided that the notes should be payable in "Spanish Milled dollars or the value thereof in gold or silver."

The Assistant Financier of the Confederation, Gouverneur Morris, proposed a decimal coinage ratio, and his plan was incorporated in a report presented by Robert Morris, Superintendent of Finance, to the Congress, January 15, 1782. Plans for a mint were advanced, and a uniform national currency to relieve the confused money conditions was outlined. Morris's unit, 1/1440 of a dollar, was calculated to agree without a fraction with all the different valuations of the Spanish milled dollar in the various States. Although a government mint was approved February 21, 1782, no immediate action was taken. During 1784 Thomas Jefferson, then a member of the House of Representatives, brought in a report concerning the plan, and expressed disagreement with Morris' complicated money unit. He advocated the simple dollar unit because he believed the dollar was already as familiar and convenient a unit of value as the British pound. He favored the decimal system and remarked that, "The most easy ratio of multiplication and division is that of ten. George Washington referred to it as 'a measure, which in my opinion, has become indispensibly necessary.' "

The Grand Committee in May 1785 recommended a gold five-dollar piece; a dollar of silver with fractional coins, of the same metal, in denominations of half, quarter, tenth, and twentieth parts of a dollar; and copper pieces valued at one-hundredth and one two-hundredth of a dollar.

In 1783 Robert Morris submitted a series of pattern pieces in silver which were designed by Dudley to carry out the decimal idea for United States money. These are known as the Nova Constellatio Patterns and consist of the "Mark" or 1,000 units, the "Quint" or 500 units, and the "Bit" or 100 units. The unit was to be a quarter grain of silver. This was not the first attempt at a dollar coin, for the Continental currency piece of dollar size, dated 1776, had been struck in such metals as brass, pewter, and silver. The variety in silver probably saw limited service as a dollar.

Congress gave formal approval to the basic dollar unit and decimal coinage ratio in its resolution of July 6, 1785, but other more pressing matters delayed further action. Not until the Constitutional Convention had placed the country on firm ground and the new nation had elected George Washington President, did the Congress again turn attention to the subject of currency, a mint, and a coinage system.

The Massachusetts cents and half-cents struck in 1787 and 1788 were the first official coins to bear a stated value in terms of decimal parts of the dollar unit in this country. The cent represented a hundredth part of a Spanish dollar.

The first federally authorized coin was the Fugio Cent, sometimes called the Franklin Cent, as he was supposed to have supplied the design and composed the legends. This piece, similar in design to the Continent Currency dollar of 1776, was privately struck in 1787 by contract with the Government.

Alexander Hamilton, then Secretary of the Treasury, reported his views on monetary matters January 21, 1791. He concurred in all essentials with the decimal subdivisions and multiples of the dollar contained in the earlier resolutions and urged the use of both gold and silver in our standard money.

Congress passes a resolution March 3, 1791, that a mint be established, and authorized the President to engage artists and procure machinery for the making of coins. No immediate steps were taken, but when Washington delivered his third annual address, he recommended immediate establishment of a mint.

On April 2, 1792, a bill was finally passed providing "that the money of account of the United States should be expressed in dollars or units, dismes or tenths, cents or hundredths, and milles or thousandths; a disme being the tenth part of a dollar, a cent the hundredth part of a dollar, a mille the thousandth part of a dollar . . . "

Denominations specified in the act were as follows:

	Value of	Grains Pure	Grains Standard
Gold Eagle	$10.00	247 - 4/8	270
Gold Half Eagle	5.00	123 - 6/8	135
Gold Quarter Eagle	2.50	61 - 7/8	67 - 4/8
Silver Dollar	1.00	371 - 4/16	416
Silver Half-Dollar.............	.50	185 - 10/16	208
Silver Quarter-Dollar..........	.25	92 - 13/16	104
Silver Disme (dime)...........	.10	37 - 2/16	41 - 3/5
Silver Half-Disme.............	.05	18 - 9/16	20 - 4/5
Copper Cent..................	.01	11 pennyweights	
Copper Half-Cent	.005	5½ pennyweights	

The word "pure" meant unalloyed metal; "standard" meant, in the case of gold, 11/12 fine or 11 parts pure metal to one part alloy, which was mixed with the pure metal to improve the wearing qualities of the coins. The fineness for silver coins was 1485/1664 or approximately 892.43 thousandths, in contrast with the gold coins of 22 karats, or 916 2/3 thousandths fine.

The law also provided for free coinage of gold and silver coins at the fixed ratio of 15 to one, and a token coinage of copper cents and half-cents. Under the free coinage provision no charge was to be made for converting gold or silver bullion into coins "weight for weight." At the depositor's option, however, he could demand an immediate exchange of coins for his bullion, for which privilege a deduction of one-half of one per cent was to be imposed.

Washington appointed David Rittenhouse, a well-known philosopher and scientist, as the first Director of the Mint. A mint building was started nearly four months after the passage of the Act of April 2, 1792. It was located on Seventh Street near Arch in Philadelphia.

The first coin struck at the new mint was the half-disme. Fifteen hundred of these pieces were produced during the month of July 1792 before the mint was completed. Washington supplied some of his own silverware to the value of about one hundred dollars for those first mint coins. Dismes also were probably struck at this time or a short while later. The portrait on these pieces is presumed to have been modeled by Martha Washington.

Copper for cents and half-cents was covered in the Act of May 8, 1792 when the purchase of not over 150 tons was authorized. On September 11, 1792, six pounds of old copper were purchased, this being the first purchase of copper for coinage, which was probably used for the striking of patterns.

Planchets with upset rims for cents and half-cents were purchased from Boulton of Birmingham, England from 1798 to 1838.

Several pattern coins were prepared in 1792 before regular mint operations commenced. These included the silver center cent by Voigt, a smaller piece than that of regular issue. The small plug of silver, worth about three-quarters of a cent, was evidently intended to bring the intrinsic value of the coin up to the value of one cent and permit production of a coin of more convenient size. Alexander Hamilton had mentioned a year before that the proposed "intrinsic value" cent would be too large, and suggested that the amount of copper could be reduced and a trace of silver added. The pattern cent with a silver center may have been designed to conform to this recommendation.

The cents by Robert Birch are equally interesting. These patterns are identified by their legends which read "LIBERTY PARENT OF SCIENCE AND INDUS-TRY" and "TO BE ESTEEMED BE USEFUL." The quarter with an eagle on the reverse side belongs among the early patterns devised before regular issues were struck.

The first depositor of silver was the bank of Maryland, which sent $80,715.73½ in French coins to the mint July 18, 1794. Moses Brown, a Boston merchant, deposited the first gold in the form of ingots, February 12, 1795, amounting to $2,276.22, receiving silver coin in payment. The first coins transferred to the Treasurer consisted of 11,178 cents on March 1, 1793. The first return of coined silver was made on October 15, 1794, and the first gold coins were delivered July 31, 1795, 744 half-eagles.

File marks on early U. S. coins are a mint process of weight adjustment.

Regular Mint Issues

Cents and half-cents exclusively were coined during the year 1793, and by 1799 approximately $50,000 in these coins had been placed in circulation. This amount proved insufficient for the requirements of commerce, and small denomination coins of the states and of foreign countries continued in use during the first few years of the nineteenth century.

One of the most serious problems confronting the commercial interests during the early years was the failure of the government to provide a sufficient volume of circulating coins. The fault, contrary to popular opinion at the time, did not lie with any lack of effort on the part of the mint. Other circumstances tended to interfere with the expected steady flow of new coinage into the channels of trade.

Free circulation of United States gold and silver coins was greatly hindered by speculators. For example, worn Spanish dollars of reduced weight and value were easily exchanged for U. S. silver dollars, which meant the export of most of the new dollars as fast as they were minted, and a complete loss to American trade channels.

Gold coins failed to circulate for similar reasons. The ratio of 15 to 1 between gold and silver was close to the world ratio when Hamilton recommended it, but by 1799 the ratio in European commercial centers had reached 15¾ to 1. At this rate the undervalued gold coins tended to flow out of the country, or were reduced for bullion. After 1800, therefore, United States gold coins were rarely seen in general circulation. As no remedy could be found, coinage of the

Eagle and the silver dollar was suspended by President Jefferson in 1804 and 1806 respectively. It is generally conceded that the silver dollar was discontinued in 1804, although the last coins minted for the period were dated 1803.

Lacking gold coins and silver dollars, the half-dollar became the desirable coin for large transactions, bank reserves, and foreign payments. Until 1830, in fact, half-dollars circulated very little as they were mainly transferred from bank to bank. This will account for the relatively good supply of half-dollars of this period which are still available to collectors in better than average condition. A senate committee of 1830 reported that United States silver coins were considered so much bullion and were accordingly "lost to the community as coins."

There was only a negligible coinage of quarters, dimes, and half-dimes from 1794 to 1834. It has been estimated that there was less than one piece for each person in the country in the year 1830. This period has been described as one of nondescript currency made up of banknotes, underweight foreign gold coins, foreign silver coins of many varieties, and domestic fractional silver coins. Notes of "wildcat banks" flooded the country before 1830 and were much more common than silver ones.

On June 28, 1834, a new law was passed reducing the weight of standard gold, which had the effect of placing our money on a gold standard. Trade and finance were greatly benefited by this act, which also proved a boon to the gold mines of Georgia and North Carolina. Branch mints in Dahlonega, Georgia, and Charlotte, North Carolina, were established two or three years later to handle the newly-mined gold at the source. The Templeton Reid and Bechtler issues of private gold coins were struck in this area.

The law of January 18, 1837, completely revised and standardized the mint and coinage laws. Legal standards, mint charges, legal tender, mint procedure, tolerance in coin weights, accounting methods, a bullion fund, standardization of gold and silver coins to 900 thousandths fine, and other desirable regulations were covered by the new legislation. Results of importance to the collector were the changes in type for the various coin denominations and the resumption of coinage of the Eagle and silver dollar shortly thereafter.

The political and financial elements underwent a crisis at about this time. The familiar "Jackson Tokens" and fractional notes of banks and commercial establishments completely eclipsed the circulation of metallic currency. This was the era of "shinplasters."

The California gold discovery in 1848 was responsible for an interesting series of private, state, and territorial gold issues in the Western states, culminating in the establishment of a branch mint at San Francisco in 1854.

Two new regular gold issues were adopted in 1849. In that year the double Eagle and gold dollar joined our American family of coins. The California gold fields greatly influenced the world gold market, making the exportation of silver profitable. For example, the silver in two half-dollars was worth $1.03½ in gold. The newly introduced gold dollars soon took over the burden and hastened the disappearance of silver coins from trade channels. This was the situation when the new three-cent postage rate brought about the bill authorizing the coinage of the silver three-cent piece in 1851. This was our country's first subsidiary coin, for its value was intrinsically 86% of its face value, an expedient designed to prevent its withdrawal from circulation.

The three-dollar gold piece was authorized by the act of February 21, 1853. Never a popular or necessary coin, it nevertheless was issued regularly until 1889.

On February 21, 1853, fractional silver coins were made subsidiary resulting from the fact that the weight of all silver pieces, excepting the dollar, was reduced. As the coins were now worth less than their face value free coinage of silver was prohibited, and the mint was authorized to purchase its silver requirements on its own account using the bullion fund of the mint, and, according to law, "the profit of said coinage shall be, . . . transferred to the account of the treasury of the United States."

Arrows were placed at the date on all silver coins except three-cent pieces and dollars, and on the quarters and half-dollars rays were added on the reverse side to denote the change of weight. In 1854 the rays were removed, and in 1856 the arrows disappeared. Production of silver coins in large quantities during this period greatly relieved the demands on gold dollars and three-cent pieces. Consequently for the first time in our nation's history there was a sufficient supply of fractional coins in general circulation.

The law of 1857 was designed primarily to reform the copper coinage. No matter how interesting and valuable the large cents and half-cents may have become in the eyes of the modern collector, they were very unpopular with the people and cost the mint too much to produce.

The new law abolished the half-cent piece, and reduced the size and changed the design of the cent. The new Flying Eagle cent contained 88% copper and 12% nickel. Several hundred experimental cents were stamped from dies bearing the date 1856 although no authority for the issue existed before 1857. Other important effects of the law were the retirement of the Spanish silver coins from circulation, and dispersal of the new cents in such excessive quantities as to create a nuisance to business houses, particularly in the eastern cities. The Indian head device replaced the Eagle in 1859, and in 1864 the weight of the cent was further reduced and its composition changed to a proportion of 95% copper and 5% tin and zinc. This bronze composition was the standard for our cent except for the years 1943, and 1944 to 1946. In 1962 the alloy was changed to 95% copper and 5% zinc.

Both Jefferson and Hamilton had contended in their day that the currency of money of small value benefits society. The history of our cent and its daily use proves the soundness of this principle.

Abundance turned to scarcity following the outbreak of the Civil War. Anticipation of a scarcity and depreciation of the paper money was sufficient to induce hoarding. The large volume of greenbacks in circulation caused a premium on gold, and subsidiary silver as a result of the sudden depreciation quickly vanished in the North. Resort was soon made to postage stamps for small change. All types of fractional notes were put out at this time by municipalities and the Government. "Postage currency" became widely used, and in 1863 a great variety of tokens appeared to help fill the vacuum. Like the tokens of 1837 they were of two general classes, tradesmen's coins and imitations of legal cents. The latter were usually produced at a profit, many of which were political or patriotic in character, with slogans typical of the times.

The Law of 1864, which effected changes in the cent, provided also for the new bronze two-cent piece. The act, moreover, provided legal tender status for these two coins up to ten times their value. The two-cent piece was the first coin to bear the motto IN GOD WE TRUST. The new coin was readily accepted by the people but proved an unnecessary denomination, going out of fashion and being discontinued only nine years later.

Secretary Chase had issued a great many currency notes of three-cent denomination early in 1865. The nickel interests seized upon this circumstance to fight for a new three-cent coin for redemption of the paper money. A law was quickly passed and signed by the president as of March 3, 1865, providing for a three-cent coin of 75-25 copper-nickel composition. Our country now possessed two types of three-cent pieces. The nickel three-cent piece was struck continuously until 1889; the three-cent silver until 1873.

The new copper-nickel alloy ratio was selected for the five-cent coin, adopted May 16, 1866, to be thereafter known as a "nickel." Again the people had a coin value available in two forms. The silver half-dime, like the three-cent piece, was retired from service in 1873.

The Carson City Mint was established in 1870 as a convenient depository for the miners in that area and operated until 1893.

The Law of March 3, 1871, was a redemption measure and was passed to provide a means for the disposal to the United States Treasury of millions of minor coins which had accumulated in the hands of postmasters, newsdealers, and others. Small-denomination coins as a result of this new law were placed on an equal footing and could be redeemed when presented in lots of twenty dollars.

There was a general revision of the coinage laws in 1873. Several years of study and debate preceded the final enactment. The legislative history of the bill occupies hundreds of pages of the Congressional Globe, and the result was considered by many a clumsy attempt and a failure. The law has sometimes been referred to as the "Crime of '73." One consequence of the bill, which achieved final enactment February 12, 1873, was the elimination of the silver dollar. In its stead the Trade dollar of greater weight was provided for use in commerce with the Orient in competition with the Mexican dollar. The legal tender provision, which unintentionally gave the trade dollar currency within our borders, was repealed the following year.

The charge for converting standard gold bullion into coin was reduced by the act to one-fifth of one per cent. The same rate was imposed on silver bullion for coining trade dollars only.

It may be a surprise to some collectors to learn that the silver dollar had not circulated to any great extent in the United States after 1803. The coin had been turned out steadily since 1840, but for various reasons such as exportation, melting, and holding in bank vaults, the dollar was virtually an unknown coin. The Law of 1873 in effect demonetized silver and committed our country to a gold standard. The silver mining interests came to realize what had occurred a little later, and the ensuing quarter century of political and monetary history was filled with their voluble protests. There was a constant bitter struggle for the return to bimetallism.

From an economic point of view the inadequate supply of gold was responsible for a gradual decline in prices throughout the world. This brought about a gradual business depression in our country, particularly in the South and Middle-West. Private silver interests influenced great sections of the West for bimetallism as a remedy for the failing price level. Authorities have concluded that a world-wide adoption of bimetallism would have improved economic conditions, but the United States alone proceeding to place its money on a double standard at the old 16 to 1 ratio would have led only to a worse situation.

Of particular importance to collectors, however, were those features of the Law of 1873 which affected the status and physical properties of the individual coins. The weight of the half-dollar, quarter, and dime, was slightly changed and arrows were placed at the date for the ensuing two years to indicate the difference in weight. Silver three-cent pieces, half-dimes, and two-cent pieces were abolished by the act, and the manufacture of minor coins was restricted to the Mint at Philadelphia.

The short-lived twenty-cent piece was authorized March 3, 1875. It was created for the Western states where the Spanish "bit" had become equivalent to a U. S. dime. The five-cent piece did not circulate there, so when a quarter was offered for a "bit" purchase, only a dime change was returned. However, it was confused with the quarter-dollar and was discontinued after 1878.

The Bland-Allison Act of February 28, 1878, gave the Secretary authority to purchase two to four million dollars worth of silver bullion each month to be coined into silver dollars. The coin, never popular, was produced in minimum quantities. This was not a bimetallic law, nor was it a free coinage act. Strictly speaking it was a subsidiary coinage law, called by some "a wretched compromise."

The North and East so disliked the silver dollars that they did not actively circulate there and eventually found their way back to the Treasury, mostly through tax payments. Secretary Manning transferred ownership to the people and removed them from Treasury holdings by the simple expedient of issuing silver certificates in small bills to effect a wide circulation.

The Bland-Allison Act was repealed in 1890 and the Sherman Act took its place. Under this new law 4,500,000 ounces of silver per month could be paid for with Treasury Notes that were to be legal tender, and redeemable in gold or silver dollars coined from the bullion purchased. Important in this case was the fact that the notes were constantly being redeemed for gold which was mainly exported. The measure was actually a government subsidy for the silver miners and as such it was marked for failure, and was hastily repealed. The Bland-Allison Act and the Sherman Act gave a total of 570 million silver dollars to our monetary stocks.

The "Gold Standard Act" of 1900 gave our country a single standard, but reaffirmed the fiction that the silver dollar was a standard coin. It still enjoyed unlimited, legal tender, but was as much a subsidiary coin, practically speaking, as the dime, for its value in terms of standard gold, even before the gold surrender executive order, was far below its face value.

The lapse in coinage after 1904 and until 1921 was due to lack of bullion. Legislation authorizing further metal supplies for silver dollars was not forthcoming until 1918 when the Pittman Act provided silver for the new dollars.

Before the first World War the value of gold was equal to the value of gold coined into money. In order to encourage a steady flow of gold to the mints the government (with the exception of the period 1853-1873) had adopted a policy of gratuitous coinage. The cost of converting gold into coin had generally been considered an expense chargeable to the government.

In practice the mint made fine bars for commercial use or mint bars for coinage at its discretion. The bars in later years were stored in vaults and gold or silver certificates issued in place of the coins.

On March 6, 1933 an order was issued by the President prohibiting banks from paying out gold and gold certificates without permission, and gold currency was thus kept for reserve purposes. Gold imports and newly mined domestic gold could only be sold to the government. Gold bullion and coins may now be collected and saved by anyone as all restrictions were removed in 1975.

Under the Coinage Act of 1965, the composition of dimes, quarters and half dollars was changed to eliminate or reduce the silver content of these coins. The "clad" dimes and quarters were composed of an outer layer of copper-nickel (75% copper and 25% nickel) bonded to an inner core of pure copper. Starting 1971 the half dollar and dollar composition was changed to that of the dime and quarter. All silver clad coins have an outer layer of 80% silver bonded to an inner core of 21% silver, with a total content of 40% silver.

By the Law of September 26, 1890, changes in designes of United States coins cannot be made oftener than once every twenty-five years. Since that date, there have been design changes in all denominations and there have been many gold and silver commemorative issues. These factors are largely responsible for the ever increasing interest in coin collecting.

QUANTITIES OF COINS STRUCK

Collectors are cautioned that mint reports are not always reliable for estimating the rarity of coins. In the early years of the mint, dies of previous years were often used until they became worn or broken.

It should also be emphasized that quantities reported, particularly for gold and silver, cover the number of coins struck and have no reference to the quantity reaching actual circulation. Many issues were deposited in the treasury as backing for paper currency and were later melted.

The rarity of gold pieces struck before 1834, particularly half eagles, can be traced to the fact that the gold content was reduced in 1834, making previous issues greater in value than face, causing melting and reminting.

The quantities reported by the mint of three dollar gold pieces from 1873 to 1877 and half cents from 1832 to 1836 are subject to doubt.

Coinage figures shown for 1964 through 1966 are for coins bearing those dates. Some of them were struck in more than one year and at various mints, both with and without mint marks.

Mint quantities are shown adjacent to each date throughout the book. Figures shown in italic are estimates based on the most accurate information available. PROOF TOTALS ARE SHOWN IN PARENTHESES.

I. THE BRITISH COLONIES IN AMERICA
SOMMER ISLANDS (Bermuda)

This coinage, the first struck for the English colonies in America, was issued about 1616. The coins were known as "Hogge Money" or "Hoggies."

The pieces were made of copper lightly silvered, in four denominations; shilling, sixpence, threepence and twopence, indicated by Roman numerals. The hog is the main device and appears on the obverse side of each. SOMMER ISLANDS is inscribed within beaded circles. The reverse shows a full-rigged galleon with the flag of St. George on each of four masts.

The islands were named for Sir George Somers who was shipwrecked there in 1609 while enroute to the Virginia Plantations. Shakespeare's "The Tempest" was possibly based on this incident.

The Bermuda Islands, as they are known today, were named for Juan Bermudez who is believed to have stopped there in 1515. A few hogs which he carried for delivery to the West Indies were left behind. When Somers and his party arrived, the islands were overrun with the animals which served as a welcome source of food for the expedition.

Twopence   Threepence

Sixpence   Large Portholes   Small Portholes

Shilling ★   Small Sail   Large Sail

	Fair	Good	Fine
Twopence	$750.00	$1,750.00	$7,000.00
Threepence (V. Rare)	—	—	—
Sixpence, small holes	650.00	1,500.00	6,000.00
Sixpence, large holes	600.00	1,400.00	5,500.00
Shilling, small sail	700.00	1,500.00	6,000.00
Shilling, large sail	750.00	1,600.00	6,500.00

★ Star Throughout Colonial Section Indicates That Struck Copies Exist

Copies of certain American issues were made after 1850 to provide facsimiles of rarer issues which would otherwise be unobtainable. A star has been placed adjacent to those pieces of which deceptive copies exist. Many crude imitations have also been made in recent years, as well as forgeries intended to deceive collectors. The specimens illustrated are genuine.

MASSACHUSETTS
"NEW ENGLAND" COINAGE (1652)

The earliest medium of exchange in the New England settlements was wampum. The General Court of Massachusetts in 1637 ordered "that wampamege should passe at 6 a penny for any sume under 12 d." Wampum consisted of shells of various colors ground to the size of a grain of corn. A hole was drilled through each piece so they could be strung on leather thongs for convenience and adornment.

Corn, pelts, and bullets were frequently used in lieu of coins, which were rarely available. Silver and gold coins brought over from England, Holland and other countries tended to flow back across the Atlantic to purchase needed supplies. The colonists thus left to their own resources dealt with the friendly Indians in kind. In 1661 the law making wampum legal tender was repealed.

Agitation for a standard coinage reached its height in 1651. England, with a civil war pending between the Puritans and Royalists, ignored the colonists, who took matters into their own hands in 1652.

The General Court in 1652 ordered the first metallic currency to be struck in the English Americas (the Spaniards had established a mint in Mexico City in 1535), the New England silver threepence, sixpence, and shilling. Silver bullion was procured principally from the West Indies. Joseph Jenks made the punches for the first coins at his Iron Works in Saugus, Massachusetts, close to Boston where the mint was located. John Hull was appointed mintmaster; his assistant was Robert Sanderson (or Saunderson). Mintmaster Hull received one shilling threepence for every twenty shillings coined as his compensation. This fee was adjusted several times during his term as mintmaster.

NE Threepence (1652)   NE Sixpence (1652) ★

Note: Early American coins are rare in conditions better than listed and valued much higher.

NE Shilling (1652) ★

	Good	Fine	V. Fine
NE Threepence *(2 known)*	—	—	—
NE Sixpence *(6 known)*	—	—	—
NE Shilling	$3,000.00	$6,700.00	$12,500.00

MASSACHUSETTS
WILLOW TREE COINAGE (1653-1660)

The simplicity of the design on the N.E. coins invited counterfeiting and clipping of the edges. Therefore, they were soon replaced by the Willow, Oak and Pine Tree series. The Willow Tree coins were struck from 1653 to 1660, the Oak Trees 1660 to 1667, and the Pine Trees 1667 to 1682. All of them (with the exception of the Oak Tree twopence) bore the date 1652, however. This evasion was to give them the appearance of having been struck during the English civil war, when Cromwell was in power.

The coinage was abandoned in 1682; a proposal to renew coinage in 1686 was rejected by the General Court.

Many varieties of all of these coins exist.

Threepence   Sixpence

Shilling

	Fair	Good	Fine
Willow Tree Threepence 1652 *(3 known)*.........	——	——	——
Willow Tree Sixpence 1652.....................	——	——	——
Willow Tree Shilling 1652	$2,000.00	$6,000.00	$12,500.00

OAK TREE COINAGE (1660-1667)

Twopence ★   Threepence

	Fair	Good	Fine	V. Fine
Oak Tree Twopence 1662............	$125.00	$300.00	$550.00	$1,000.00
Oak Tree Threepence 1652	135.00	325.00	600.00	1,200.00

MASSACHUSETTS

Sixpence   Shilling ★

	Fair	Good	Fine	V. Fine
Oak Tree Sixpence 1652..............	$135.00	$325.00	$600.00	$950.00
Oak Tree Shilling 1652..............	125.00	300.00	550.00	900.00

PINE TREE COINAGE (1667-1682)

The first pine tree coins were minted on the same size planchets as the Oak Tree pieces. Subsequent issues were narrower and thicker to conform to the size of English coins.

Threepence ★   Sixpence ★

Shilling,
Large Planchet
(1667-1674) ★

Shilling,
Small Planchet
(1675-1682)

	Fair	Good	Fine	V. Fine
Pine Tree Threepence 1652................	$110.00	$225.00	$375.00	$650.00
Pine Tree Sixpence 1652	125.00	250.00	500.00	750.00
Pine Tree Shilling, large planchet 1652.....	125.00	250.00	500.00	900.00
Pine Tree Shilling, small planchet 1652.....	110.00	225.00	475.00	800.00

MARYLAND

In 1658 Cecil Calvert, the second Lord Baltimore and "Lord Proprietor of Maryland," had coinage struck in England for use in Maryland.

There were four denominations: shillings, sixpence, and fourpence (groat) in silver, and a copper penny (denarium). The silver coins have the bust of Lord Baltimore on the obverse, and the Baltimore family Arms with the denomination in Roman numerals and the legend CRESCITE ET MULTIPLICAMINI (Increase and be multiplied) on the reverse. The obverse of the penny is similar, but the reverse has a ducal coronet with two pennants and the inscription DENARIUM, TERRAE-MARIAE (Penny, Maryland). Numerous die varieties and patterns exist in this series.

Fourpence (groat)

Lord Baltimore Shilling

Sixpence

Penny (denarium) ★

	Fair	Good	Fine	V. Fine
Penny (Copper) (Ex. Rare).........	—			
Fourpence......................	$500.00	$1,100.00	$4,000.00	$7,000.00
Sixpence	350.00	900.00	2,200.00	4,500.00
Shilling	450.00	1,000.00	3,000.00	5,750.00

NEW JERSEY
ST. PATRICK OR MARK NEWBY COINAGE

Mark Newby, who came from Dublin, Ireland, in November 1681, brought some halfpenny pieces believed by numismatists to have been struck in Dublin c. 1673. These were called St. Patrick Halfpence.

The coin received wide currency in the New Jersey Province, having been authorized to pass as legal tender by the General Assembly in May 1682.

These have a brass insert at the crown so that when the coin was struck it would appear as though it were a golden crown. On some pieces this insert has been removed or does not show.

The smaller piece, known as a farthing, was never authorized for circulation in the Colonies. The obverses show a crowned king kneeling playing a harp. The legend FLOREAT REX (May the King prosper) is separated by a crown. The reverse side of the halfpence shows St. Patrick with a crozier in his left and a trefoil in his right hand, surrounded by people. At his left is a shield. The legend is ECCE GREX (Behold the flock).

The farthing reverse shows St. Patrick driving away reptiles and serpents, as he holds a Metropolitan cross in his left hand. The legend reads QUIESCAT PLEBS (May the people be at ease). Numerous die variations exist.

NEW JERSEY

St. Patrick Farthing

St. Patrick Halfpenny

	V. Good	Fine	V. Fine
St. Patrick Farthing	$75.00	$160.00	$385.00
St. Patrick Farthing — Silver pattern	600.00	1,500.00	2,750.00
St. Patrick Farthing — Gold pattern			(Unique)
St. Patrick Halfpenny	120.00	275.00	470.00

II. COINAGE AUTHORIZED BY ROYAL PATENT
AMERICAN PLANTATIONS TOKEN

These tokens struck in nearly pure tin were the first authorized coinage for the British colonies in America. They were made under a franchise granted in 1688 to John Holt. Bright, unblemished specimens are more valuable. Restrikes were made about 1828 from original dies.

	Fine	E. Fine	Unc.
(1688) James II Plantation Token,			
1/24 PART REAL — Tin	$225.00	$400.00	$925.00
1/24 PART REAL — Tin. Sidewise 4 in 24	—	—	—
Restrike	175.00	275.00	750.00

COINAGE OF WILLIAM WOOD
ROSA AMERICANA COINS

William Wood, an Englishman, obtained a patent from George I to make tokens for Ireland and the American Colonies.

The first pieces struck were undated; others bear the dates 1722, 1723, 1724 and 1733. The Rosa Americana pieces were issued in three denominations, halfpenny, penny and twopence, and were intended for America. This type had a full-blown rose on the reverse with the words ROSA AMERICANA UTILE DULCI (American Rose — the useful with the pleasant).

ROSA AMERICANA

The obverse, common to both Rosa Americana and Hibernia pieces, shows the head of George I and the legend GEORGIUS D:G: MAG: BRI: FRA: ET. HIB: REX. (George, by the Grace of God, King of Great Britain, France and Ireland) or abbreviations thereof. Rosa Americana tokens, however, were rejected by the American Colonists. The coins are made of a composition of 75% copper, 24.7% zinc, and .3% silver known as Bath metal.

	V. Good	*Fine*	*E. Fine*
Twopence (no date)	$85.00	$165.00	$375.00
Twopence (no date) motto without label (*3 known*)	—	—	—

1722 Halfpenny D. G. REX ROSA AMERI.			
UTILE DULCI	$85.00	$150.00	$350.00
1722 Halfpenny DEI GRATIA REX UTILE DULCI	65.00	110.00	260.00
1722 Halfpenny VTILE DVLCI	—	—	—

1722 Penny UTILE DULCI	$55.00	$110.00	$260.00
1722 Penny VTILE DVLCI	50.00	100.00	250.00
1722 Penny GEORGIVS	—	—	—

ROSA AMERICANA

	V. Good	Fine	E. Fine
1722 Twopence, period after REX.....................	$85.00	$165.00	$335.00
1722 Twopence, no period after REX.................	85.00	165.00	335.00

1723 Halfpenny....................................	50.00	90.00	225.00
1723 Halfpenny, uncrowned rose...................	——	——	——

1723 Penny..	55.00	100.00	240.00
1723 Twopence (illustrated)........................	85.00	160.00	350.00

1724 Penny (Pattern)...............................		——	——
1724 Penny (undated) ROSA: SINE: SPINA. (3 known)		——	——

ROSA AMERICANA

1724 Twopence (Pattern) .... Rare

★

1733 Twopence (Pattern) Proof.. Rare

The 1733 twopence is a pattern piece and bears the bust of George II facing to the left. Issued by the successors to the coinage patent, since William Wood had died in 1730.

WOOD'S HIBERNIA COINAGE

The type intended for Ireland had a seated figure with a harp on the reverse side and the word HIBERNIA. Denominations struck were halfpenny and farthing with dates 1722, 1723 and 1724. Hibernia coins were unpopular in Ireland, so many of them were sent to the American Colonies.

First Type   Second Type   1723 over 22

	V. Good	V. Fine	E. Fine
1722 Farthing, D: G: REX (Ex. Rare).................		$225.00	$365.00
1722 Halfpenny, D: G: REX (Ex. Rare)................	—	—	—
1722 Halfpenny, first type, harp at left	$17.50	55.00	120.00
1722 Halfpenny, second type, harp at right	17.50	65.00	130.00
1723 over 22 Halfpenny	17.50	70.00	160.00
1723 Halfpenny...................................	12.50	30.00	90.00
1723 Halfpenny — Silver pattern	—	—

[21]

WOOD'S HIBERNIA COINAGE

1723 Hibernia Farthing   1724 Hibernia Halfpenny

	V. Good	V. Fine	E. Fine
1723 Hibernia Farthing — DEI. GRATIA. REX	$20.00	$40.00	$100.00
1723 Hibernia Farthing — D.G. REX. (Ex. Rare)		235.00	450.00
1723 Hibernia Farthing — Silver pattern		900.00	1,250.00
1724 Hibernia Farthing	40.00	75.00	150.00
1724 Hibernia Halfpenny	20.00	55.00	125.00

VIRGINIA HALFPENNY

In 1773 coinage of a copper halfpenny was authorized for Virginia by the Crown. The pattern in proof struck on a large planchet with wide milled border is often referred to as a penny.

The silver piece dated 1774 is referred to as a shilling, but may have been a pattern or trial for a halfpenny or a guinea.

	V. Good	V. Fine	Unc.
1773 Halfpenny, period after GEORGIVS	$25.00	$55.00	$325.00
1773 Halfpenny, no period after GEORGIVS	35.00	85.00	375.00

"Penny"   "Shilling" 1774

	Proof
1773 "Penny"	$4,500.00
1774 "Shilling" (6 known)	—

III. EARLY AMERICAN TOKENS
Struck in America or England for use by American Merchants

LONDON ELEPHANT TOKENS

Struck c. 1664-1666 during the reign of Charles II, the London Token, an early historian states, was produced during the great plague raging in London. The legend on this piece relates directly to that crisis. It has also been stated that the London Token was to have been current in Tangier, Africa, but was never used in that locality. No date appears on this token.

It is unlikely that many ever circulated in America. They are associated with the 1694 pieces through use of a common obverse die.

	V. Good	V. Fine	E. Fine
(1664) Halfpenny GOD PRESERVE LONDON (Thick planchet)	$85.00	$175.00	$335.00
(1664) Halfpenny GOD PRESERVE LONDON (Thin planchet)	100.00	225.00	385.00
(1664) Halfpenny GOD PRESERVE LONDON (Diagonals in center of shield)	150.00	325.00	600.00
(1664) Halfpenny, similar. Variety with sword in second quarter of shield instead of first	——	——	——
(1664) Halfpenny LON DON	650.00	1,400.00	——

CAROLINA AND NEW ENGLAND ELEPHANT TOKENS

Although no law is known authorizing coinage for Carolina, two very interesting pieces known as Elephant Tokens were made with the date 1694. These copper tokens were of halfpenny denomination. The reverse reads GOD PRESERVE CAROLINA AND THE LORDS PROPRIETERS. 1694.

The second and more common variety has the last word spelled PROPRIETORS. The correction was made on the original die, for the E shows plainly beneath the O. The elephant's tusks nearly touch the milling on the second variety.

The Elephant Pieces were probably struck in England and perhaps intended only as tokens, or, as we might say today, as an advertising stunt to enliven interest in the Carolina Plantation.

Like the Carolina Tokens, the New England Elephant Tokens were believed to have been struck in England as a promotional piece to increase interest in the American Colonies.

CAROLINA ELEPHANT TOKENS

★

	V. Good	Fine
1694 PROPRIETERS (Ex. Rare)..........................	—	—
1694 PROPRIETORS, O OVER E...........................	$1,500.00	$4,000.00

NEW ENGLAND ELEPHANT TOKEN

★

1694 NEW ENGLAND (Ex. Rare).......................... — —

THE NEW YORKE TOKEN

Little is known about the origin of this token. The style of design and execution seem to be Dutch, and it is probable that the dies were prepared in Holland. There is no date on the piece which evidently belongs to the period between 1664, when the name New Yorke was first adopted, and 1710 after which it was rarely spelled that way.

UNDATED

	V. Good	Fine
Brass..............	$2,000.00	$3,500.00
Pewter	—	—

GLOUCESTER TOKENS

S. S. Crosby, in his book "The Early Coins of America" stated that this coin appears to have been intended as a pattern for a shilling; a private coinage by Richard Dawson of Gloucester (county), Virginia. The only specimens known are struck in brass.

The denomination XII indicates that a silver coinage (one shilling) was planned but never issued. Known specimens are imperfect and the full legend cannot be discerned.

The building may represent some public building, possibly the court house. The legend on the reverse may have read GLOUCESTER COURT HOUSE VIRGINIA.

GLOUCESTER TOKENS

1714 Shilling (2 known) Brass .... 1976 A.N.A. Sale $35,000.00

HIGLEY OR GRANBY COPPERS

Dr. Samuel Higley owned a private copper mine near Granby, Connecticut. He worked the mine as an individual, smelting his own ore and making his own dies for the coins that he issued. After his death in 1737 his brother John continued the coinage.

The Higley coppers were never officially authorized. All the tokens were made of pure copper. There were seven obverse and four reverse dies. The first issue, in 1737, bore the legend THE VALUE OF THREEPENCE. After a time the quantity exceeded the local demand, and a protest arose against the value of the piece. Higley, a resourceful individual, promptly created a new design, still with the Roman III, but with the inscription VALUE ME AS YOU PLEASE. On the reverse appeared the words I AM GOOD COPPER.

(Electrotypes and Casts Exist)

★

	Good	V. Good
1737 THE • VALVE • OF • THREE • PENCE. — 3 Hammers — CONNECTICVT	$5,000.00	$8,500.00
1737 THE • VALVE • OF • THREE • PENCE. — 3 Hammers — I • AM • GOOD • COPPER...............	6,250.00	10,000.00

1737 VALUE • ME • AS • YOU • PLEASE — 3 Hammers — I • AM • GOOD • COPPER................	5,000.00	8,500.00
1737 VALVE • ME • AS • YOU • PLEASE — 3 Hammers — I • AM • GOOD • COPPER................	(Ex. Rare)	
(1737) VALUE • ME • AS • YOU • PLEASE — Broad Axe — J • CUT • MY • WAY • THROUGH.........	6,250.00	9,000.00
1739 VALUE • ME • AS • YOU • PLEASE — Broad Axe — J • CUT • MY • WAY • THROUGH.........	8,500.00	16,000.00

HIBERNIA-VOCE POPULI

These coins, struck in the year 1760, were prepared by one Roche, of King Street, Dublin, who was at that period engaged in the manufacture of buttons for the army, for which he held a contract with home government. Like other Irish tokens, some of these pieces found their way to Colonial America. The piece apparently dated 1700 is from a defective die. They possibly circulated in Colonies with numerous other counterfeit halfpence and "Bungtown Tokens."

Farthing 1760

Halfpenny 1760

Halfpenny "1700"

VOOE POPULI

	Good	V. Fine	E. Fine
1760 Farthing, large letters (pictured)	$125.00	$450.00	$900.00
1760 Farthing, small letters	——	——	——
1700 Halfpenny	——	——	——
1760 Halfpenny	20.00	65.00	125.00
1760 Halfpenny VOOE POPULI	30.00	90.00	160.00
1760 Halfpenny, P below bust	50.00	125.00	190.00
1760 Halfpenny, P in front of face	50.00	125.00	190.00

PITT TOKENS

William Pitt, who endeared himself to America, is the subject of these pieces, probably intended as commemorative medalets. The halfpenny served as currency during a shortage of regular coinage. The reverse legend refers to Pitt's efforts to have the stamp act repealed. The Pitt farthing-size token, struck in brass or copper on cast planchets, is rare.

1766 Farthing	V. Rare	
1766 Halfpenny		
V. Good	Fine	E. Fine
$150.00	$250.00	$650.00

RHODE ISLAND SHIP MEDAL

Although this medal has a Dutch inscription, the spelling and design indicate an English or Anglo-American origin. The satirical theme depicts the retreat from Rhode Island by Continental troops. Specimens are known in brass, copper, tin and pewter.

1778-1779
Rhode Island
Ship Medal

	V. Fine	E. Fine
VLUGTENDE (fleeing) below ship		—
Wreath below ship	$375.00	$900.00
Without wreath below ship	350.00	850.00

J. CHALMERS — Annapolis, Maryland

John Chalmers, a goldsmith, struck a series of silver tokens at Annapolis in 1783. The shortage of change and the refusal of the people to use underweight cut Spanish coins, or "bits," prompted the issuance of these pieces.

The shilling with rings on the reverse is very rare. The common type shilling has two clasped hands on the obverse. The reverse shows two doves competing for a worm.

The sixpence has a star within a wreath on the obverse, and a cross with hands clasped on the reverse. The threepence has the clasped hands on the obverse side, and the reverse shows a branch encircled by a wreath.

	Good	Fine
1783 Threepence	$500.00	$1,400.00
1783 Sixpence, small date	800.00	1,750.00
1783 Sixpence, large date	650.00	1,600.00

	V. Good	V. Fine
1783 Shilling — Birds, long worm	400.00	1,250.00
1783 Shilling — Birds, short worm (pictured)	375.00	1,150.00
1783 Shilling — Rings (Ex. Rare)	—	—

IV. THE FRENCH COLONIES

None of the coins of the French regime is strictly American. They were all general issues for the French colonies of the New World. The coinage of 1670 was authorized by an edict of Louis XIV dated February 19, 1670, for use in New France, Acadia, the French settlements in Newfoundland, and the French West Indies. The copper of 1717 to 1722 was authorized by edicts of 1716 and 1721 for use in New France, Louisiana, and the French West Indies.

ISSUE OF 1670

The coinage of 1670 consisted of silver 5 and 15 sols. A copper 2 deniers was also authorized but never struck. A total of 200,000 of the 5 sols was struck, and 40,000 of the 15 sols, at Paris. Nantes was to have coined the copper, but did not; the reasons for this may never be known, since the archives of the Nantes mint before 1700 were destroyed. The only known specimen is a pattern struck at Paris. The silver coins were raised in value by a third in 1672 to keep them circulating, but in vain. They rapidly disappeared, and by 1680 none was to be seen. Later they were restored to their original value.

	V. Good	Fine	V. Fine	E. Fine	Unc.
5 Sols 1670 (200,000)	$125.00	$300.00	$500.00	$800.00	$1,300.00
15 Sols 1670 (40,000)	5,000.00	9,000.00	15,000.00	——	——

COINAGE OF 1717-1720

The copper 6 and 12 deniers of 1717 were authorized by an edict of Louis XV dated December 1716, to be struck at Perpignan. The order could not be carried out, for the supply of copper was too brassy. A second attempt in 1720 also failed, probably for the same reason. All these coins are extremely rare, the 6 deniers of 1720 probably being unique.

Copper

	V. Good	Fine
6 Deniers 1717 ...	$1,250	$1,750
6 Deniers 1720 ...		Unique
12 Deniers 1717 ...	1,500	2,000

BILLON COINAGE

The piece of 30 deniers was called a *mousquetaire,* and was coined at Metz and Lyons. The 15 deniers was coined only at Metz. The sou marque and half were coined at almost every French mint, those of Paris being commonest. The half sou of 1740 is the only commonly available date. Specimens of the sou marque dated after 1760 were not used in North America.

FRENCH COLONIES
BILLON COINAGE

30 Deniers		Sou Marque		
	V. Good	Fine	V. Fine	E. Fine
15 Deniers 1710-1713AA..................	$100.00	$175.00	$250.00	$400.00
30 Deniers 1709-1713AA..................	80.00	125.00	175.00	250.00
30 Deniers 1709-1713D	80.00	125.00	175.00	250.00
Half sou marque 1738-1748.......	50.00	75.00	100.00	150.00
Sou marque 1738-1760, various mints	25.00	35.00	`50.00	85.00

COINAGE OF 1721-1722

The copper coinage of 1721-1722 was authorized by an edict of Louis XV dated June 1721. The coins were struck on copper blanks imported from Sweden. Rouen and La Rochelle struck pieces of 9 deniers in 1721 and 1722. New France received 534,000 pieces, mostly from the mint of La Rochelle, but only 8,180 were successfully put into circulation as the colonists disliked copper. In 1726 the rest of the issue was sent back to France.

COPPER SOU OR NINE DENIERS

	V. Good	Fine
1721-B (Rouen)	$65.00	$100.00
1721-H		
(La Rochelle)	32.50	55.00
1722-H	35.00	60.00
1722-H, 2 over 1	60.00	100.00

FRENCH COLONIES IN GENERAL

Coined for use in the French colonies and only unofficially circulated in Louisiana along with other foreign coins and tokens. Most were counterstamped RF (République Française) for use in the West Indies.

	Good	Fine	E. Fine
1767 French Colonies, Sou........................	$35.00	$90.00	$260.00
1767 French Colonies, Sou. Counterstamped RF......	17.50	45.00	120.00

V. SPECULATIVE ISSUES, TOKENS & PATTERNS

THE CONTINENTAL DOLLAR

The Continental Dollars were probably a pattern issue only and never reached general circulation. It was the first silver dollar size coin ever proposed for the United States. The dies were engraved by someone whose initials were E. G. (possibly Elisha Gallaudet). Some of them have his signature "EG FECIT" on the obverse. The coins were probably struck in Philadelphia.

Varieties result from differences in the spelling of the word CURRENCY and the addition of EG FECIT. These coins were struck in silver, pewter and brass, those in silver probably having done service as a dollar. Pewter coins in original bright uncirculated condition are worth an additional premium.

Copies were struck in various metals for the 1876 Centennial Exposition in Philadelphia and also restruck from hubbed copy dies circa 1961.

"CURRENCY"   "CURENCY"

	Good	Fine	E. Fine	Unc.
1776 CURENCY — Pewter	$950	$2,250	$4,000	$9,000
1776 CURENCY — Brass (2 varieties)	——	——	——	——
1776 CURENCY — Silver	——	——	——	——
1776 CURRENCY — Pewter	1,100	3,000	6,000	10,000
1776 CURRENCY —Pewter, EG FECIT	1,000	2,500	5,000	9,500
1776 CURRENCY — Silver, EG FECIT	——	——	——	——
1776 CURRENCEY — Pewter	——	——	——	——

★ Star Throughout Colonial Section Indicates That Struck Copies Exist.

NOVA CONSTELLATIO COPPERS

The Nova Constellatio pieces were struck supposedly by order of Gouverneur Morris who had been Assistant Financier of the Confederation. The tokens were turned out in fairly large quantities in the years 1783 and 1785. Evidence indicates that they were struck in Birmingham from dies made there by Thomas Wyon, and imported for American circulation as a private business venture by Gouverneur Morris.

1783
"CONSTELLATIO"
Pointed Rays, Small U.S.

V. Good..............	$25.00
Fine	62.50
Ex. Fine	180.00

1783
"CONSTELLATIO"
Pointed Rays, Large U.S.

V. Good..............	$25.00
Fine	75.00
Ex. Fine	225.00

1783
"CONSTELATIO"
Blunt Rays

V. Good..............	$25.00
Fine	70.00
Ex. Fine	200.00

1785
"CONSTELATIO"
Blunt Rays

V. Good..............	$30.00
Fine	80.00
Ex. Fine	230.00

1785
"CONSTELLATIO"
Pointed Rays

V. Good..............	$25.00
Fine	65.00
Ex. Fine	170.00

1786 (Similar) ....   ——

NOVA CONSTELLATIO PATTERNS (Silver)

These Nova Constellatio pieces undoubtedly represent the first patterns for a coinage of the United States. They were designed by Benjamin Dudley for Gouverneur Morris to carry out his ideas for a decimal coinage system. The 1000 unit designation he called a "mark," the 500 a "quint." These denominations, together with the smaller 100 unit piece, were designed to standardize the many different coin values among the several States. These pattern pieces represent the first attempt at a decimal ratio, and were the forerunners of our present system of money values. Neither the proposed denominations nor the coins advanced beyond the pattern stage. The pieces are all dated 1783 and are extremely rare. There are two types of the "quint."

★ Sets of Mickley Electrotypes Exist

BIT 100 Units

QUINT Type 1   Reverse   QUINT Type 2

MARK

1783 (Bit) "100," Silver (2 varieties) .... each unique
1783 (Quint) "500," Silver — Type 1 .... unique
1783 (Quint) "500," Silver — Type 2 .... unique
1783 (Mark) "1000," Silver .... unique

IMMUNE COLUMBIA PIECES

These are considered experimental or pattern pieces. No laws describing them are known. There are several types with the seated figure of Justice device. These dies were possibly the work of Thomas Wyon.

1785 Copper, 13 stars .... —
1785 Silver, 13 stars .... —

IMMUNE COLUMBIA PIECES

1785 Ptd. Rays CONSTELLATIO
Copper. Extra star in legend   ——
1785 Blunt Rays CONSTELATIO
Copper........ (2 known)   ——
Gold .... (Unique)   ——
A gold specimen in the National Coin
Collection was acquired from Stickney
in exchange for an 1804 dollar.

1785
George III Obverse
Good...... $1,600   Fine..... $4,250

1785
Vermon Auctori Obverse
Good...... $1,350   Fine..... $4,000

1787
IMMUNIS COLUMBIA
Eagle Reverse
Dies by James Atlee

Good	$175.00
Fine	350.00
V. Fine	900.00
Ex. Fine	2,000.00

CONFEDERATIO COPPERS

The Confederatio Coppers are experimental or pattern pieces. This will explain why the die with the CONFEDERATIO legend was combined with other designs such as bust of George Washington, Libertas et Justitia of 1785, Immunis Columbia of 1786, the New York "Excelsiors," Inimica Tyrannis Americana and others. There were in all thirteen dies struck in fourteen combinations. Some of the dies were believed to have been made by Thomas Wyon of Birmingham, England.

There are two types of the Confederatio reverse. In one instance the stars are contained in a small circle; in the other larger stars are in a larger circle.

Typical Obverse

Small Circle Reverse

Large Circle Reverse

1785 Stars in small circle — various obverses.........................	V. Rare
1785 Stars in large circle — various obverses...........................	V. Rare

SPECULATIVE PATTERNS

The motto and shield design used on some of these patterns was later adopted for use on the New Jersey copper coins.

1786 IMMUNIS COLUMBIA   Eagle Reverse   Shield Reverse

	Good	Fine
1786 IMMUNIS COLUMBIA, eagle reverse......................	—	—
1786 IMMUNIS COLUMBIA, shield reverse	—	—

	Good	Fine
1786 (No date) Washington obverse	—	—
1786 Eagle obverse	—	—
1786 Washington obverse, eagle reverse (Unique)	—	—

VI. COINAGE OF THE STATES
NEW HAMPSHIRE

New Hampshire was the first of the states to consider the subject of coinage following the Declaration of Independence.

William Moulton was empowered to make a limited quantity of coins of pure copper authorized by the State House of Representatives in 1776. Although cast patterns were prepared, it is believed that they were not approved. Little of the proposed coinage was ever actually circulated.

Other purported patterns are of doubtful origin. These include a unique engraved piece and a rare struck piece with large initials WM on the reverse.

	V. Good
1776 New Hampshire copper	$5,500.00

[34]

MASSACHUSETTS
MASSACHUSETTS PINE TREE COPPER

Nothing is known regarding the origin of the Pine Tree pattern dated 1776. The obverse has a crude pine tree with the letters 1d LM at its base; Inscription, MASSACHUSETTS STATE. The reverse has a figure probably intended to represent the Goddess of Liberty, seated on a globe and holding a liberty cap and staff. A dog sits at her feet. The legend LIBERTY AND VIRTUE surrounds the figure.

1776 Pine Tree pattern (Unique) . . . .   ——

A similar pattern, probably from the same source, has an Indian with bow on the obverse, and seated figure on the reverse.

1776 Indian pattern (Unique) . . . .   ——

MASSACHUSETTS HALFPENNY

This pattern piece is sometimes called the "Janus Copper." There are three heads facing left, front and right on the obverse with the inscription STATE OF MASSA. ½ D. The reverse shows the Goddess of Liberty, seated resting against a globe facing right, inscribed GODDESS LIBERTY 1776.

1776 Halfpenny, 3 heads on obverse (Unique) . . . .   ——

An "Act for establishing a mint for the coinage of gold, silver and copper" was passed by the Massachusetts General Court October 17, 1786. The next year the Council directed that the design should incorporate "the figure of an Indian with a bow and arrow and a star at one side, with the word 'Commonwealth," the reverse, a spread eagle with the words 'of Massachusetts A.D. 1787'."

MASSACHUSETTS

The coinage of Massachusetts copper cents and half cents in 1787 and 1788 was under the direction of Joshua Witherle. These were the first coins bearing the denomination Cent as established by Congress. Many varieties exist, the most valuable being that with arrows in the eagle's right talon.

Most of the dies for these coppers were made by Joseph Callender. Jacob Perkins of Newburyport also engraved some of the dies.

The mint was abandoned early in 1789 as the venture was unprofitable.

1787 Half Cent	
Good	$32.50
Fine	60.00
V. Fine	120.00
Ex. Fine	200.00

Obverse   Arrows in Eagle's Right Talon   Arrows in Left Talon

	Good	Fine	V.F.	E.F.
1787 Cent, arrows in right talon (Ex. Rare)				
1787 Cent, arrows in left talon	$25.00	$50.00	$100.00	$200.00
1787 Cent, "horn" (die break) from eagle's head	25.00	55.00	120.00	260.00

1788 Half Cent	
Good	$37.50
Fine	65.00
Very Fine	150.00
Ex. Fine	285.00

1788 Cent	
Period after Massachusetts	
Good	$25.00
Fine	50.00
V. Fine	100.00
Ex. Fine	200.00
No period after Massachusetts	
Good	$30.00
Fine	60.00
V. Fine	125.00
Ex. Fine	250.00

★

★

CONNECTICUT

Authority for establishing a mint near New Haven was granted by the State to Samuel Bishop, Joseph Hopkins, James Hillhouse and John Goodrich in 1785.

Available records indicate that most of the Connecticut coppers were coined under a sub-contract by Samuel Broome and Jeremiah Platt, former New York merchants. Abel Buel and James Atlee were the principal die-sinkers.

1785 Copper
Bust Facing Right
Good............. $25.00
Fine 80.00
V. Fine............. 140.00

1785 Copper
African Head
Good............. $27.50
Fine 100.00
V. Fine.......... 175.00

1785 Copper
Bust facing left
Good............. $115.00
Fine 250.00
V. Fine.......... 450.00

1786 Copper
ETLIB INDE
Good............... $50.00
Fine................ 100.00
V. Fine............. 200.00

1786 Copper
Large Head Facing Right
Good............... $50.00
Fine................ 125.00
V. Fine............. 250.00

CONNECTICUT

1786 Copper
Mailed Bust Facing Left
Good $25.00
Fine 65.00
V. Fine 150.00

1786 Copper
Mailed Bust Facing Left
Hercules Head
Good $55.00
Fine 160.00
V. Fine 375.00

1786 Copper
Draped Bust
Good $50.00
Fine 150.00
V. Fine 265.00

The Connecticut coppers, especially those dated 1787 and 1788, were usually crudely struck and on imperfect planchets.

1787 Copper
Mailed Bust Facing Left
IND ET LIB
1787 over 1788
Good $55.00
Fine 175.00
V. Fine 350.00

1787 Copper
Small Head Facing Right
ETLIB INDE
Good $55.00
Fine 160.00
V. Fine 350.00

Small Head Type of 1787 and 1788

1787 Copper
Mailed Bust Facing Right
INDE ET LIB
Good $60.00
Fine 200.00
V. Fine 700.00

1787 Muttonhead Variety
Good $55.00
Fine 150.00
V. Fine 300.00

CONNECTICUT

	Good	Fine	V. Fine
1787 Mailed bust facing left	$20.00	$50.00	$100.00
1787 Similar, laughing head variety................	20.00	55.00	120.00
1787 Similar, Hercules head (see 1786)	175.00	400.00	700.00
1787 Similar, dated 1787 over 1877	40.00	125.00	250.00

1787 Similar, horned bust variety...................	20.00	50.00	150.00
1787 Similar, CONNECT variety......................	50.00	150.00	250.00

1787 Draped bust facing left (many varieties)........	15.00	35.00	75.00
1787 Similar, AUCIORI variety.......................	20.00	50.00	100.00
1787 Similar, AUCTOPI variety.......................	25.00	60.00	140.00
1787 Similar, AUCTOBI variety......................	25.00	70.00	175.00
1787 Similar, CONNFC variety.......................	20.00	50.00	120.00
1787 Similar, CONNLC variety.......................	40.00	110.00	175.00
1787 Similar, FNDE variety	20.00	50.00	100.00
1787 Similar, ETLIR variety	20.00	50.00	100.00
1787 Similar, ETIIB variety.........................	25.00	60.00	125.00

1788 Mailed bust facing right.......................	30.00	75.00	170.00
1788 Similar, small head (see picture page 38)	125.00	400.00	950.00

CONNECTICUT

	Good	Fine	V. Fine
1788 Mailed bust facing left	$22.50	$60.00	$125.00
1788 Mailed bust left CONNLC......................	27.50	70.00	155.00

1788 Draped bust facing left........................	23.00	70.00	135.00
1788 Similar, CONNLC variety......................	50.00	125.00	200.00
1788 Similar, INDL ET LIB variety	40.00	100.00	180.00

NEW YORK
THE BRASHER DOUBLOON

Perhaps the most famous pieces coined before the establishment of the U.S. Mint at Philadelphia were those produced by a well-known goldsmith and jeweler, Ephraim Brasher, neighbor of George Washington, in New York.

Brasher produced a gold piece weighing about 408 grains, approximately equal in value to a Spanish doubloon (about $16.00).

The punch-mark EB appears in either of two positions as illustrated. This mark is found on some foreign gold coins as well, and probably was so used by Brasher as evidence of his testing of their value.

V. Fine

1787 Doubloon, punch on breast. Gold (Unique)	——
1787 Doubloon, punch on wing. Gold.......................................	——

★ Star Throughout Colonial Section Indicates That Struck Copies Exist.

NEW YORK

No coinage was authorized for New York following the Revolutionary War although several propositions were considered. The only coinage laws passed were those regulating coins already in use.

A partnership headed by Thomas Machin was formed in 1787 for the purpose of striking copper coins, near Newburgh. The establishment was called a "Manufactory of hardware," but the operations there were conducted in secret and looked upon as illegal.

Subsequently, Reuben Harmon, Jr., who operated the mint at Rupert, Vermont, and William Coley were listed as copartners "in such trades and merchandizing and in the coinage of copper for the state of Vermont, Connecticut and New York, for their most benefit advantage and profit."

Many of the pieces classified as Connecticut coins, the Vermon Auctori with the Britannia reverse and the counterfeit George III halfpence were products of this "hardware manufactory" known as Machin's Mills.

COPPER COINAGE

1786
NON VI VIRTUTE VICI

(Believed to be the bust of Washington.)

Good $2,250.00
Fine 4,500.00
V. Fine 9,000.00

	Good	Fine	V. Fine
1787 EXCELSIOR copper, eagle on globe facing right.	$500.00	$1,200.00	$3,500.00
1787 EXCELSIOR copper, eagle on globe facing left	450.00	1,000.00	3,250.00

1787
Large Eagle on Reverse

Arrows and branch
transposed (Ex. Rare). . . . . ——

NEW YORK

1787 George Clinton
Good	$3,000.00
Fine.	6,000.00
V. Fine	15,000.00

1787
Indian and N.Y. Arms
Good	$1,500.00
Fine	3,500.00
V. Fine	6,000.00

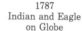

1787
Indian and Eagle
on Globe
Good	$1,750.00
Fine.	3,800.00
V. Fine	7,000.00

1787
Indian and
George III Reverse
(3 known)

MACHIN'S MILLS COINAGE (1786-1789)

The most prevalent Machin's Mills coins are lightweight imitations of the British halfpenny, with bust obverse and Britannia seated reverse. These can be distinguished by their crude die work and single outline in the crosses of Britannia's shield. Dates used are 1747, 1771, 1772, 1774, 1776, 1778, 1787, and 1788. These pieces are not to be confused with other American, or English-made George III counterfeits, some of which have identical dates, or genuine George III British halfpence, which were dated 1770 to 1775.

	Good	Fine
Machin's Mills Copper, various dates		
GEORGIUS III REX/BRITANNIA	$50.00	$100.00

NEW YORK
THE NOVA EBORACS

1787
NOVA EBORAC
Reverse Seated
Figure Facing Right

Fair	$17.50
Good	70.00
Fine	175.00
V. Fine	300.00

1787
NOVA EBORAC
Reverse Seated
Figure Facing Left

Fair	$15.00
Good	50.00
Fine	135.00
V. Fine	250.00

1787
NOVA EBORAC
Small Head

Fair	$150.00
Good	325.00
Fine	700.00
V. Fine	1,400.00

1787
NOVA EBORAC
Large Head

Fair	$50.00
Good	200.00
Fine	400.00
V. Fine	825.00

NEW JERSEY

On June 1, 1786, the New Jersey Colonial legislature granted to Thomas Goadsby, Albion Cox and Walter Mould authority to coin some three million coppers weighing six pennyweight and six grains apiece, not later than June 1788, on condition that they delivered to the Treasurer of the State, "one-tenth part of the full sum they shall strike and coin," in quarterly installments. These coppers were to pass current at 15 to the shilling.

In an operation of this kind the contractors purchased the metal and assumed all expenses of coining. The difference between these expenses and the total face value of the coins issued represented the profit.

NEW JERSEY

Later Goadsby and Cox asked authority to coin two-thirds of the total independently. Their petition was granted November 22, 1786. Mould was known to have produced his coins at Morristown, while Cox (and probably Goadsby) operated in Rahway. Coins were also minted in Elizabethtown and Newburgh, New York.

The series offers many varieties. The obverse shows a horse's head with plow and the legend NOVA CAESAREA (New Jersey). The reverse has a United States shield and legend E PLURIBUS UNUM (One composed of many).

1786 Date Under Draw Bar

1786 No Coulter

	Good	Fine	V. Fine
1786 Date under draw bar..........................			
1786 No coulter...................................	$100.00	$300.00	$400.00

Narrow Shield

Wide Shield

	Good	Fine	V. Fine
1786 Narrow shield	22.50	55.00	120.00
1786 Wide shield	35.00	70.00	150.00
1786 Similar, bridle variety........................	30.00	60.00	140.00

Pluribs Variety, Lg. Planchet

Small Planchet

Outlined Shield

	Good	Fine	V. Fine
1787 Pronounced outline to shield..................	20.00	60.00	100.00
1787 Small planchet, plain shield..................	20.00	60.00	100.00
1787 Large planchet, plain shield	20.00	60.00	100.00
1787 Similar, PLURIBS variety.....................	35.00	100.00	250.00

NEW JERSEY

Serpent Head

Fox Variety

	Good	Fine	V. Fine
1787 Serpent head variety.........................	$35.00	$100.00	$225.00
1788 Horses head facing right	20.00	50.00	100.00
1788 Similar, running fox before legend	35.00	100.00	250.00
1788 Horse's head facing left	100.00	250.00	400.00

VERMONT

Reuben Harmon, Jr., of Rupert, Vermont, was granted permission to coin copper pieces for a period of two years beginning July 1, 1785. The well-known Vermont plow coppers were first produced in that year. The franchise was extended for eight years in 1786.

Harmon's mint was located in the northeast corner of Rupert near a stream known as Millbrook. Col. William Coley, a New York goldsmith, made the first dies.

Some of the late issues were made near Newburgh, N.Y. by the Machin's Mills coiners.

1785 IMMUNE COLUMBIA

1785 VERMONTS

	Good	Fine		Good	Fine
1785 IMMUNE COLUMBIA ...	$1,350	$4,000	1785 VERMONTS	$90.00	$350.00

1785 VERMONTIS

1786 VERMONTENSUM

	Good	Fine		Good	Fine
1785 VERMONTIS ...	150.00	400.00	1786 VERMON-TENSIUM	70.00	275.00

VERMONT

1786 Baby Head

1787 BRITANNIA

	Good	Fine
1786 Baby head	$150.00	$550.00

	Good	Fine
1787 BRITANNIA.....	$50.00	$150.00

Reverse of this coin is always weak

1786 Bust Left

1786 Bust left	75.00	300.00

1788 (Several Varieties)

1788 (Several var.)..	50.00	175.00
1788 VERMON		
AUƆTORI.......	—	—
1788 *ET LIB*		
*INDE	125.00	350.00

1787 Bust Left

1787 Bust left	—	—

1788 GEORGIVS III REX

1788 GEORGIVS III		
REX	115.00	400.00

This piece should not be confused with the common English halfpence with similar design and reverse legend BRITANNIA.

1787 Bust Right

1787 Bust right (Several var.)..	50.00	175.00

Most Vermont coppers are struck on poor and defective planchets. Well struck coins on smooth full planchets command higher prices.

VII. PRIVATE TOKENS AFTER CONFEDERATION
NORTH AMERICAN TOKEN

This piece was struck in Dublin, Ireland. The obverse shows the seated figure of Hibernia facing left. The date of issue is believed to have been much later than that shown on the token.

Like many Irish tokens, this issue found its way to America in limited quantities and was accepted near the Canadian border.

Copper or Brass

	V. Good	Fine	V. Fine
1781...	$12.50	$27.50	$60.00

THE BAR "CENT"

The Bar "Cent" is undated and of uncertain origin. It has thirteen parallel and unconnected bars on one side. On the other side is the large roman letter USA monogram. The design was supposedly copied from a Continental button.

The significance of the design is clearly defined by its extreme simplicity. The separate thirteen states (bars) unite into a single entity as symbolized by the interlocking letters (USA).

This coin is believed to have been issued at the same time as the Nova Constellatio coppers by Thomas Wyon at Birmingham, England, for America. It first circulated in New York during November, 1785.

On the less valuable struck copy made by J. A. Bolen c. 1862 the A passes under, instead of over, the S.

★

	V. Good	Fine	E. Fine
Undated (about 1785) Bar "Cent" ...	$275.00	$550.00	$1,100.00

AUCTORI PLEBIS TOKEN

This token is sometimes included with the coins of Connecticut as it greatly resembles issues of that state. It was struck in England by an unknown maker, possibly for use in America. The reverse was also used with various other dies.

1787
AUCTORI PLEBIS

Good	$40.00
Fine	100.00
V. Fine	200.00

THE MOTT TOKEN

This was one of the first tradesman's tokens issued in America. Manufactured in England, they were issued by Messrs. Mott of New York in 1789. The firm was composed of William and John Mott, located at 240 Water Street, a fashionable section of New York at that time.

	V. Good	Fine	E. Fine
1789 Mott Token, thick planchet....................	$80.00	$125.00	$300.00
1789 Mott Token, thin planchet.....................	100.00	175.00	500.00
1789 Mott Token, entire edge engrailed	135.00	300.00	900.00

STANDISH BARRY, BALTIMORE, MARYLAND

Standish Barry, a Baltimore silversmith, circulated a silver threepence in 1790. He was a watch and clockmaker, engraver and later a silversmith. The tokens were believed to have been an advertising venture at a time when small change was scarce. The precise date, July 4, 90, on this piece may indicate that Barry intended to commemorate Independence Day, but there are no records to substantiate this belief. The head shown on the obverse is probably that of George Washington. The legend BALTIMORE TOWN JULY 4, 90 appears in the border. STANDISH BARRY THREE PENCE is on the reverse.

1790 Threepence... —— ——

ALBANY CHURCH PENNY

The First Presbyterian Church of Albany, New York authorized an issue of one thousand copper uniface tokens in 1790. These passed at twelve to a shilling and were used to stop contributions of worn and counterfeit coppers. Two varieties were made, one with the addition of a large D above the word CHURCH.

Albany Church Penny

	V. Good
(1790) Without D......................	$1,500.00
(1790) With D added..................	1,500.00

KENTUCKY TOKEN

These tokens were struck in England about 1792-94. Each star in the triangle represents a state, identified by its initial letter. These pieces are usually called Kentucky Cents because the letter K (for Kentucky) happens to be at the top. Some of the edges are plain; others are engrailed with an oblique reeding, and some have the edge lettered: "PAYABLE IN LANCASTER LONDON OR BRISTOL," or "PAYABLE AT BEDWORTH NUNEATON OR HINKLEY."

	V. Good	V. Fine	E. Fine	Unc.
Cent, (1792-94) plain edge	$40.00	$85.00	$135.00	$360.00
Cent, engrailed edge		300.00	450.00	825.00
Cent, lettered edge PAYABLE AT BEDWORTH, etc.	—	—	—	—
Cent, lettered edge PAYABLE IN LANCASTER, etc.	60.00	125.00	200.00	360.00
Cent, lettered edge PAYABLE AT I. FIELDING, etc.	—	—	—	—

FRANKLIN PRESS

This piece is an English tradesmans' token but, being associated with Benjamin Franklin, has accordingly been included in American collections.

1794 Franklin Press Token	40.00	85.00	135.00	225.00

TALBOT, ALLUM & LEE CENTS

Talbot, Allum & Lee, engaged in the India trade and located at 241 Pearl Street, New York, placed a large quantity of English-made coppers in circulation during 1794 and 1795. ONE CENT appears on the 1794 issue, and the legend PAYABLE AT THE STORE OF on the edge. The denomination is not found on the 1795 reverse but the edge legend was changed to read: WE PROMISE TO PAY THE BEARER ONE CENT.

1794 Cent with NEW YORK	
V. Good..................	$30.00
V. Fine	85.00
Unc.....................	450.00

1794 Cent Without NEW YORK	
V. Good..................	200.00
V. Fine	600.00
Unc.....................	—

TALBOT, ALLUM & LEE CENTS

1795 Cent
V. Good $20.00
V. Fine 60.00
Unc. 325.00

MYDDELTON TOKENS

These tokens were struck at the Soho Mint of Boulton and Watt near Birmingham, England. They are unsurpassed in beauty and design by any piece of this period.

1796
Myddelton Token
Proof
Copper $8,000.00
Silver 6,000.00

COPPER COMPANY OF UPPER CANADA

The obverse of this piece is the same as the Myddleton token. The new reverse legend was apparently intended for Canadian circulation, or it was used to give the token creditability.

Proof
1796 Copper $1,500.00

THE CASTORLAND MEDAL

This medal is dated 1796 and alludes to a proposed French settlement known as Castorland in Carthage, New York, at the time of the French Revolution.

1796 Silver original. (Reeded edge) . . . . ——
1796 Copper original. (Reeded edge, unbroken dies) . . . . ——
Copy dies are still available and have been used for restriking throughout the years. The illustration is a modern restrike.

NEW YORK THEATRE TOKEN

Token penny issued by Park Theatre, New York circa 1797.

	E. Fine	Unc.
Penny, THE • THEATRE • AT • NEW YORK • AMERICA	$2,000	$3,000

NORTH WEST COMPANY TOKEN

These tokens were probably valued at one beaver and struck in Birmingham in 1820 by John Walker & Co. All but one known specimen are holed, and all have been found in the region of the lower Columbia River valley in Oregon.

	V. Good
1820	$800.00
1820 Copper	800.00

VIII. WASHINGTON PIECES

An interesting series of coins and tokens dated from 1783 to 1795 bear the portrait of George Washington. The likenesses in most instances were faithfully reproduced and were designed to honor Washington. Many of these pieces were of English origin and made later than the dates indicate.

The legends generally signify a strong unity among the states and a marked display of patriotism which pervaded the new nation during that period. We find among these tokens an employment of what were soon to become our official coin devices, namely, the American eagle, the United States shield and stars. The denomination One Cent is used in several instances, while on some of the English pieces Halfpenny will be found. Several of these pieces were private patterns for proposed coinage contracts.

GEORGIUS TRIUMPHO TOKEN

Although the head shown on this token bears a strong resemblance to that upon some coins of George III, many collectors consider the Georgius Triumpho (Triumphant George) a token intended to commemorate the successful termination of the Revolutionary War — a triumph justly claimed for Washington.

The reverse side shows the Goddess of Liberty behind a framework of thirteen bars and fleur de lis. She holds an olive branch in her right hand and staff of liberty in her left. VOCE POPOLI (By the Voice of the People) 1783.

	Good	Fine	V. Fine
1783 GEORGIUS TRIUMPHO	$50.00	$100.00	$250.00

WASHINGTON PIECES

Military Bust

Large Military Bust
Point of Bust Close to W

	Fine	V. Fine	E. Fine
1783 Large military bust	$27.50	$60.00	$125.00
1783 Small military bust, plain edge	35.00	75.00	160.00
1783 Small military bust, engrailed edge	50.00	120.00	200.00

1783 Draped bust, no button......................	30.00	65.00	135.00
1783 Draped bust, with button....................	65.00	125.00	225.00

		Proof
1783 Draped bust. Copper restrike, plain edge		$275.00
1783 Draped bust. Copper restrike, engrailed edge		175.00
1783 Draped bust. Silver restrike, engrailed edge		375.00

UNITY STATES

V. Good	$30.00
V. Fine..............	90.00
Ex. Fine.............	160.00

Undated
Double Head
Cent

Fine.................	$50.00
V. Fine..............	75.00
Ex. Fine.............	150.00

Satirical Medal
1784 Ugly head....... (Ex. Rare)
Presumably of American origin.

WASHINGTON PIECES

1791 Cent
Edge Lettered: UNITED STATES OF AMERICA

	Fine	E. Fine	Unc.
1791 Cent, small eagle	$125.00	$325.00	$825.00
1791 Cent, large eagle	115.00	275.00	700.00

1791 Liverpool
Halfpenny
Lettered Edge

Fine	$650.00
Ex. Fine	1,350.00
Unc.	2,150.00

1792 Eagle with Stars

Copper	—
Silver	—
Gold	—

(1792) Undated Cent
"WASHINGTON BORN VIRGINIA"

1792 Cent
"WASHINGTON PRESIDENT"

	Fine
Copper	$2,000.00
Silver	—

Restrike of Obverse by Albert Collis, 1959

	Fine
Plain edge	$5,500.00
Lettered edge	—

WASHINGTON PIECES

★

	Good	*Fine*
1792 Small eagle. Silver	—	
1792 Small eagle. Copper	$1,200.00	$3,500.00
1792 Same. Ornamented edge (circles and squares)	—	
1792 Same. Silver	—	—
1792 Large eagle. Silver		(Unique)

**1792 Cent
Roman Head**

Lettered Edge:
UNITED STATES OF
AMERICA
Proof .... —

**1793 Ship
Halfpenny**

Lettered Edge
Fine $75.00
V. Fine.......... 150.00
Ex. Fine............ 250.00
Plain edge (Rare) . —

**1795 Halfpenny
Grate Token**

(Large coat buttons
variety pictured.)

	V. Fine	*E. Fine*	*Unc.*
1795 Large buttons, lettered edge	$350.00	$575.00	$950.00
1795 Large buttons, reeded edge	70.00	150.00	350.00
1795 Small buttons, reeded edge	160.00	325.00	650.00

WASHINGTON PIECES

Liberty and Security Halfpenny

	V. Good	Fine	E. Fine
1795 Halfpenny, plain edge	$75.00	$150.00	$375.00
1795 Halfpenny, LONDON edge	50.00	85.00	225.00
1795 Halfpenny, BIRMINGHAM edge	60.00	110.00	300.00
1795 Halfpenny, ASYLUM edge	125.00	250.00	500.00

Liberty and
Security Penny
Undated (1795)

Fine	$125.00
V. Fine	200.00
Ex. Fine	350.00
Unc.	900.00
Dated 1795	——

SUCCESS MEDALS

	Fine	V. Fine	E. Fine
SUCCESS medal, large. Plain or reeded edge	$125.00	$200.00	$325.00
SUCCESS medal, small. Plain or reeded edge	125.00	200.00	325.00

NORTH WALES HALFPENNY

	Good	Fine
1795 NORTH WALES Halfpenny	$65.00	$175.00
Lettered edge	——	——
Two stars at each side of harp	——	——

IX. THE FUGIO CENTS

The first coins issued by authority of the United States were the "Fugio" cents. Entries in the Journal of Congress supply interesting information about proceedings relating to this coinage.

"Saturday, April 21, 1787. . . .

"That the board of treasury be authorized to contract for three hundred tons of copper coin of the federal standard, agreeable to the proposition of Mr. James Jarvis, ... That it be coined at the expense of the contractor, etc."

On Friday, July 6, 1787, there was "Resolved, that the board of treasury direct the contractor for the copper coinage to stamp on one side of each piece the following device, viz: thirteen circles linked together, a small circle in the middle, with the words 'United States,' around it; and in the centre, the words 'We are one'; on the other side of the same piece the following device, viz: a dial with the hours expressed on the face of it; a meridian sun above on one side of which is the word 'Fugio,' (The meaning is, 'time flies') and on the other the year in figures '1787' below the dial, the words 'Mind Your Business.' "

The legends have been credited to Benjamin Franklin by many, and the coin, as a consequence, has been referred to as the Franklin Cent.

These cents were coined in New Haven, Conn., and possibly elsewhere. Most of the copper used in this coinage came from military stores. It is believed to have been the copper bands which held together the powder kegs sent to us by the French. The dies were made by Abel Buel of New Haven.

1787 WITH CLUB RAYS

	V. Good	Fine	V. Fine
Club Rays. Rounded ends	$85.00	$175.00	$400.00
Club Rays. Concave ends to rays:			
FUCIO (c instead of G). (Ex. Rare).........	——	——	——
Club Rays. Concave ends, FUGIO	——	——	——

1787 WITH POINTED RAYS

	V.G.	Fine	V.F.	E.F.	Unc.
UNITED above, STATES below. (Rare)	——	——	——	——	——
UNITED STATES at sides of circle	$50.00	$85.00	$125.00	$200.00	$450.00

THE FUGIO CENTS

	V.G.	V.F.	E.F.	Unc.
STATES UNITED at sides of circle. Cinquefoils (small, five bladed clover design) on label	$55.00	$150.00	$210.00	$475.00
STATES UNITED. 8-pointed stars on label	75.00	165.00	275.00	——
STATES UNITED. Label with raised rims (simply two concentric circles). Large letters in WE ARE ONE	80.00	250.00	500.00	——

Note: The preceding types with pointed rays have regular obverses punctuated with four cinquefoils.

Obv. no cinquefoils. Cross after date.

	V.G.	V.F.	E.F.	Unc.
Rev. UNITED STATES	150.00	450.00	——	——
Same obv., rev. STATES UNITED	175.00	475.00	——	——
Same obv., rev. label with raised rims				(Ex. Rare)

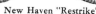

American Congress

New Haven "Restrike"

		E.F.	Unc.
Reverse with rays and AMERICAN CONGRESS. (Ex. Rare)	Gold (2 known)	——	——
	Silver	——	$450.00
	Copper or Brass	——	200.00

New Haven "restrikes" were supposedly struck from dies discovered by the fourteen-year-old C. Wyllys Betts in 1858 on the site of the Broome & Platt Store in New Haven, Conn., where the originals were made. Three pairs of dies were reportedly found and are still extant. Actually, the "restrikes" were made from copy dies c. 1860.

BIBLIOGRAPHY

Baker, W. S. *Medallic Portraits of Washington.* Philadelphia 1885 (reprinted 1965).
Crosby, S. S. *The Early Coins of America.* Boston 1875 (reprinted 1945, 1965, 1975).
Dickeson, M. W. *The American Numismatic Manual.* Philadelphia 1859, 1860, 1865.
Kessler, Alan. *The Fugio Cents.* Newtonville, Massachusetts 1976.
Maris, Edward. *A Historic Sketch of the Coins of New Jersey.* Philadelphia 1881 (reprinted 1925).
Miller, Henry C. and Hillyer Ryder. *The State Coinages of New England.* New York 1920.
Nelson, Philip. *The Coinage of William Wood 1722-1733.* London 1903 (reprinted 1959).
Newman, Eric P. *Coinage for Colonial Virginia.* New York 1957.
Noe, Sydney P. *The New England and Willow Tree Coinage of Massachusetts.* New York 1943. *The Oak Tree Coinage of Massachusetts.* New York 1947, and *The Pine Tree Coinage of Massachusetts.* New York 1952. (all reprinted 1973). *Studies on Money in Early America.* American Numismatic Society. New York, 1976.
Wurtzbach, Carl. *Massachusetts Colonial Silver Money.* 1937.

FIRST UNITED STATES MINT ISSUES

Many members of the House favored a representation of the president's head on the obverse of each coin. Others considered the idea a monarchical practice. Washington is believed to have expressed disapproval of the use of his portrait on our coins.

The majority considered a figure emblematic of Liberty more appropriate and the Senate finally concurred in this opinion. Robert Birch was an engraver employed at designing proposed devices for our coins. He, perhaps together with Adam Eckfeldt, engraved the dies for the disme and half disme. He has also been associated with a large copper cent of unusual design, which is known as the Birch Cent.

1792 SILVER CENTER CENT

	Fine	E. Fine
Cent. Silver center......	——	——
Cent. No silver center ...	——	——

1792 BIRCH CENT

Copper (V. Rare).. ——
G.W. PT. (George Washington President) below wreath, white metal (Unique)

1792 HALF DISME

	Good	Fine	V. Fine
Silver....	$1,200	$2,500	$4,500
Copper......................			(Unique)

1792 DISME

	E. Fine	Unc.
Silver (3 known)........	——	——
Copper................	——	——

1792 PATTERN QUARTER DOLLAR
Copper.......... (2 known)
White Metal...... (Unique)

MINTS AND MINT MARKS

Coins struck at Philadelphia (except 1942 to 1945 five-cent pieces) do not carry a mint mark. The mint mark is found only on coins struck at the branch mints. It is a small letter, usually found on the reverse side; the Lincoln cent is an early exception to this. All coins minted after 1967 have the mint mark on the obverse. The letters that signify the various mints are as follows:

C — Charlotte, North Carolina (gold coins only). 1838-1861.
CC — Carson City, Nevada. 1870-1893.
D — Dahlonega, Georgia (gold coins only). 1838-1861.
D — Denver, Colorado. 1906 to date.
O — New Orleans, Louisiana. 1838-1909.
P — Philadelphia, Pennsylvania. 1793 to date.
S — San Francisco, California. 1854 to date.

All dies for United States coins are made at the Philadelphia Mint. Dies for use at branch mints are hand stamped with the appropriate mint mark before they are shipped from Philadelphia. Because of this hand operation, the exact positioning and size of the mint mark may vary slightly, depending on where and how deeply the punch was impressed. This also accounts for double-punched and superimposed mint marks such as the 1938 D over D, and D over S Buffalo nickels. Polishing of dies may also alter the apparent size of fine details. Occasionally the mint mark is inadvertently left off a die sent to a branch mint, as was the case with some of the 1968, 1970 and 1975 proof dimes, and the 1971 proof nickel.

Prior to 1900, punches for mint marks varied greatly in size. This is particularly noticeable in the 1850 to 1880 period in which the letters range from very small to very large. An attempt to standardize sizes started in 1892 with the Barber series, but exceptions are seen in the 1892 O half dollar and 1905 O dime, both of which have normal and "microscopic" mint marks. A more or less standard size small mint mark was used on all minor coins starting in 1909, and on all dimes, quarters and halves after the Barber series was replaced in 1916. Slight variations in mint mark size occur through 1940 with notable differences in 1928, when small and large S mint marks were used.

In recent years a single D or S punch has been used to mark all branch mint dies. The change to the larger D for Denver coins occurred in 1933. Dimes, half dollars and dollars of 1934 exist with either the old, smaller size mint mark or the new, larger size D. All other denominations of 1934 and after are standard. The San Francisco mint mark was changed to its present larger size during 1941 and, with the exception of the half dollar, all 1941 S coins are known with either small or large size mint mark. Halves were not changed until 1942, and the 1942 S pieces exist both ways. The 1945 S dime with "microscopic" S is an unexplained abnormality.

PROOF COINS

A "proof" is a specimen striking of coinage for presentation, souvenir, exhibition, or numismatic purposes. Pre-1968 proofs were made only at the Philadelphia Mint. Current proofs are made only at San Francisco.

The term "proof" refers to the method of manufacture and not the condition of a coin. Regular production coins in mint state have coruscating, frosty luster, soft details, and minor imperfections. Proof coins can usually be distinguished by their sharpness of detail, high wire edge, and extremely brilliant, mirrorlike surface. All proofs are originally sold by the mint at a premium.

Very few proof coins were made prior to 1856. Because of their rarity and infrequent sales, they are not all listed in this catalog.

Frosted proofs were issued prior to 1936. These have a brilliant mirrorlike field with contrasting dull or frosted design and lettering. With modern proofs the first 15-20 coins struck from new proof dies are also frosted, but this feature is lost as soon as the dies are repolished.

Matte proofs have a granular "sandblast" surface instead of the mirror finish. Matte proof cents, nickels, and gold coins were issued from 1908 to 1916; a few 1921 and 1922 silver dollars were also struck this way.

Brilliant proofs have been issued from 1936 to date. These have a uniformly brilliant mirrorlike surface and sharp, high relief details.

"Prooflike" coins are occasionally seen. These are specimens from the first few impressions of regular coinage dies from any mint. They are not true proofs, but may have most of the characteristics of a proof coin and generally command a premium. Collectors should beware of coins that have been buffed to look like proofs; a magnifying glass will reveal myriad hair lines and lack of detail.

How A Proof Coin Is Made . . .

Selected dies are inspected for perfection and are highly polished and cleaned. They are again wiped clean or polished after every 15 to 25 impressions and are replaced frequently to avoid imperfections from worn dies. Coinage blanks are polished and cleaned to assure high quality in striking. They are then hand fed into the coinage press one at a time, each blank receiving two blows from the dies to bring up sharp, high relief details. The coinage operation is done at slow speed with extra pressure. Finished proofs are individually inspected and are handled by gloves or tongs. They also receive a final inspection by packers before being sonically sealed in special plastic cases.

MODERN PROOF COINS

After a lapse of twenty years, proof coins were struck at the Philadelphia Mint from 1936 to 1942 inclusive. In 1942, when the composition of the five-cent piece was changed, there were two types of this denomination available to collectors. The striking of proof coins was temporarily suspended from 1943 to 1949, and again from 1965 to 1967; during the latter period special mint sets were struck. Proof sets were resumed in 1968. They are delivered from the mint only during the year of issue. Sets from 1936 through 1972 include the cent, nickel, dime, quarter and half; starting in 1973 the dollar is included.

Figures in parentheses represent the total number of full sets minted.

1936 (3,837)	$1,600	1962 (3,218,019)...............	$4.75
1937 (5,542)	825.00	1963 (3,075,645)...............	4.90
1938 (8,045)	410.00	1964 (3,950,762)...............	5.00
1939 (8,795)	350.00	1968S (3,041,506)	4.00
1940 (11,246)	275.00	1968S 10¢ without mint mark .	—
1941 (15,287)	275.00	1969S (2,934,631)	4.00
1942 both nickels ⎱ (21,120) ⋯	320.00	1970S (2,632,810)	8.00
1942 one nickel ⎰	275.00	1970S with sm. date 1¢........	47.00
1950 (51,386)	165.00	1970S 10¢ without mint mark	
1951 (57,500)	100.00	(estimated 2,200)........	550.00
1952 (81,980)	65.00	1971S (3,220,733)	4.00
1953 (128,800)	45.00	1971S 5¢ without mint mark	
1954 (233,300)	22.00	(estimated 1,655)........	900.00
1955 box pack ⎱ (378,200) ⋯⋯	21.00	1972S (3,260,996)	4.00
1955 flat pack ⎰ ⋯⋯	22.00	1973S (2,760,339)	10.00
1956 (669,384)	11.00	1974S (2,612,568)	11.00
1957 (1,247,952)...............	6.00	1975S (2,845,450)	21.00
1958 (875,652)	11.50	1975S 10¢ without mint mark	—
1959 (1,149,291)...............	6.25	1976S (4,149,730)	7.75
1960 (1,691,602 both kinds)		1976S three piece set (3,295,714)	10.00
with lg. date 1¢..........	5.75	1977S (3,251,152)	10.00
1960 with sm. date 1¢.........	20.00	1978S......................	10.00
1961	4.75		

SPECIAL MINT SETS

1965 (2,360,000)...... $3.00   1966 (2,261,583)..... $3.25   1967 (1,863,344) $4.00

UNITED STATES REGULAR ISSUES
HALF CENTS — 1793-1857

From the standpoint of face value the half cent is the smallest coin struck by the United States. All half cents are scarce, but the series has never enjoyed the popularity of some of the other series, hence the more common dates and varieties are reasonably priced.

There were various intermissions in coinage, and during most of the period 1836 to 1849 the coinage was very small, causing a very noticeable lapse in the series for the average collector. While 1796 is the most valuable date, the originals and restrikes of 1831, 1836 and 1840 through 1849, and rare varieties are all difficult to obtain.

The half cent was authorized to be coined April 2, 1792. Originally the weight was to have been 132 grains, but this was changed to 104 grains by the Act of January 14, 1793, before coinage commenced. The weight was again changed to 84 grains January 26, 1796 by presidential proclamation in conformity with the Act of March 3, 1795. Coinage was discontinued by the Act of February 21, 1857. All were coined at the Philadelphia Mint.

LIBERTY CAP TYPE 1793-1797

AG-3 ABOUT GOOD—*Clear enough to identify.*

G-4 GOOD—*Outline of bust clear, no details. Date readable. Reverse lettering incomplete.*

VG-8 VERY GOOD—*Some hair details. Reverse lettering complete.*

F-12 FINE—*Most of hair detail shows. Leaves worn but all visible.*

VF-20 VERY FINE—*Hair near ear and forehead worn, other areas distinct. Some details in leaves show.*

Head Facing Left 1793

Designer Adam Eckfeldt; weight 6.74 grams; composition: copper; approx. diameter 22 mm; edge: TWO HUNDRED FOR A DOLLAR.

	Quan. Minted	AG-3	G-4	VG-8	F-12	VF-20
1793	35,334	$250.00	$500.00	$700.00	$1,125	$1,800

Head Facing Right 1794-1797

1794 — Designer Robert Scot; weight 6.74 grams; composition: copper; approx. diameter 23.5 mm; edge: TWO HUNDRED FOR A DOLLAR.

1795 — Designer John Smith Gardner; weight 6.74 grams; composition: copper; approx. diameter 23.5 mm; edge: TWO HUNDRED FOR A DOLLAR.

1795-1797 (thin planchet) — Weight 5.44 grams; composition: copper; approx. diameter 23.5 mm; edge: plain (some 1797 experimentally lettered).

1794	81,600	60.00	100.00	150.00	250.00	475.00

HALF CENTS

Pole to Cap

Punctuated Date

No Pole to Cap

	Quan. Minted	AG-3	G-4	VG-8	F-12	VF-20
1795 Lettered edge, with pole.........	} 25,600	$55.00	$90.00	$135.00	$240.00	$475.00
1795 Lettered edge, punctuated date ..		55.00	90.00	135.00	240.00	475.00
1795 Plain edge, punctuated date .	} 109,000	50.00	85.00	130.00	225.00	440.00
1795 Pl. edge, no pole		50.00	85.00	130.00	225.00	440.00
1796 With pole*........... 5,090		850.00	1,500	2,400	400.00	6,500
1796 No pole 1,390		1,300	3,150	4,500	7,300	12,500

*The deceptive "Dr. Edwards" struck copy of this coin has a different head and larger letters.

1797 Plain Edge

1797, 1 above 1, Plain Edge

1797 All kinds........... 119,215					
1797 Lettered edge..............	150.00	285.00	435.00	700.00	1,500
1797 Plain edge.................	50.00	85.00	125.00	225.00	400.00
1797, 1 above 1, plain edge	47.50	80.00	115.00	200.00	350.00

DRAPED BUST TYPE 1800-1808

AG-3 ABOUT GOOD—*Clear enough to identify.*
G-4 GOOD—*Bust outline clear, no details, date readable. Reverse lettering worn and incomplete.*
VG-8 VERY GOOD—*Some drapery shows. Date and legends complete.*
F-12 FINE—*Shoulder drapery and hair over brow worn smooth.*
VF-20 VERY FINE—*Only slight wear in above areas. Slight wear on reverse.*

Designer Robert Scot: weight 5.44 grams; composition: copper; approx. diameter 23.5 mm; plain edge.

A modified reverse design was introduced during 1802, and used through 1808.

1800 211,530	13.00	23.00	29.00	39.00	62.50

HALF CENTS

	Quan. Minted	AG-3	G-4	VG-8	F-12	VF-20
1802, 2 over 0, rev. of 1800	} 14,366	$350.00	$750.00	$1,300	$1,850	$3,200
1802, 2 over 0, new rev.		70.00	140.00	200.00	400.00	700.00
1803	97,900	13.00	21.00	27.50	37.50	60.00

Plain 4   Crosslet 4   Stemless Wreath   Stems to Wreath

		AG-3	G-4	VG-8	F-12	VF-20
1804 Plain 4, stems		14.00	24.00	34.00	48.00	90.00
1804 Pl. 4, stemless		12.50	20.00	27.00	36.00	58.00
1804 Cr. 4, stems	} 1,055,312	12.50	20.00	27.00	36.00	58.00
1804 Cr. 4, stemless		12.50	20.00	27.00	36.00	58.00
1804 "Spiked chin"		14.00	24.00	31.00	43.00	75.00

1804 "Spiked Chin" Variety   Small 5   Large 5

		AG-3	G-4	VG-8	F-12	VF-20
1805 Sm. 5, stemless		12.50	20.00	27.00	36.00	58.00
1805 Small 5, stems	} 814,464	47.50	78.00	132.50	325.00	585.00
1805 Large 5, stems		12.50	20.00	27.00	36.00	58.00

Small 6   Large 6   1808, 8 over 7   Normal Date

		AG-3	G-4	VG-8	F-12	VF-20
1806 Small 6, stems		21.00	44.00	67.50	130.00	200.00
1806 Sm. 6, stemless	} 356,000	13.00	21.00	27.50	37.50	60.00
1806 Large 6, stems		13.00	21.00	27.50	37.50	60.00
1807	476,000	13.00	21.00	27.50	37.50	60.00
1808, 8 over 7	} 400,000	35.00	45.00	67.50	125.00	250.00
1808 Normal date		13.00	21.00	27.50	37.50	60.00

CLASSIC HEAD TYPE 1809-1836

Designer John Reich. Standards same as previous issue.

AG-3 ABOUT GOOD—*Worn, but clear enough to identify.*
G-4 GOOD—*LIBERTY only partly visible on hair band. Lettering, date, stars, worn but visible.*
VG-8 VERY GOOD—*LIBERTY entirely visible on hair band. Lower curls worn.*
F-12 FINE—*Only part wear on LIBERTY and hair at top worn in spots.*
VF-20 VERY FINE—*Lettering clear-cut. Hair only slightly worn.*
MS-60 UNCIRCULATED—*Typical brown to red surface. No trace of wear.*

HALF CENTS

1809 Circle Inside 0   1809 Normal Date

	Quan. Minted	G-4	VG-8	F-12	VF-20	MS-60
1809 Circle inside 0 ..	⎫	$19.00	$25.00	$35.00	$60.00	$400.00
1809, 9 over 6	⎬ 1,154,572	19.00	25.00	35.00	60.00	385.00
1809 Normal date....	⎭	19.00	25.00	35.00	60.00	385.00
1810 215,000		21.00	32.00	44.00	77.50	650.00
1811 63,140		50.00	78.00	135.00	300.00	1,250
1811 Rev. of 1802. Unofficial restrike. Extremely Rare.						
1825 63,000		21.00	24.00	32.50	50.00	350.00
1826 234,000		19.00	23.00	31.00	38.00	315.00

Brilliant red uncirculated half cents are worth more than prices shown.

13 Stars   12 Stars

1828, 13 Stars	⎱ 606,000	19.00	23.00	31.00	38.00	250.00
1828, 12 Stars	⎰	20.00	26.00	36.00	55.00	500.00
1829	487,000	19.00	23.00	31.00	38.00	335.00

Original Large Berries   Restrike Small Berries

Beginning in 1831 new coinage equipment and modified dies produced a raised rim on each side of these coins. Proofs and restrikes were made at the mint for sale to collectors. They are believed to have been struck after 1850.

	Quan. Minted			MS-60	Proof
1831 Original. (Beware of altered date).................... 2,200				$2,200	$3,000
1831 Restrike. Large berries (Rev. of 1836)					1,900
1831 Restrike. Small berries (Rev. of 1840-1857)................					3,900

	Quan. Minted	VG-8	F-12	VF-20	MS-60	Proof
1832 .... 154,000*		23.00	28.00	36.00	315.00	1,200
1833 .... 120,000*		23.00	28.00	36.00	315.00	1,200
1834 .... 141,000*		23.00	28.00	36.00	315.00	1,200
1835 .... 398,000*		23.00	28.00	36.00	315.00	1,200
1836 Original...................						1,800
1836 Restrike. (Rev. of 1840-1857)						3,000

*The figures given here are thought to be correct, although official mint records report these quantities for 1833-36 rather than 1832-35.

HALF CENTS

No half cents were struck in 1837. Because of the great need for small change, however, a large number of tokens similar in size to current half cents and large cents were issued privately by businessmen who needed them in commerce. One of the most popular pieces is listed and illustrated below.

	G-4	VG-8	F-12	VF-20	MS-60
1837 Token (not a coin)	$17.50	$27.50	$40.00	$80.00	$240.00

BRAIDED HAIR TYPE 1840-1857

Designer Christian Gobrecht; weight 5.44 grams; composition: copper; diameter 23 mm; plain edge.

	Proof		Proof
1840 Original................	$1,250	1845 Original.................	$1,400
1840 Restrike...............	1,100	1845 Restrike	1,250
1841 Original................	1,250	1846 Original.................	1,300
1841 Restrike...............	1,300	1846 Restrike	1,200
1842 Original................	1,325	1847 Original.................	1,200
1842 Restrike...............	1,150	1847 Restrike	1,200
1843 Original................	1,275	1848 Original.................	1,300
1843 Restrike...............	1,225	1848 Restrike	1,200
1844 Original................	1,300	1849 Original. Small date	1,500
1844 Restrike...............	1,250	1849 Restrike. Small date	1,200

Brilliant or red uncirculated half cents are worth more than prices shown.

G-4 GOOD—*Some of LIBERTY shows and beads partly distinct.*

VG-8 VERY GOOD—*Beads uniformly distinct. Hairlines show in spots.*

F-12 FINE—*Hairlines above ear worn. Beads sharp.*

VF-20 VERY FINE—*Lowest curl shows wear, hair otherwise distinct.*

MS-60 UNCIRCULATED—*No trace of wear, light blemishes.*

Small Date   Large Date

	Quan. Minted	G-4	F-12	VF-20	MS-60	Proof
1849 Large date	39,864	27.50	33.00	49.00	350.00	——
1850	39,812	27.50	33.00	49.00	350.00	——
1851	147,672	25.00	30.00	39.00	300.00	——
1852 Original...................						——
1852 Restrike...................						1,400
1853	129,694	25.00	30.00	39.00	300.00	
1854	55,358	25.00	30.00	39.00	300.00	1,100
1855	56,500	25.00	30.00	39.00	300.00	1,200
1856	40,430	27.50	35.00	42.00	300.00	1,000
1857	35,180	30.00	37.50	55.00	325.00	1,200

BIBLIOGRAPHY

Cohen, Roger S., Jr. *American Half Cents—The "Little Half Sisters".* 1971.
Crosby, S. S. *United States Coinage of 1793—Cents and Half Cents.* Boston, 1897.
Frossard, Edward. *United States Cents and Half Cents 1793-1857.* Irvington, New York, 1879.
Gilbert, Ebenezer, *United States Half Cents.* New York, 1916. Hewitt Reprint, Chicago.

LARGE CENTS — 1793-1857

Cents and half cents were the first coins struck under the authority of the United States Government. Coinage began in 1793 with laws specifying that the cent should weigh exactly twice as much as the half cent. Large cents were coined every year from 1793 to 1857 with the exception of 1815, when a lack of copper prevented production. All were coined at the Philadelphia Mint. Mintage records in some cases may be inaccurate, as many of the early pieces were struck later than the dates shown on the coins. Varieties listed are those most significant to collectors. Numerous other die varieties may be found because each of the early dies was individually made. Values of varieties not listed in this guide depend on collector interest, rarity and demand. Proof large cents were first made in 1817; all proofs are rare, as they were not made available to the general public until the 1850's.

FLOWING HAIR, CHAIN TYPE REVERSE 1793

Designer Henry Voight; weight 13.48 grams; composition: copper; approx. diameter 26-27 mm; edge: bars and slender vine with leaves.

AG-3 ABOUT GOOD—*Date and devices clear enough to identify.*

G-4 GOOD—*Lettering worn but readable. Bust has no detail.*

VG-8 VERY GOOD—*Date and lettering distinct, some details of head visible.*

F-12 FINE—*About half of hair, etc. details show.*

VF-20 VERY FINE—*Ear visible. Most of details can be seen.*

EF-40 EXTREMELY FINE—*Highest points of hair and back of temple show wear.*

| Obverse | AMERI. Reverse | AMERICA Reverse |

	Quan. Minted	AG-3	G-4	VG-8	F-12	VF-20	EF-40
1793 Chain	36,103						
1793 AMERI. in legend		$300.00	$600.00	$1000	$2200	$4250	$8500
1793 AMERICA*		275.00	550.00	900.00	2000	3750	7000

*Varieties with or without periods after date and LIBERTY.

FLOWING HAIR, WREATH TYPE REVERSE 1793

The reverse of this type bears a "single-bow" wreath, as distinguished from the wreath tied with a double bow on the following type. A three-leaf sprig appears above the date on the obverse, and both sides have borders of small beads. Introduction of this reverse answered criticism of the chain design, but the stronger modeling of the face and hair still failed to gain acceptance as representative of Liberty. After three months' production the design was abandoned in favor of the Liberty Cap type.

Instead of the normal sprig above the date, the rare "strawberry leaf" variety has a spray of trefoil leaves and a small blossom. The trefoils match those found on the normal wreath reverse. It is not clear why this variety was created. All known specimens are badly worn.

LARGE CENTS

Designer Adam Eckfeldt; weight 13.48 grams; composition: copper; approx. diameter 26-28 mm; edge: vine and bars, or lettered ONE HUNDRED FOR A DOLLAR followed by either a single or double leaf.

Wreath Type   Strawberry Leaf Var.

Quan. Minted	AG-3	G-4	VG-8	F-12	VF-20	EF-40
1793 Wreath 63,353						
1793 Vine/bars edge ...	$110.00	$250.00	$450.00	$900.00	$1650	$3750
1793 Lettered edge.....	125.00	275.00	500.00	950.00	1900	4250
1793 Strawberry leaf...			Ex. Rare			

LIBERTY CAP TYPE 1793-1796

Another major change was made in 1793 to satisfy continuing objections to the obverse portrait. This version appears to have been more successful, as it was continued into 1796. The 1793 pieces had beaded borders, but a border of denticles or "teeth" was adopted in 1794. A famous 1794 variety is the probably whimsical "starred" reverse, with a border of 94 tiny 5-pointed stars under the denticles.

Portrait variations listed below for 1794 are the result of several changes of die engravers. The so-called "Jefferson head" of 1795 is now thought to be a sample for a proposed coinage contract by a private manufacturer, John Harper.

Planchets became too thin for edge lettering after the weight reduction ordered late in 1795. The variety with reeded edge was probably an experimental substitute, rejected in favor of a plain edge.

1793-1795 (thick planchet) — Designer Joseph Wright; weight 13.48 grams; composition: copper; approx. diameter 29 mm; edge: ONE HUNDRED FOR A DOLLAR followed by a single leaf.

1795-1796 (thin planchet) — Designer John Smith Gardner; weight 10.89 grams; composition: copper; approx. diameter 29 mm; plain edge.

Liberty Cap Type

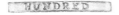

1793 Vine and Bars edge
Chain and Wreath type only

Lettered edge 1793-1795
ONE HUNDRED FOR A DOLLAR   Beaded Border, 1793 Only

LARGE CENTS

1793-1794	1794 Only	1794-1796
"Head of 1793" Head is in high rounded relief	"Head of 1794" Well defined hair, hook on lowest curl	"Head of 1795" Head in low relief, no hook on lowest curl

	Quan. Minted	AG-3	G-4	VG-8	F-12	VF-20	EF-40
1793 Lib. Cap...	11,056	$225.00	$450.00	$775.00	$1400.00	$3750.00	$8000.00
1794 All kinds..	918,521						
1794 "Head of 1793"...		90.00	175.00	300.00	700.00	1750.00	4000.00
1794 "Head of 1794"...		22.50	40.00	75.00	125.00	275.00	800.00
1794 "Head of 1795"...		22.50	40.00	75.00	130.00	285.00	825.00
1794 Starred rev.......		750.00	1300.00	2250.00	4000.00	9000.00	
1795 Ltd. ed.	37,000	35.00	67.50	125.00	200.00	450.00	1100.00
1795 Plain ed...	501,500	22.50	45.00	80.00	125.00	225.00	575.00

Reeded Edge

1795 Reeded edge......			Ex. Rare			
1795 Jefferson Head (not a regular mint issue)						
Plain ed.	700.00	1200.00	2000.00	3250.00	7000.00	
Ltd. ed.			Ex. Rare			
1796 Lib. Cap... 109,825	30.00	60.00	100.00	150.00	300.00	750.00

Obverse 1796-1807

1794 Starred Reverse

"Jefferson Head"

This head was modified slightly in 1798. See following page for details.

DRAPED BUST TYPE 1796-1807

Designer Robert Scot; weight 10.89 grams; composition: copper; approx. diameter 29 mm; plain edge.

AG-3 ABOUT GOOD—*Clear enough to identify.*

G-4 GOOD—*Lettering worn, but clear; date clear. Bust lacks details.*

VG-8 VERY GOOD—*Drapery partly visible. Less wear in date and lettering.*

F-12 FINE—*Hair over brow is smooth, some detail showing elsewhere.*

VF-20 VERY FINE—*Hairlines slightly worn. Hair over brow better defined.*

EF-40 EXTREMELY FINE—*Hair above forehead and left of eye outlined and detailed. Only slight wear on olive leaves.*

LARGE CENTS

1794-1796	1795-1798	1796-1807

"Reverse of 1794"
Note double leaf at top
right; 14-16 leaves left,
16-18 leaves right.

"Reverse of 1796"
Note single leaf at top
right; 17-21 leaves left,
16-19 leaves right.

"Reverse of 1797"
Note double
leaf at top right;
16 leaves left,
19 leaves right.

	Quan. Minted	AG-3	G-4	VG-8	F-12	VF-20	EF-40
1796 Dr. Bust...	363,375						
1796 reverse of 1794		$25.00	$50.00	$85.00	$150.00	$275.00	$675.00
1796 reverse of 1796		27.50	55.00	90.00	155.00	300.00	725.00
1796 reverse of 1797		30.00	60.00	100.00	175.00	350.00	775.00
1796 LIHERTY error.....		40.00	75.00	125.00	210.00	425.00	1100.00

LIHERTY
error

Gripped or
Milled Edge

Stems   Stemless

		AG-3	G-4	VG-8	F-12	VF-20	EF-40
1797 All kinds..	897,510						
1797 Gr. Ed., '96 rev....		15.00	30.00	60.00	110.00	225.00	525.00
1797 Pl. edge, '96 rev...		17.00	33.00	65.00	125.00	250.00	575.00
1797, '97 rev., Stems ...		10.00	20.00	37.50	70.00	175.00	400.00
1797, '97 rev., Stemless.		20.00	42.00	75.00	150.00	300.00	700.00

1798, 8 over 7

Style 1 hair appears on all 1796-
97, many 1798 varieties and 1800
over 1798. Style 2 hair, used 1798-
1807, is most easily recognized by
the extra curl near the shoulder.

Style 1 Hair   Style 2 Hair

1798 All kinds	1,841,745						
1798, 8 over 7		17.00	33.00	70.00	135.00	275.00	800.00
1798, reverse of 1796...		17.00	33.00	65.00	125.00	250.00	700.00
1798, 1st hair style.....		9.00	19.00	35.00	70.00	150.00	375.00
1798, 2nd hair style		9.00	19.00	31.00	62.50	140.00	350.00

[69]

LARGE CENTS

1799, 9 over 8

1800 over 1798

1800, 80 over 79

	Quan. Minted	AG-3	G-4	VG-8	F-12	VF-20	EF-40
1799, 9 over 8 ... *		$225.00	$450.00	$750.00	$1500	$3500	——
1799 Nor. date...	42,540	200.00	425.00	700.00	1300	3250	——
1800 All kds..	2,822,175						
1800 over 1798,							
Style 1 hair		7.00	16.00	27.50	52.50	140.00	$475.00
1800, 80 over 79,							
Style 2 hair		6.00	14.00	25.00	45.00	110.00	300.00
1800 Normal date......		6.00	14.00	25.00	42.50	100.00	275.00

*Mintage for 1799, 9 over 8 variety is included with the 1798 figure.

Fraction 1/000

Corrected Fraction

1801 Reverse, 3 Errors

Error-fraction dies appear on cents of 1801, 1802, and 1803, but all of these dies originated in 1801, possibly all by the same blunderer.

	AG-3	G-4	VG-8	F-12	VF-20	EF-40
1801 All kds.. 1,362,837						
1801 Normal rev.......	6.00	14.00	25.00	45.00	100.00	275.00
1801, 3 errors: 1/000, one						
stem & IINITED ...	15.00	35.00	50.00	120.00	250.00	700.00
1801 Fraction 1/000....	9.00	18.00	30.00	65.00	140.00	425.00
1801, 1/100 over 1/000.	10.00	22.00	36.00	85.00	175.00	500.00
1802 All kds. 3,435,100.						
1802 Normal rev.......	6.00	12.00	20.00	40.00	85.00	225.00
1802 Fraction 1/000....	7.50	15.00	27.50	50.00	125.00	325.00
1802 Stemless wreath ..	7.00	14.00	25.00	45.00	115.00	275.00

1803 Sm. Date, Blunt 1

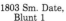

1803 Large Date Pointed 1

Small Fraction

Large Fraction

All small date varieties have a blunt 1 in date. Large dates have pointed 1 and noticeably larger 3.

LARGE CENTS

	Quan. Minted	AG-3	G-4	VG-8	F-12	VF-20	EF-40
1803 All kds..	3,131,691						
1803 Sm. dt., sm. fract .		$6.00	$12.00	$20.00	$40.00	$85.00	$225.00
1803 Sm. dt., lg. fract ..		6.00	12.00	20.00	40.00	85.00	225.00
1803 Lg. dt., sm. fract..	175.00	275.00	500.00	900.00	1800.00		
1803 Lg. dt., lg. fract...	25.00	45.00	85.00	150.00	275.00	800.00	
1803, 1/100 over 1/000 .	9.00	20.00	40.00	65.00	150.00	400.00	
1803 Stemless wreath ..	8.50	17.50	30.00	50.00	140.00	375.00	

1804 With Broken Dies (see arrows)

All genuine 1804 Cents have a crosslet 4 in the date and a large fraction. The 0 in the date is in line with the O in OF on the reverse of the coin.

1804	96,500	165.00	250.00	425.00	750.00	1,300	2,300

Restrike of 1804 Cent

A fake 1804 was manufactured from discarded mint dies. An altered 1803 die was used for the obverse and a die of the 1820 cent used for the reverse. They were struck about the year 1860 to satisfy the demand for this rare date. Known as the "restrike," it was a patchwork job and is easily distinguished from a genuine 1804 cent.

1804 Unofficial restrike of 1860 (Uncirculated)							250.00
1805	941,116	6.00	12.00	20.00	40.00	85.00	225.00
1806	348,000	9.00	20.00	35.00	65.00	160.00	375.00

Small 1807, 7 over 6, blunt 1

Lg. 1807, 7 over 6, pointed 1

"Comet" Variety

1807 All kinds...	829,221						
1807 Small 7 over 6, ... Blunt 1............		100.00	200.00	350.00	600.00	1,200	——
1807 Large 7 over 6.....		6.00	12.00	20.00	45.00	100.00	275.00
1807 Small fraction		7.50	16.00	32.00	60.00	140.00	450.00
1807 Large fraction		6.00	12.00	20.00	40.00	90.00	250.00
1807 "Comet" variety (die break behind head)		8.00	17.50	35.00	80.00	175.00	500.00

LARGE CENTS

CLASSIC HEAD TYPE 1808-1814

1808 to 1814 — This group does not compare in sharpness and quality to those struck before (1793-1807), nor to those struck after (1816 on). The copper used was "softer," having less metallic impurities. This impaired the wearing quality of the series. For this reason collectors find greater difficulty in obtaining these dates in choice condition.

Designer John Reich. Standards same as previous issue.

AG-3 ABOUT GOOD—*Details clear enough to identify.*

G-4 GOOD—*Legends, stars, date worn, but plain.*

VG-8 VERY GOOD—*LIBERTY all readable. Ear shows. Details worn but plain.*

F-12 FINE—*Hair on forehead and before ear nearly smooth. Ear and hair under ear sharp.*

VF-20 VERY FINE—*All hairlines show some detail. Leaves on rev. show slight wear.*

EF-40 EXTREMELY FINE—*All hairlines sharp. Very slight wear on high points.*

	Quan. Minted	AG-3	G-4	VG-8	F-12	VF-20	EF-40
1808	1,007,000	$12.00	$19.00	$35.00	$62.50	$150.00	$400.00
1809	222,867	32.00	52.50	90.00	175.00	360.00	850.00

1810, 10 over 09   1810 Normal Date   1811, last 1 over 0   1811 Normal Date

	Quan. Minted	AG-3	G-4	VG-8	F-12	VF-20	EF-40
1810 All kds...	1,458,500						
1810, 10 over 09		10.00	16.00	30.00	55.00	125.00	375.00
1810 Normal date		10.00	16.00	30.00	52.50	120.00	350.00
1811 All kds.....	218,025						
1811 Last 1 over 0		25.00	40.00	72.50	135.00	275.00	700.00
1811 Normal date		22.50	36.00	67.50	120.00	250.00	650.00

1812 Small date   1812 Large date   1814 Plain 4   1814 Crosslet 4

	Quan. Minted	AG-3	G-4	VG-8	F-12	VF-20	EF-40
1812 Sm. dt....	1,075,500	10.00	16.00	30.00	52.50	120.00	350.00
1812 Lg. dt....		10.00	16.00	30.00	52.50	120.00	350.00
1813	418,000	14.00	25.00	47.50	90.00	185.00	475.00
1814 Plain 4....	357,830	10.00	17.00	32.00	55.00	125.00	375.00
1814 Crosslet 4 .		10.00	17.00	32.00	55.00	125.00	375.00

LARGE CENTS

CORONET TYPE 1816-1857

G-4 GOOD—*Head details partly visible. Even wear in date and legends.*
VG-8 VERY GOOD—*LIBERTY, date, stars, legends clear. Part of hair cord visible.*
F-12 FINE—*All hairlines show. Hair cords show uniformly.*
VF-20 VERY FINE—*Hair cords only slightly worn. Hairlines only partly worn, all well defined.*
EF-40 EXTREMELY FINE—*Both hair cords stand out sharply. All hairlines sharp.*

Designer Robert Scot; weight 10.89 grams; composition: copper; approx. diameter 28-29 mm; plain edge.

MATRON HEAD 1816-1835

1817, 15 Stars

	Quan. Minted	G-4	VG-8	F-12	VF-20	EF-40	MS-60*
1816	2,820,982	$5.00	$6.50	$10.00	$25.00	$50.00	$275.00
1817, 13 stars	} 3,948,400	5.00	6.50	10.00	25.00	45.00	225.00
1817, 15 stars		7.00	10.00	17.50	35.00	85.00	500.00
1818	3,167,000	5.00	6.50	9.00	22.50	45.00	225.00

1819, 9 over 8   1819 Large Date   1819 Small Date

1819, 9 over 8	} 2,671,000	7.00	9.00	15.00	27.50	55.00	400.00
1819 Large date		5.00	6.50	10.00	25.00	45.00	250.00
1819 Small date		5.00	6.50	10.00	22.50	45.00	250.00

1820, 20 over 19
note 1 under 2

1820 Large Date
note plain-topped 2

1820 Small Date
note curl-topped 2

*Values shown are for average condition. Red to bright red uncirculated large cents with attractive surface (not cleaned) command higher prices. Beware of slightly worn copper coins which have been cleaned and recolored to simulate uncirculated luster.

LARGE CENTS

	Quan. Minted	G-4	VG-8	F-12	VF-20	EF-40	MS-60*
1820, 20 over 19	⎫	$6.00	$7.50	$12.00	$27.50	$55.00	$325.00
1820 Large date	⎬ 4,407,550	5.00	6.50	9.00	22.50	40.00	250.00
1820 Small date	⎭	5.00	6.50	9.00	25.00	50.00	275.00
1821	389,000	10.00	15.00	25.00	65.00	185.00	1,000
1822	2,072,339	5.00	6.50	9.00	22.50	60.00	375.00

1823, 3 over 2   1823 Restrike

		G-4	VG-8	F-12	VF-20	EF-40	MS-60*
1823, 3 over 2	⎫	20.00	27.50	60.00	110.00	400.00	——
1823 Normal date...	⎬	22.50	30.00	65.00	125.00	600.00	——
1823 Unofficial restrike, from broken obverse die						80.00	220.00

The 1823 unofficial restrike was made at the same time and by the same people as the 1804 restrike copy (qv), using a discarded 1823 obverse and an 1813 reverse die. The dies are heavily rusted (lumps on coin) and most examples have both dies cracked across.

1824, 4 over 2   1826, 6 over 5

		G-4	VG-8	F-12	VF-20	EF-40	MS-60*
1824, 4 over 2	⎫ 1,193,939	10.00	15.00	25.00	60.00	135.00	——
1824 Normal date...	⎭	6.00	8.00	15.00	30.00	70.00	550.00
1825	1,461,100	5.00	6.50	10.00	27.50	55.00	350.00
1826, 6 over 5	⎫ 1,517,425	10.00	15.00	25.00	50.00	100.00	500.00
1826 Normal date.....	⎭	5.00	6.50	10.00	25.00	45.00	275.00
1827	2,357,732	5.00	6.50	10.00	25.00	50.00	300.00

This date-size appears on cents before 1828   This date-size appears on cents after 1828

		G-4	VG-8	F-12	VF-20	EF-40	MS-60*
1828 Lg. nar. date	⎫ 2,260,624	5.00	6.50	10.00	25.00	50.00	325.00
1828 Sm. wide date ...	⎭	6.00	7.50	15.00	35.00	75.00	425.00

*See footnote page 73.

LARGE CENTS

This letter-size appears on cents of 1808-1834

note individual letter-size and proximity.

This letter-size appears on cents of 1829-1837

note isolation of letters, esp. STATES.

	Quan. Minted	G-4	VG-8	F-12	VF-20	EF-40	MS-60*
1829 Large letters	} 1,414,500	$5.00	$6.50	$10.00	$25.00	$50.00	$275.00
1829 Med. letters		6.00	7.50	17.50	35.00	80.00	400.00
1830 Large letters	} 1,711,500	5.00	6.50	10.00	25.00	50.00	275.00
1830 Med. letters		15.00	25.00	50.00	100.00	225.00	——
1831 Large letters	} 3,359,260	4.50	6.00	9.00	17.50	45.00	275.00
1831 Med. letters		4.50	6.00	9.00	17.50	45.00	275.00
1832 Large letters	} 2,362,000	4.50	6.00	9.00	17.50	40.00	250.00
1832 Med. letters		4.50	6.00	9.00	17.50	40.00	250.00
1833	2,739,000	4.50	6.00	9.00	17.50	40.00	250.00

Large 8 and Stars

Large 8, Small Stars

Small 8, Large Stars

1834 All kinds 1,855,100							
1834 Lg. 8, stars & rev. letters...		7.00	10.00	15.00	30.00	75.00	350.00
1834 Lg. 8 & stars, med. letters..		15.00	25.00	40.00	75.00	150.00	——
1834 Lg. 8, sm. stars, med. let....		5.00	6.50	10.00	25.00	55.00	300.00
1834 Sm. 8, lg. stars, med. let. ...		5.00	6.50	10.00	22.50	50.00	275.00

Large 8 and Stars, Matron Head

Small 8 and Stars, Matron Head

"Head of 1836" 1835-1837 Slim Bust

1835 Lg. 8 & stars	} 3,878,400	7.00	9.00	15.00	30.00	70.00	300.00
1835 Sm. 8 & stars....		7.00	9.00	15.00	30.00	70.00	300.00
1835 "Head of 1836" ..		5.00	6.50	10.00	22.50	45.00	225.00
1836	2,111,000	6.00	7.50	10.00	22.50	45.00	250.00

*See footnote page 73.

LARGE CENTS

G-4 GOOD—*Considerably worn. LIBERTY readable.*
VG-8 VERY GOOD—*Hairlines smooth but visible, outline of ear clearly defined.*
F-12 FINE—*Hairlines at top of head and behind ear worn but visible. Braid over brow plain, ear clear.*
VF-20 VERY FINE—*All details more sharp. Hair over brow shows only slight wear.*
EF-40 EXTREMELY FINE—*Hair above ear detailed, but slightly worn.*

Designer Christian Gobrecht; weight 10.89 grams; composition: copper; diameter 27.5 mm; plain edge.

1829-1837
Medium Letters
note proximity
of letters

"Head of 1838"
Beaded Cords
note slim bust
with beaded cords

1837-1839
Small Letters
note isolation
of letters

	Quan. Minted	G-4	VG-8	F-12	VF-20	EF-40	MS-60*
1837 Pl. crd., sm. let ..	} 5,558,300	$6.00	$8.00	$15.00	$30.00	$60.00	$300.00
1837 Pl. crd., med. let .		5.00	6.50	10.00	17.50	40.00	225.00
1837 Head of 1838		5.00	6.50	10.00	17.50	40.00	225.00
1838	6,370,200	5.00	6.50	10.00	17.50	40.00	225.00

1839 Over 1836
note closed 9,
plain cords

Silly Head
note browlock
at forehead

Booby Head
note back tip of
shoulder exposed

1839 All kinds 3,128,661						
1839, 9 over 6, plain cords	80.00	110.00	225.00	350.00	1,300	——
1839 Head of 1838, beaded cords.	6.00	8.00	15.00	25.00	60.00	325.00
1839 Silly Head.................	6.00	8.00	17.50	30.00	70.00	450.00
1839 Booby Head	6.00	8.00	15.00	30.00	70.00	400.00
1839 Petite head...............	6.00	8.00	15.00	25.00	60.00	350.00

The last two 1839 heads use a modified reverse which omits the line under CENT (see illustration at 1843).

*See footnote page 73.

LARGE CENTS

1840 Large Date

1840 Small Date

Small Date
over Large 18

	Quan. Minted	G-4	VG-8	F-12	VF-20	EF-40	MS-60*
1840 Large date	} 2,462,700	$5.50	$7.00	$10.00	$17.50	$35.00	$250.00
1840 Small date		5.50	7.00	10.00	17.50	35.00	250.00
1840 Sm. dt., lg. 18...		7.00	10.00	15.00	25.00	50.00	325.00
1841 Small date	1,597,367	6.00	8.00	10.00	17.50	40.00	300.00

1842 Small Date

1842 Large Date

Small Letters
1839-1843

1842 Small date	} 2,383,390	6.00	8.00	10.00	15.00	32.50	225.00
1842 Large date		6.00	8.00	10.00	15.00	32.50	225.00

"Head of 1840"
Petite Head
1839-1843

"Head of 1844"
Mature Head
1843-1857

Large Letters
1843-1857

1843 Petite, sm. let...	} 2,428,320	6.00	8.00	12.00	17.50	40.00	250.00
1843 Petite, lg. let ...		10.00	15.00	25.00	50.00	25.00	600.00
1843 Mature, lg. let ..		8.00	10.00	17.50	32.50	65.00	300.00
1844 Normal date....	} 2,398,752	6.00	8.00	10.00	17.50	30.00	225.00
1844 over 81 (error)..		8.00	10.00	20.00	40.00	100.00	600.00
1845	3,894,804	6.00	7.00	9.00	12.50	30.00	200.00

*See footnote page 73.

LARGE CENTS

1846 Small Date
note squat date
with closed 6

1846 Medium Date
note medium height
with ball-top 6

1846 Tall Date
note vertically-stretched
date with open-mouthed 6

	Quan. Minted	G-4	VG-8	F-12	VF-20	EF-40	MS-60*
1846 Small date	} 4,120,800	$5.00	$6.00	$8.00	$12.50	$30.00	$200.00
1846 Medium date ...		6.00	7.00	10.00	17.50	35.00	225.00
1846 Tall date		6.00	7.00	10.00	17.50	35.00	225.00
1847	} 6,183,669	4.50	6.00	8.00	12.50	25.00	180.00
1847, 7 over "sm." 7 .		8.00	10.00	20.00	35.00	70.00	300.00

1847, 7 over "Small" 7

1848	6,415,799	4.50	6.00	8.00	12.50	25.00	180.00
1849	4,178,500	4.50	6.00	8.00	12.50	30.00	225.00
1850	4,426,844	4.50	6.00	8.00	12.50	25.00	180.00

1844, 44 over 81   1851, 51 over 81

Both of these errors actually
have their final two digits
punched over an inverted 18.

These are not true overdates, but are some of the more spectacular of several
date-punch blunders of the 1844-1854 period. The so-called "overdates" of 1844
and 1851 each have the date punched upside-down, then corrected normally.

1851 Normal date....	} 9,889,707	4.00	5.00	7.00	10.00	25.00	180.00
1851 over 81 (error)..		6.00	8.00	15.00	35.00	75.00	300.00
1852	5,063,094	4.00	5.00	7.00	10.00	25.00	180.00
1853	6,641,131	4.00	5.00	7.00	10.00	25.00	180.00
1854	4,236,156	4.00	5.00	7.00	10.00	25.00	180.00

*See footnote page 73.

LARGE CENTS

1855 Upright 5's

1855 Slanting 5's

Original sketches of engraver James B. Longacre's work reveal that slanting 5's were a peculiarity of his work. The figure punch for an upright 5 was probably the work of an apprentice.

	Quan. Minted	G-4	VG-8	F-12	VF-20	EF-40	MS-60*
1855 All kinds	1,574,829						
1855 Upright 5's		$5.00	$6.00	$8.00	$12.50	$27.50	$200.00
1855 Slanting 5's		5.00	6.00	8.00	12.50	27.50	200.00
1855 Slanting 5's, knob on ear		6.00	8.00	10.00	25.00	40.00	275.00
1856 Upright 5	2,690,463	5.00	6.00	8.00	12.50	27.50	200.00
1856 Slanting 5		5.00	6.00	8.00	12.50	27.50	200.00

1857 Large Date

1857 Small date

1857 Large date	333,456	20.00	25.00	35.00	45.00	60.00	300.00
1857 Small date		22.50	27.50	40.00	50.00	65.00	325.00

*See footnote page 73.

Passing of the Large Cent and Half Cent

By 1857 the cost of making and distributing copper coins had risen. Mint Director Snowden reported that they "barely paid expenses." Both cents and half cents had become unpopular, in fact, they hardly circulated outside of the larger cities. The practice of issuing subsidiary silver coins which began in 1853, brought about a reform of the copper coinage. The half cent was abandoned and a smaller cent was introduced late in 1857.

The law of 1857 brought important benefits to the citizens. By its terms Spanish coins were redeemed and melted at the Mint in exchange for new small cents. The decimal system became popular and official thereafter, and the old method of reckoning in reals, medios, shillings, etc., was gradually given up, although the terms, "two bits" and "penny" are still commonly used. The new, convenient small cent won popular favor and soon became a useful instrument of retail trade and a boon to society generally.

BIBLIOGRAPHY
Sheldon, Wm. H. *Penny Whimsy (1793-1814)*. New York, 1958.
Newcomb, H. R. *United States Copper Cents 1816-1857*. New York, 1944.
PENNY-WISE, official publication of Early American Coppers, Inc. (EAC)

SMALL CENTS — 1856 to Date
FLYING EAGLE TYPE 1856-1858

The Act of February 21, 1857 provided for the coinage of the small cent, and made uncurrent the coins of other countries, particularly the Spanish and Mexican dollars. The new cents weighed 72 grains. Composition, 88% copper, 12% nickel.

The 1856 Eagle cent was not an authorized mint issue, as the law governing the new size coin was enacted after the date of issue. It is believed that about 1,000 of these pieces were struck. They are properly referred to as patterns.

Collectors are advised to inspect any 1856 Flying Eagle cent carefully.

A few tests will aid in establishing genuineness of this cent, as follows: If the lower half of the 6 is thick it is probably an altered 1858. A magnifying glass will often reveal poor workmanship.

The figure 5 slants slightly to the right on a genuine 1856. The vertical bar points to the center of the ball just beneath. On the 1858, this bar points *outside* the ball.

The 1858 cent is found in two minor varieties. The A and M in the word AMERICA are joined in the large letter variety, and separated in the small letter variety. The reverse design of the eagle cents is dominated by a wreath of corn, wheat, cotton and tobacco.

G-4 GOOD—*All details worn, but readable.*
VG-8 VERY GOOD—*Feather details and eye of eagle are evident, but worn.*
F-12 FINE—*Eagle head details and feather tips sharp.*
VF-20 VERY FINE—*Feathers in right wing and tail show considerable detail.*
EF-40 EXTREMELY FINE—*Slight wear, all details sharp.*
MS-60 UNCIRCULATED—*No trace of wear. Light blemishes.*

Designer James B. Longacre; weight 4.67 grams; composition: .880 copper, .120 nickel; diameter 19 mm; plain edge. All coined at Philadelphia Mint.

| 1858, 8 over 7 | 1856-1858 Large Letters | 1858 Small Letters |

Quan. Minted		Quan. Minted
1856 .... est. *1,000*	1858 Lg. letters ...... *(80)*	
1857 17,450,000	1858 Sm. letters..... *(200)*	24,600,000

	G-4	VG-8	F-12	VF-20	EF-40	MS-60	Proof
1856	$750.00	$875.00	$1,175	$1,350	$1,600	$2,100	$2,500
1857	7.50	9.00	13.00	24.00	60.00	475.00	2,900
1858 Lg. let ...	8.50	10.00	13.50	25.00	65.00	485.00	2,900
1858, 8 over 7 .				200.00	400.00	750.00	
1858 Sm. let...	8.50	10.00	13.50	25.00	65.00	485.00	2,900

SMALL CENTS
INDIAN HEAD TYPE 1859-1909

The small cent was redesigned in 1859, and a representation of an Indian girl was adopted as the obverse device. The 1859 reverse was also changed to represent a laurel wreath. In 1860 the reverse was modified to display an oak wreath with a small shield at the top. The weight and composition of the coin were not changed.

Designer James B. Longacre; weight 4.67 grams; composition: .880 copper, .120 nickel; diameter 19 mm; plain edge. All coined at Philadelphia Mint.

G-4 GOOD—*No LIBERTY visible.*
VG-8 VERY GOOD—*At least half of LIBERTY readable.*
F-12 FINE—*LIBERTY completely visible.*
VF-20 VERY FINE—*Slight but even wear on LIBERTY.*
EF-40 EXTREMELY FINE—*LIBERTY sharp. All other details sharp. Only slight wear on ribbon end.*
MS-60 UNCIRCULATED—*No trace of wear. Light blemishes.*

Without Shield at Top of Wreath
1859 Only

With Shield on Reverse
1860 to 1909

Variety 1 — Copper-nickel, Laurel Wreath Reverse 1859

	Quan. Minted	G-4	VG-8	F-12	VF-20	EF-40	MS-60	Proof
1859	36,400,000	$4.50	$5.75	$11.00	$22.00	$60.00	$400.00	$750.00

Variety 2 — Copper-nickel, Oak Wreath with Shield 1860-1864

	Quan. Minted	G-4	VG-8	F-12	VF-20	EF-40	MS-60	Proof
1860 . . *(1,000)*	20,566,000	3.75	5.00	8.75	14.00	27.50	115.00	550.00
1861 . . *(1,000)*	10,100,000	8.50	11.50	17.50	25.00	37.50	140.00	600.00
1862 . . . . *(550)*	28,075,000	3.25	4.25	6.50	10.00	17.50	100.00	430.00
1863 . . . . *(460)*	49,840,000	3.25	4.25	6.50	10.00	17.50	95.00	425.00
1864 . . . . *(300)*	13,740,000	6.00	8.25	14.00	18.00	29.00	125.00	650.00

Variety 3 — Bronze 1864-1909

During the year 1864 the alloy of the cent was changed to 95 per cent copper and five per cent tin and zinc. The weight was reduced to 48 grains, resulting in a thinner coin than the so-called "white" cents of 1856-1864. The design remained unchanged. Before 1864 cents did not have the designer's initial L on the bonnet ribbon; late in that year the letter appeared on only a small quantity. The initial appeared on all dates of Indian cents thereafter. Consult the illustration details.

Indian Head Cent with "L"

If the coin is turned slightly (so Indian faces observer) the highlighted details of the "L" will appear to better advantage. The point of the bust is pointed on the variety with "L"; rounded without "L." The "L" is the initial of the engraver, Longacre.

SMALL CENTS

Designer James B. Longacre; weight 3.11 grams; composition: .950 copper, .050 tin and zinc; diameter 19 mm; plain edge; mints: Philadelphia, San Francisco.

	Quan. Minted	G-4	VG-8	F-12	VF-20	EF-40	MS-60	Proof
1864								
All kinds.....	39,233,714							
1864 No L............ (150)		$2.50	$5.50	$8.50	$17.50	$27.50	$75.00	$825.00
1864 L must show ..... (20)		14.75	27.50	50.00	70.00	95.00	275.00	——
1865* ... (500)	35,429,286	2.75	4.00	7.50	15.00	25.00	70.00	350.00
1866 .. (725)	9,826,500	13.00	17.50	29.00	45.00	70.00	155.00	350.00
1867 .... (625)	9,821,000	13.00	17.50	29.00	45.00	70.00	155.00	350.00
1868 .... (600)	10,266,500	13.00	17.50	29.00	45.00	70.00	155.00	350.00

| 1869, "9 over 8" | | | Closed 3 | | | Open 3 | | |

	Quan. Minted	G-4	VG-8	F-12	VF-20	EF-40	MS-60	Proof
1869 over 8*.. }	6,420,000	250.00	75.00	145.00	250.00	420.00	900.00	
1869 .... (600)		20.00	35.00	60.00	90.00	130.00	325.00	550.00
1870 .. (1,000)	5,275,000	17.50	27.50	50.00	67.50	90.00	200.00	375.00
1871 .... (960)	3,929,500	22.00	35.00	60.00	80.00	115.00	240.00	440.00
1872 .... (950)	4,042,000	25.00	40.00	70.00	95.00	130.00	295.00	490.00
1873 All kinds..	11,676,500							
1873 Closed 3 (1,100)......		6.00	9.00	16.50	25.00	42.50	100.00	275.00
1873 Doubled LIBERTY.....		——	——	——				
1873 Open 3..............		6.00	9.00	16.50	25.00	42.50	100.00	
1874 .... (700)	14,187,500	6.00	9.00	16.50	25.00	42.50	100.00	250.00
1875 .... (700)	13,528,000	6.00	9.00	16.50	25.00	42.50	100.00	250.00
1876 .. (1,150)	7,944,000	9.50	12.00	25.00	35.00	52.50	110.00	225.00
1877 .... (510)	852,500	125.00	150.00	225.00	310.00	450.00	925.00	1,200
1878 .. (2,350)	5,799,850	9.50	12.00	30.00	45.00	60.00	125.00	170.00
1879 .. (3,200)	16,231,200	2.25	3.50	6.50	12.50	21.00	60.00	120.00
1880 .. (3,955)	38,964,955	1.20	1.70	3.60	5.75	11.00	40.00	110.00
1881 ... 3,575)	39,211,575	1.20	1.70	3.60	5.75	11.00	40.00	110.00
1882 .. (3,100)	38,581,100	1.20	1.70	3.60	5.75	11.00	40.00	110.00
1883 .. (6,609)	45,598,109	1.20	1.70	3.60	5.75	11.00	40.00	110.00
1884 .. (3,942)	23,261,742	1.75	3.25	6.00	9.25	15.00	52.50	120.00
1885 .. (3,790)	11,765,384	3.75	6.50	10.00	15.00	27.50	65.00	130.00
1886 .. (4,290)	17,654,290	2.10	3.25	6.00	10.00	20.00	55.00	115.00

On coins 1859-1886 the last feather of the headdress points between I and C of AMERICA; from mid-1886 to 1909 it points between C and A.

| 1887 .. (2,960) | 45,226,483 | 1.00 | 1.50 | 2.25 | 3.50 | 8.00 | 45.00 | 100.00 |

1888, last 8 over 7

| 1888 over 7 } | | | | | —— | —— | —— | |
| 1888 .. (4,582) } | 37,494,414 | 1.00 | 1.50 | 2.25 | 3.50 | 8.00 | 45.00 | 110.00 |

*One variety of 1865 appears to show traces of a 4 under the 5 in the date. The 9 is doubled on some varieties of the 1869; on others it appears to be over an 8.

SMALL CENTS

	Quan. Minted	G-4	VG-8	F-12	VF-20	EF-40	MS-60	Proof
1889 .. (3,336)	48,869,361	$1.00	$1.50	$2.25	$3.50	$8.00	$40.00	$110.00
1890 .. (2,740)	57,182,854	1.00	1.50	2.25	3.50	8.00	40.00	110.00
1891 .. (2,350)	47,072,350	1.00	1.50	2.25	3.50	8.00	40.00	110.00
1892 .. (2,745)	37,649,832	1.00	1.50	2.25	3.50	8.00	40.00	110.00
1893 .. (2,195)	46,642,195	1.00	1.50	2.25	3.50	8.00	40.00	110.00
1894 .. (2,632)	16,752,132	1.75	3.75	6.75	11.50	17.50	50.00	120.00
1895 .. (2,062)	38,343,636	.75	1.00	1.60	2.75	6.50	34.00	110.00
1896 .. (1,862)	39,057,293	.75	1.00	1.60	2.75	6.50	34.00	110.00
1897 .. (1,938)	50,466,330	.75	1.00	1.60	2.75	6.50	32.50	110.00
1898 .. (1,795)	49,823,079	.75	1.00	1.60	2.75	6.50	32.50	110.00
1899 .. (2,031)	53,600,031	.75	1.00	1.60	2.75	6.50	32.50	110.00
1900 .. (2,262)	66,833,764	.75	.90	1.30	2.30	6.00	32.50	110.00
1901 .. (1,985)	79,611,143	.75	.90	1.30	2.30	6.00	32.50	110.00
1902 .. (2,018)	87,376,722	.75	.90	1.30	2.30	6.00	32.50	110.00
1903 .. (1,790)	85,094,493	.75	.90	1.30	2.30	6.00	32.50	110.00
1904 .. (1,817)	61,328,015	.75	.90	1.30	2.30	6.00	32.50	110.00
1905 .. (2,152)	80,719,163	.75	.90	1.30	2.30	6.00	32.50	110.00
1906 .. (1,725)	96,022,255	.75	.90	1.30	2.30	6.00	32.50	110.00
1907 .. (1,475)	108,138,618	.75	.90	1.30	2.30	6.00	32.50	110.00

Location of mint mark S
on reverse of Indian cent
(1908 and 1909 only).

1908 .. (1,620)	32,327,987	.75	.90	1.30	2.30	6.00	35.00	110.00
1908S	1,115,000	20.00	22.50	27.50	32.50	45.00	137.50	
1909 .. (2,175)	14,370,645	1.10	1.75	2.40	3.50	8.00	45.00	120.00
1909S	309,000	75.00	85.00	100.00	125.00	160.00	300.00	

Choice brilliant Unc. and Proof small cents command higher prices.

LINCOLN TYPE, WHEAT EARS REVERSE 1909-1958

Victor D. Brenner designed this cent which was issued to commemorate the hundredth anniversary of Lincoln's birth. The designer's initials VDB appear on a limited quantity of cents of 1909. The San Francisco mint produced the smallest issue before the initials were removed, creating the scarcest though not the highest priced Lincoln cent. The initials were restored, in 1918, to the obverse side as illustrated on page 84. This type cent was the first to have the motto IN GOD WE TRUST.

Matte proof coins were made for collectors from 1909 through 1916, and an exceptional specimen dated 1917 is also known to exist.

Designer Victor D. Brenner; weight 3.11 grams; composition: .950 copper, .050 tin and zinc; diameter 19 mm; plain edge; mints: Philadelphia, Denver, San Francisco.

Location of mint mark
S or D on obverse of
Lincoln cent.

SMALL CENTS

G-4 GOOD—*Date worn but apparent. Lines in wheat ears missing. Full rims.*

VG-8 VERY GOOD—*Half of lines show in upper wheat ears.*

F-12 FINE—*Wheat lines worn but visible.*

VF-20 VERY FINE—*Cheek and jaw bones worn but separated. No worn spots on wheat ears.*

EF-40 EXTREMELY FINE—*Slight wear. All details sharp.*

MS-60 UNCIRCULATED—*No trace of wear. Light blemishes.*

CHOICE UNCIRCULATED—*No trace of wear. Barely noticeable blemishes.*

Choice brilliant uncirculated cents command higher prices.
Cents with well struck mint marks are also worth more.

 Location of
designer's
initials V.D.B.
on 1909 only.

 No
V.D.B.
on
Reverse
1909-1958

Variety 1 — Bronze 1909-1942

	Quan. Minted	G-4	VG-8	F-12	VF-20	EF-40	MS-60	Matte Proof
1909 V.D.B.								
(420) ...	27,995,000	$1.75	$2.00	$2.50	$2.85	$3.50	$12.50	$425.00
1909S, V.D.B.	484,000	135.00	145.00	160.00	180.00	200.00	340.00	
1909 (2,198) .	72,702,618	.40	.45	.60	.70	1.50	10.00	100.00
1909S	1,825,000	26.00	29.00	33.00	40.00	50.00	85.00	
1910 (2,405) .	146,801,218	.20	.30	.45	.80	1.60	11.00	100.00
1910S	6,045,000	5.75	6.75	7.75	9.00	12.00	53.00	
1911 (1,733) .	101,177,787	.20	.30	.60	1.25	4.00	14.00	100.00
1911D	12,672,000	2.50	3.50	5.00	8.50	16.00	60.00	
1911S	4,026,000	9.00	10.00	11.50	14.50	20.00	75.00	
1912 (2,145) .	68,153,060	.25	.40	1.25	3.00	6.50	20.00	100.00
1912D	10,411,000	2.50	3.50	5.25	11.00	20.00	70.00	
1912S	4,431,000	8.00	9.00	11.00	14.75	23.00	75.00	
1913 (2,848) .	76,532,352	.20	.35	1.25	3.50	7.00	21.00	100.00
1913D	15,804,000	1.35	1.90	3.00	7.00	17.50	67.50	
1913S	6,101,000	5.00	6.00	7.25	8.50	16.00	67.50	
1914 (1,365) .	75,238,432	.25	.40	1.70	4.00	7.75	37.50	190.00
1914D*	1,193,000	50.00	60.00	70.00	105.00	210.00	750.00	
1914S	4,137,000	6.50	7.50	8.50	11.00	20.00	92.50	
1915 (1,150) .	29,092,120	.60	1.00	4.25	9.00	22.00	80.00	250.00
1915D	22,050,000	.60	1.00	1.50	5.00	11.00	37.50	
1915S	4,833,000	5.00	5.75	7.00	8.50	17.00	65.00	
1916 (1,050) .	131,833,677	.20	.30	.40	1.00	2.25	11.00	275.00
1916D	35,956,000	.25	.40	.85	2.85	6.75	30.00	
1916S	22,510,000	.55	.80	1.25	2.85	6.90	37.50	
1917	196,429,785	.15	.20	.35	.85	2.00	11.00	——
1917D	55,120,000	.25	.35	.75	2.85	6.75	37.50	
1917S	32,620,000	.25	.35	.75	2.85	6.75	37.50	

Designer's initials restored
starting 1918.

1918	288,104,634	.20	.25	.40	.80	2.25	13.00
1918D	47,830,000	.25	.35	.70	2.00	6.00	37.50
1918S	34,680,000	.25	.35	.70	2.00	6.00	38.50

*Beware of altered date or mint mark. No VDB on shoulder of genuine 1914D cent.

SMALL CENTS

	Quan. Minted	G-4	VG-8	F-12	VF-20	EF-40	MS-60	Proof
1919	392,021,000	$ .20	$ .25	$ .40	$ .80	$2.00	$10.00	
1919D.	57,154,000	.25	.35	.70	2.75	5.25	25.00	
1919S	139,760,000	.25	.35	.50	1.25	3.00	22.00	
1920	310,165,000	.20	.25	.35	.60	2.00	9.50	
1920D.	49,280,000	.25	.35	.60	1.50	4.50	36.00	
1920S	46,220,000	.25	.35	.60	1.50	4.50	36.00	
1921	39,157,000	.25	.35	.60	1.50	4.50	31.00	
1921S	15,274,000	.60	.85	1.25	3.00	11.00	195.00	
1922D.	} 7,160,000	4.75	5.75	6.75	9.00	16.00	65.00	
1922 Plain*.		70.00	90.00	125.00	170.00	300.00	2,000	
1923	74,723,000	.15	.20	.35	.75	2.00	9.50	
1923S	8,700,000	1.40	1.75	2.50	4.75	14.00	260.00	
1924	75,178,000	.15	.20	.35	.75	3.50	22.00	
1924D.	2,520,000	8.00	9.00	11.00	16.00	28.50	300.00	
1924S	11,696,000	.60	.80	1.40	3.50	7.00	125.00	
1925	139,949,000	.15	.25	.35	.75	2.00	9.00	
1925D.	22,580,000	.30	.40	.60	1.30	4.50	40.00	
1925S	26,380,000	.25	.35	.55	1.25	4.25	40.00	
1926	157,088,000	.15	.25	.35	.75	2.00	9.00	
1926D.	28,020,000	.25	.35	.60	1.30	3.25	37.50	
1926S	4,550,000	3.00	3.60	5.00	6.00	12.50	165.00	
1927	144,440,000	.15	.20	.30	.55	2.00	8.50	
1927D.	27,170,000	.25	.35	.50	.85	2.75	25.00	
1927S	14,276,000	.40	.55	.90	1.75	4.25	48.00	
1928	134,116,000	.15	.20	.30	.55	1.70	8.00	
1928D.	31,170,000	.20	.30	.40	.80	1.75	22.50	
1928S†	17,266,000	.25	.35	.60	1.25	2.50	35.00	
1929	185,262,000	.15	.20	.30	.60	1.35	6.75	
1929D.	41,730,000	.15	.25	.35	.65	1.35	10.00	
1929S	50,148,000	.15	.25	.35	.60	1.35	8.00	
1930	157,415,000	.10	.15	.25	.40	1.00	5.00	
1930D.	40,100,000	.15	.20	.30	.45	1.00	9.00	
1930S	24,286,000	.15	.20	.30	.50	1.00	7.00	
1931	19,396,000	.25	.35	.45	.85	1.80	16.00	
1931D.	4,480,000	3.00	3.25	4.00	5.00	7.00	55.00	
1931S	866,000	25.00	27.00	30.00	32.50	35.00	52.50	
1932	9,062,000	.90	1.25	1.50	2.00	3.00	16.00	
1932D.	10,500,000	.60	.80	1.20	1.90	3.00	16.00	
1933	14,360,000	.50	.60	.70	1.00	2.00	17.50	
1933D.	6,200,000	1.60	1.90	2.25	3.00	4.00	20.00	
1934	219,080,000	. . . . .	.10	.15	.30	.60	3.00	
1934D.	28,446,000	.15	.25	.30	.45	1.25	18.50	
1935	245,388,000	. . . . .	.10	.15	.20	.40	1.50	
1935D.	47,000,000	. . . . .	.10	.15	.25	.40	2.25	
1935S	38,702,000	. . . . .	.10	.20	.30	.60	5.00	
1936 . . (5,569)	309,637,569	. . . . .	.10	.15	.20	.30	1.40	$145.00
1936D.	40,620,000	. . . . .	.10	.20	.30	.45	1.50	
1936S	29,130,000	. . . . .	.10	.25	.40	.55	2.25	
1937 . . (9,320)	309,179,320	. . . . .		.10	.15	.30	1.50	37.50
1937D.	50,430,000	. . . . .	.10	.15	.25	.35	1.50	
1937S	34,500,000	. . . . .	.10	.20	.30	.40	2.00	
1938 . (14,734)	156,696,734	. . . . .	.10	.15	.20	.30	1.60	27.50
1938D.	20,010,000	.15	.20	.30	.45	.65	2.50	

*The 1922 without D caused by defective die. Beware removed mint mark.
†Large and small mint mark varieties, see page 59.

SMALL CENTS

	Quan. Minted	G-4	VG-8	F-12	VF-20	EF-40	MS-65	Proof
1938S	15,180,000	$ .25	$ .35	$ .45	$ .55	$ .75	$3.50	
1939 . (13,520)	316,479,520			.10	.15	.25	1.10	$25.00
1939D.........	15,160,000	.35	.45	.55	.65	.85	4.50	
1939S.........	52,070,000	.10	.15	.20	.30	.40	1.75	
1940 . (15,872)	586,825,872	.....	.....	.....	.10	.20	1.00	22.00
1940D.........	81,390,000	.....	.....	.10	.15	.25	1.00	
1940S.........	112,940,000	.....	.....	.10	.15	.25	1.00	
1941 . (21,100)	887,039,100	.....	.....		.10	.20	.75	21.00
1941D.........	128,700,000	.....	.....	`	.10	.25	2.75	
1941S*........	92,360,000	.....	.....	.10	.15	.30	4.00	
1942 . (32,600)	657,828,600	.....	.....		.10	.20	.45	21.00
1942D.........	206,698,000	.....	.....		.10	.20	.65	
1942S.........	85,590,000	.10	.15	.25	.30	.45	6.00	

*Large and small mint mark varieties, see page 59.

Variety 2 — Zinc-coated Steel 1943 Only

Owing to a shortage of copper during the critical war year 1943 the Treasury Department resorted to the use of zinc coated steel for our cents. No bronze cents were officially issued in 1943. A few specimens struck on bronze planchets by error are known to exist. Through a similar error, a few of the 1944 cents were struck on steel planchets.

1943 — Weight 2.70 grams; composition: steel, coated with zinc; diameter 19 mm; plain edge.

1943	684,628,670	.....	.15	.25	.30	.70
1943D........	217,660,000	.....	.15	.25	.30	1.00
1943S........	191,550,000	.....	.30	.45	.55	1.75

Variety 1 Resumed 1944-1958

Cartridge cases were salvaged for coinage of 1944 through 1946. Although the color was slightly different for uncirculated specimens, the coins proved satisfactory in every respect. The original alloy of 1864-1942 was resumed in 1947.

1944-1946 — Weight 3.11 grams; composition: .950 copper, .050 zinc; diameter 19 mm; plain edge.

	Quan. Minted	VF-20	EF-40	MS-65
1944	1,435,400,000	$ .10	$ .20	$ .30
1944D.........................		.10	.15	.30
1944D, D over S (2 varieties) .... }	430,578,000			
1944S.........................	282,760,000	.10	.20	.35
1945	1,040,515,000	.10	.15	.35
1945D.........................	266,268,000	.10	.20	.70
1945S.........................	181,770,000	.10	.20	.50
1946	991,655,000	.10	.15	.25
1946D.........................	315,690,000	.10	.20	.30
1946S.........................	198,100,000	.10	.20	.70
1947	190,555,000	.10	.20	.30
1947D.........................	194,750,000	.10	.20	.30
1947S.........................	99,000,000	.15	.25	.80
1948	317,570,000	.10	.20	.60
1948D.........................	172,637,500	.10	.20	.30
1948S.........................	81,735,000	.15	.30	.90
1949	217,775,000	.10	.20	.75
1949D.........................	153,132,500	.10	.20	.60
1949S.........................	64,290,000	.20	.30	1.40

SMALL CENTS

		Quan. Minted	VF-20	EF-40	MS-65	Proof
1950	(51,386)	272,686,386	$ .10	$ .20	$ .50	$37.50
1950D		334,950,000	.10	.20	.30	
1950S		118,505,000	.10	.25	.55	
1951	(57,500)	284,633,500	.10	.25	1.70	16.00
1951D		625,355,000	.10	.15	.25	
1951S		136,010,000	.15	.25	1.00	
1952	(81,980)	186,856,980	....	.15	.60	12.50
1952D		746,130,000	....	.15	.25	
1952S		137,800,004	....	.20	.65	
1953	(128,800)	256,883,800	....	.10	.25	11.50
1953D		700,515,000	....	.10	.25	
1953S		181,835,000	....	.15	.45	
1954	(233,300)	71,873,350	.25	.35	.50	6.50
1954D		251,552,500	....	.10	.25	
1954S		96,190,000	....	.20	.35	

1955 Doubled Die Error

Enlarged Detail of
1972 Doubled Die Error

These coins were made from improperly prepared dies that show full doubled outline of date and legend. Do not confuse with less valuable pieces showing only minor traces of doubling.

		Quan. Minted	VF-20	EF-40	MS-65	Proof
1955 Doubled die obv		330,958,200	215.00	250.00	*550.00	
1955	(378,200)			.10	.20	3.00
1955D		563,257,500		.10	.25	
1955S		44,610,000	.30	.40	.50	
1956	(669,384)	421,414,384	....		.25	2.00
1956D		1,098,201,100	....		.20	
1957	(1,247,952)	283,787,952	....		.20	2.00
1957D		1,051,342,000	....		.20	
1958	(875,652)	253,400,652	....		.25	3.00
1958D		800,953,300	....		.20	

*Value is for MS-60 Uncirculated.

LINCOLN TYPE, MEMORIAL REVERSE 1959 TO DATE

Frank Gasparro designed the Lincoln Memorial reverse which was introduced in 1959 on the 150th anniversary of Lincoln's birth.

1959-1962 — Designer: Obv. V. D. Brenner, Rev. Frank Gasparro; weight 3.11 grams; composition: .950 copper, .050 tin and zinc; diameter 19 mm; plain edge; mints: Philadelphia, Denver, San Francisco. 1962-Composition changed to: .950 copper, .050 zinc.

		Quan. Minted		MS-65	Proof
1959	(1,149,291)	610,864,291	....	$ .10	$1.75
1959D		1,279,760,000	....	.10	

SMALL CENTS

Small Date	Large Date	Small Date Numbers aligned at top	Large Date Low 7 in date

		Quan. Minted		*MS-65*	*Proof*
1960 Large date ...	⎰ (1,691,602)	588,096,602	....	$ .10	$ 1.35
1960 Sm. date	⎱		....	3.00	19.50
1960D Large date............	⎰	1,580,884,000	....	.10	
1960D Small date............	⎱		....	.30	
1961 .... (3,028,244)		756,373,244	....	.10	1.00
1961D........................		1,753,266,700		.10	

Starting in September 1962 the composition of the cent was changed to 95% copper and 5% zinc. In 1969 the dies were modified to strengthen the design, and Lincoln's head was made slightly smaller. In 1973 dies were further modified and engraver's initials FG made larger. The initials were reduced slightly in 1974.

	MS-65	*Proof*		*MS-65*	*Proof*
1962 (3,218,019)			1972 Doubled die obv.		
.... 609,263,019	$ .10	$1.00	See page 87	$135.00	
1962D 1,793,148,400	.10		1972........ 2,933,255,000	.10	
1963 (3,075,645)			1972D 2,665,071,400	.10	
.... 757,185,645	.10	1.00	1972S (3,260,996)		
1963D 1,774,020,400	.10		 380,200,104	.10	$ .75
1964 (3,950,762)			1973........ 3,728,245,000	.10	
.... 2,652,525,762	.10	1.00	1973D 3,549,576,588	.10	
1964D 3,799,071,500	.10		1973S (2,760,339)		
1965........ 1,497,224,900	.10		 319,937,634	.10	1.50
1966........ 2,188,147,783	.10		1974........ 4,232,140,523	.10	
1967........ 3,048,667,100	.10		1974D 4,235,098,000	.10	
1968........ 1,707,880,970	.15		1974S (2,612,568)		
1968D 2,886,269,600	.10		 412,039,228	.10	1.75
1968S (3,041,506)			1975........ 5,451,476,142	.10	
.... 261,311,510	.10	.85	1975D 4,505,275,300	.10	
1969........ 1,136,910,000	.15		1975S Proof only		
1969D 4,002,832,200	.10		.... (2,845,450)		19.50
1969S (2,934,631)			1976........ 4,674,292,426	.10	
.... 547,309,631	.10	.75	1976D 4,221,592,455	.10	
1970........ 1,898,315,000	.15		1976S Proof only		
1970D 2,891,438,900	.10		.... (4,149,730)		9.00
1970S (2,632,810)			1977........ 4,469,930,000	.10	
.... 693,192,814			1977D 4,194,062,300	.10	
1970S Sm. date..........	1.35	35.00	1977S Proof only (3,251,152)		5.00
1970S Lg. date (low 7) ...	.10	.75	1978.....................	.10	
1971........ 1,919,490,000	.10		1978D	.10	
1971D 2,911,045,600	.10		1978S..................		
1971S (3,220,733)					
.... 528,354,192	.10	.75			

TWO-CENT PIECES — 1864-1873

The Act of April 22, 1864, which changed the weight and composition of the cent, included a provision for the bronze two-cent piece. The weight was specified as 96 grains, the alloy being the same as for the cent.

The two-cent piece is one of the short-lived issues of United States coinage. The motto "In God We Trust" appeared for the first time. Its presence on the new coin was due largely to the increased religious sentiment during the Civil War crisis.

There are two varieties for the first year of issue, 1864: the small motto and the large motto. The differences are explained in the illustrations below. The small motto variety of 1864 is scarce.

1864 Small Motto

1864 Large Motto

Details explain the differences in these two well-known varieties. On the obverse the D in God is narrow on the large motto. The stem to the leaf shows plainly on the small motto variety. There is no stem on the large motto coin.

The first T in TRUST touches ribbon crease at left on the small motto variety; there is a 1mm. gap on the large motto variety.

It will be noted that the shield device is very similar to the nickel five-cent piece introduced in 1866.

Designer James B. Longacre; weight 6.22 grams; composition: .950 copper, .050 tin and zinc; diameter 23 mm; plain edge. All coined at Philadelphia Mint.

G-4 GOOD—*At least IN GOD visible.*
VG-8 VERY GOOD—*WE weakly visible.*
F-12 FINE—*Complete motto visible. WE weak.*
EF-40 EXTREMELY FINE—*WE is bold.*
MS-60 UNCIRCULATED—*No trace of wear. Light blemishes.*

Brilliant red choice uncirculated and proof coins command higher prices.

	Quan. Minted	G-4	VG-8	F-12	EF-40	MS-60	Proof
1864 Sm. motto	} 19,847,500	$40.00	$55.00	$75.00	$135.00	$475.00	——
1864 Lg. motto		5.25	6.50	8.75	30.00	200.00	$450.00
1865*	13,640,000	5.25	6.50	8.75	30.00	200.00	385.00
1866	3,177,000	5.25	6.50	8.75	30.00	200.00	375.00
1867	2,938,750	5.25	6.50	8.75	30.00	200.00	375.00
1868	2,803,750	5.25	6.50	8.75	30.00	200.00	375.00
1869, 9 over 8	} 1,546,500	120.00	250.00	——	——		
1869		5.50	6.75	10.00	32.00	260.00	385.00
1870	861,250	6.50	8.00	12.00	35.00	275.00	395.00
1871	721,250	7.50	9.00	13.00	40.00	350.00	425.00
1872	65,000	40.00	55.00	70.00	120.00	450.00	450.00
1873 Closed 3. Proofs only (600). (See illustration on page 82)							800.00
1873 Open 3. Restrike (Est. 500)							825.00

*Some varieties appear to show traces of a 4 under the 5 in the date.

BIBLIOGRAPHY

Kliman, Myron M. *The Two Cent Piece and Varieties. 1977.*

THREE-CENT PIECES (NICKEL)

ISSUED 1865-1889

The three cent pieces struck in nickel composition were designed to replace the silver three cent coins. Composition is 75% copper and 25% nickel. All were coined at Philadelphia and have plain edges.

Designer James B. Longacre; weight 1.94 grams; composition: .750 copper, .250 nickel; diameter 17.9 mm; plain edge. All coined at Philadelphia Mint.

G-4 GOOD—*Date and legends complete though worn. III smooth.*

VG-8 VERY GOOD—*III is half worn. Rims complete.*

F-12 FINE—*Hair curls well defined.*

EF-40 EXTREMELY FINE—*Slight, even wear.*

MS-60 UNCIRCULATED—*No trace of wear. Light blemishes.*

	Quan. Minted	G-4	VG-8	F-12	EF-40	MS-60	Proof
1865	11,382,000	$ 5.00	$ 6.00	$ 7.00	$ 14.00	$110.00	$650.00
1866	4,801,000	5.00	6.00	7.00	14.00	110.00	225.00
1867	3,915,000	5.00	6.00	7.00	14.00	110.00	190.00
1868	3,252,000	5.00	6.00	7.00	14.00	110.00	180.00
1869	1,604,000	5.00	6.00	7.00	14.00	110.00	180.00
1870	1,335,000	6.00	7.00	8.00	15.00	110.00	180.00
1871	604,000	6.00	7.00	8.50	16.00	120.00	180.00
1872	862,000	6.00	7.00	8.50	16.00	120.00	180.00
1873 All kinds	1,173,000						
1873 Closed 3 (1,100)		6.00	7.00	8.50	16.00	120.00	180.00
1873 Open 3		6.00	7.00	8.50	16.00	120.00	
1874	790,000	6.50	7.50	9.00	17.00	125.00	180.00
1875	228,000	7.75	9.00	11.50	23.00	130.00	200.00
1876	162,000	7.75	9.00	11.50	23.00	150.00	200.00
1877 (Proofs only)							850.00
1878 (2,350)	2,350						300.00
1879 (3,200)	41,200	22.00	27.00	32.50	50.00	200.00	195.00
1880 (3,955)	24,955	25.00	30.00	37.50	52.50	220.00	195.00
1881 (3,575)	1,080,575	5.00	6.00	7.50	15.00	110.00	180.00
1882 (3,100)	25,300	24.00	30.00	37.50	55.00	200.00	190.00
1883 (6,609)	10,609	35.00	42.50	55.00	85.00	250.00	200.00
1884 (3,942)	5,642	45.00	55.00	65.00	120.00	300.00	225.00
1885 (3,790)	4,790	55.00	65.00	85.00	150.00	350.00	250.00
1886 (4,290)	4,290						275.00
1887, 7 over 6							325.00
1887 All kinds (2,960)	7,961	50.00	55.00	70.00	110.00	285.00	300.00
1888 (4,582)	41,083	22.50	27.50	35.00	50.00	180.00	180.00
1889 (3,436)	21,561	25.00	30.00	40.00	55.00	185.00	185.00

NICKEL FIVE-CENT PIECES — 1866 to Date

SHIELD TYPE 1866-1883

The shield type nickel was made possible by the act of May 16, 1866. Its weight was set at 77-16/100 grains with the same composition as the nickel three-cent piece which was authorized in 1865. In 1866 the coin was designed with rays between the stars on the reverse. Some of the pieces minted in 1867 have the same details, but later the rays were eliminated creating two varieties for that year. There was no further change in the type until it was replaced by the Liberty head device in 1883. Proofs only were struck in 1877 and 1878.

Designer James B. Longacre; weight 5 grams; composition: .750 copper, .250 nickel; diameter 20.5 mm; plain edge. All coined at Philadelphia Mint.

NICKEL FIVE-CENT PIECES

Sharply struck uncirculated coins are valued higher than the prices shown here.

G-4 GOOD—*All letters in motto readable.*
VG-8 VERY GOOD—*Motto stands out clearly. Rims worn slightly but even. Part of shield lines visible.*
F-12 FINE—*Half of each olive leaf is smooth.*
EF-40 EXTREMELY FINE—*Leaf tips show slight wear. Cross over shield slightly worn.*
MS-60 UNCIRCULATED—*No trace of wear. Light blemishes.*

Rays Between Stars 1866-1867

	Quan. Minted	G-4	VG-8	F-12	EF-40	MS-60	Proof
1866	14,742,500	$11.25	$14.50	$20.00	$ 75.00	$450.00	$1,400
1867 Rays	2,019,000	13.50	18.00	29.00	85.00	525.00	5,000

Without Rays 1867-1883

Typical example of 1883 3 over 2.
Other varieties exist
as well as pieces with recut 3.

		G-4	VG-8	F-12	EF-40	MS-60	Proof
1867 No rays	28,890,500	8.00	9.50	12.00	27.50	170.00	200.00
1868	28,817,000	8.00	9.50	12.00	27.50	170.00	200.00
1869	16,395,000	8.00	9.50	12.00	27.50	170.00	200.00
1870	4,806,000	8.50	10.50	13.00	32.50	170.00	200.00
1871	561,000	32.50	40.00	52.50	95.00	270.00	325.00
1872	6,036,000	8.50	10.50	13.00	32.50	170.00	200.00
1873 All kinds	4,550,000						
1873 Closed 3 (1,100)		8.50	10.50	13.00	32.50	170.00	200.00
1873 Open 3		8.50	10.50	13.00	32.50	170.00	
1874	3,538,000	10.00	12.00	15.00	35.00	170.00	200.00
1875	2,097,000	13.00	15.00	22.00	45.00	200.00	225.00
1876	2,530,000	13.00	15.00	22.00	42.00	185.00	225.00
1877 Est. Issued	(500) 500						1,000
1878 ...... (2,350)	2,350						350.00
1879 ...... (3,200)	29,100	45.00	55.00	70.00	110.00	300.00	275.00
1879, 9 over 8							
1880 ...... (3,955)	19,955	55.00	65.00	80.00	130.00	325.00	275.00
1881 ...... (3,575)	72,375	40.00	48.00	60.00	100.00	290.00	275.00
1882 ...... (3,100)	11,476,000	8.00	9.50	12.00	27.50	170.00	200.00
1883 ...... (5,419)	1,456,919	8.00	9.50	12.00	27.50	170.00	200.00
1883, 3 over 2		30.00	42.00	110.00	385.00		

LIBERTY HEAD TYPE 1883-1913

In 1883 the type was changed to the familiar "Liberty head." This type first appeared without the word CENTS on the coin, merely a large letter "V." These "centless" coins were goldplated and passed for five dollars. Later in that year the word CENTS was added.

Five 1913 Liberty head nickels were originally owned by Col. E. H. R. Green (son of the famous Hetty Green). These have since been dispersed and are now held in the collections of several individuals. These were not a regular issue and were never placed in circulation.

Designer Charles E. Barber; weight 5 grams; composition: .750 copper, .250 nickel; diameter 21.2 mm; plain edge; mints: Philadelphia, Denver, San Francisco.

NICKEL FIVE-CENT PIECES

Sharply struck uncirculated coins are valued higher than the prices shown here.

Variety 1 — Without CENTS 1883 Only

G-4 GOOD—*No details in head. LIBERTY obliterated.*

VG-8 VERY GOOD—*At least 3 letters in LIBERTY readable.*

F-12 FINE—*All letters in LIBERTY show.*

VF-20 VERY FINE—*LIBERTY bold, including letter I.*

EF-40 EXTREMELY FINE—*LIBERTY sharp. Corn grains at bottom of wreath show, on reverse.*

MS-60 UNCIRCULATED—*No trace of wear. Light blemishes.*

	Quan. Minted	G-4	VG-8	F-12	VF-20	EF-40	MS-60	Proof
1883 without CENTS								
(5,219)	5,479,519	$1.75	$2.50	$3.50	$5.00	$8.75	$45.00	$200.00

Variety 2 — With CENTS 1883-1913

Location of mint mark.

1883 with CENTS								
(6,783)	16,032,983	$ 5.00	$ 6.50	$ 8.75	$ 14.00	$ 22.00	$ 85.00	$150.00
1884 (3,942)	11,273,942	5.25	7.50	10.00	16.00	25.00	90.00	150.00
1885 (3,790)	1,476,490	90.00	110.00	160.00	185.00	235.00	385.00	385.00
1886 (4,290)	3,330,290	32.50	45.00	65.00	80.00	120.00	220.00	240.00
1887 (2,960)	15,263,652	3.20	4.50	10.00	15.00	25.00	85.00	150.00
1888 (4,582)	10,720,483	5.50	7.75	12.00	18.00	28.00	90.00	150.00
1889 (3,336)	15,881,361	3.20	4.50	10.00	15.00	25.00	85.00	145.00
1890 (2,740)	16,259,272	3.20	4.50	10.00	15.00	25.00	85.00	145.00
1891 (2,350)	16,834,350	3.20	4.50	10.00	15.00	20.00	85.00	145.00
1892 (2,745)	11,699,642	3.20	4.50	10.00	15.00	20.00	85.00	145.00
1893 (2,195)	13,370,195	3.00	4.25	9.00	13.00	18.00	85.00	145.00
1894 (2,632)	5,413,132	5.00	7.00	12.00	18.00	27.50	100.00	155.00
1895 (2,062)	9,979,884	2.25	4.00	9.00	13.00	18.00	85.00	145.00
1896 (1,862)	8,842,920	2.50	4.50	9.50	14.00	21.00	95.00	155.00
1897 (1,938)	20,428,735	1.00	1.75	3.25	6.50	14.00	80.00	145.00
1898 (1,795)	12,532,087	1.00	1.75	3.25	6.50	14.00	80.00	145.00
1899 (2,031)	26,029,031	1.00	1.50	3.00	6.00	13.00	80.00	145.00
1900 (2,262)	27,255,995	.60	1.00	2.00	5.00	12.00	75.00	140.00
1901 (1,985)	26,480,213	.60	1.00	2.00	5.00	12.00	75.00	140.00
1902 (2,018)	31,489,579	.60	1.00	2.00	5.00	12.00	75.00	140.00
1903 (1,790)	28,006,725	.60	1.00	2.00	5.00	12.00	75.00	140.00
1904 (1,817)	21,404,984	.60	1.00	2.00	5.00	12.00	75.00	140.00
1905 (2,152)	29,827,276	.60	1.00	2.00	5.00	12.00	75.00	140.00
1906 (1,725)	38,613,725	.60	1.00	2.00	5.00	12.00	75.00	140.00
1907 (1,475)	39,214,800	.60	1.00	2.00	5.00	12.00	75.00	140.00
1908 (1,620)	22,686,177	.60	1.00	2.00	5.00	12.00	75.00	140.00
1909 (4,763)	11,590,526	.75	1.25	2.50	6.00	13.00	75.00	140.00
1910 (2,405)	30,169,353	.60	1.00	2.00	5.00	12.00	75.00	140.00
1911 (1,733)	39,559,372	.60	1.00	2.00	5.00	12.00	75.00	140.00
1912 (2,145)	26,236,714	.60	1.00	2.00	5.00	12.00	75.00	140.00
1912D........	8,474,000	1.35	2.00	5.25	17.50	50.00	250.00	
1912S..........	238,000	31.50	37.50	50.00	85.00	145.00	475.00	
1913 Liberty Head (5 known)..........................						1972 Private Sale $100,000		

NICKEL FIVE-CENT PIECES
INDIAN HEAD or BUFFALO TYPE 1913-1938

These pieces are known as Buffalo, Bison or Indian Head nickels. In the first year of issue, 1913, there were two distinct varieties, the first showing the bison on a mound, and the second with the base redesigned to a thinner straight line.

James E. Fraser designed this nickel employing three different Indians as models. His initial F is beneath the date. The bison was modeled after "Black Diamond" in the New York Zoological Gardens.

Matte proof coins were made for collectors from 1913 to 1917.

Designer James Earle Fraser; weight 5 grams; composition: .750 copper, .250 nickel; diameter 21.2 mm; plain edge; mints: Philadelphia, Denver, San Francisco.

Variety 1 — FIVE CENTS on Raised Ground

G-4 GOOD—*Legends and date readable. Horn worn off.*

VG-8 VERY GOOD—*Half horn shows.*

F-12 FINE—*Two-thirds horn shows. Obv. rim intact.*

VF-20 VERY FINE—*Full horn shows. Indian's cheekbone worn.*

EF-40 EXTREMELY FINE—*Full horn. Slight wear on Indian's hair ribbon.*

MS-60 UNCIRCULATED—*No trace of wear. Light blemishes.*

	Quan. Minted	G-4	VG-8	F-12	VF-20	EF-40	MS-60	Matte Proof
1913 Var. 1								
(1,520)	30,993,520	$ 2.50	$ 3.25	$ 4.00	$ 6.50	$ 10.00	$ 35.00	$475.00
1913D Var. 1 ...	5,337,000	5.50	6.00	7.00	8.50	14.00	42.50	
1913S Var. 1 ...	2,105,000	6.25	8.00	10.00	15.00	20.00	60.00	

Variety 2 — FIVE CENTS Recessed

Mint mark below FIVE CENTS.   1918D, 8 over 7

	Quan. Minted	G-4	VG-8	F-12	VF-20	EF-40	MS-60	Matte Proof
1913 Var. 2								
(1,514)	29,858,700	3.00	3.75	4.75	6.00	9.00	30.00	425.00
1913D Var. 2 ...	4,156,000	23.00	27.50	35.00	45.00	55.00	100.00	
1913S Var. 2 ...	1,209,000	41.00	47.50	62.50	72.00	90.00	150.00	
1914 (1,275)	20,665,738	3.75	4.50	5.75	7.00	13.50	35.00	400.00
1914D..........	3,912,000	19.50	25.00	33.50	45.00	57.50	150.00	
1914S..........	3,470,000	4.50	5.50	8.00	11.50	19.00	90.00	
1915 (1,050)	20,987,270	1.75	2.50	3.25	5.50	11.50	35.00	400.00
1915D..........	7,569,000	5.50	7.00	11.25	16.50	25.00	90.00	
1915S..........	1,505,000	8.00	11.00	22.50	35.00	52.50	165.00	
1916 ...(600)	63,498,066	.75	1.00	1.75	2.50	6.50	25.00	500.00
1916 Doubled die					275.00	400.00	600.00	
1916D........	13,333,000	4.50	5.50	7.50	11.50	19.00	82.00	
1916S........	11,860,000	3.00	4.00	6.00	10.50	19.00	100.00	
1917	51,424,019	.85	1.25	1.90	3.00	10.00	35.00	——
1917D.........	9,910,000	3.50	5.50	9.25	25.00	45.00	140.00	
1917S.........	4,193,000	3.25	5.50	9.25	25.00	45.00	175.00	
1918	32,086,314	.85	1.50	2.75	6.00	12.50	60.00	
1918D, 8 over 7.. ⎫ 8,362,00	165.00	275.00	475.00	900.00	1,850	9,500		
1918D...... ⎭		3.50	5.50	10.00	30.00	55.00	250.00	
1918S..........	4,882,000	3.00	4.75	9.50	26.50	52.50	225.00	

NICKEL FIVE-CENT PIECES

	Quan. Minted	G-4	VG-8	F-12	VF-20	EF-40	MS-60
1919	60,868,000	$ .65	$ .85	$1.50	$3.00	$7.50	$32.50
1919D†	8,006,000	3.75	6.00	11.50	37.50	75.00	325.00
1919S†	7,521,000	2.50	4.50	8.75	26.00	65.00	300.00
1920	63,093,000	.65	.85	1.50	3.00	7.50	30.00
1920D†	9,418,000	3.00	4.50	8.75	33.50	55.00	275.00
1920S	9,689,000	1.75	2.75	6.25	26.00	51.50	285.00
1921	10,663,000	.85	1.25	3.00	6.75	14.50	75.00
1921S†	1,557,000	9.25	15.00	30.00	70.00	115.00	465.00
1923	35,715,000	.45	.65	1.25	2.75	7.00	32.50
1923S†	6,142,000	1.50	2.50	5.50	22.50	50.00	225.00
1924	21,620,000	.45	.65	1.25	3.50	8.00	55.00
1924D	5,258,000	2.25	3.00	7.75	27.50	45.00	285.00
1924S	1,437,000	4.50	6.50	14.50	60.00	140.00	800.00
1925	35,565,100	.50	.70	1.25	2.75	7.00	30.00
1925D†	4,450,000	3.50	5.50	11.00	36.50	65.00	300.00
1925S	6,256,000	2.25	4.00	6.75	18.50	52.50	300.00
1926	44,693,000	.40	.60	.95	1.50	5.00	25.00
1926D†	5,638,000	2.00	3.75	9.00	28.50	60.00	300.00
1926S	970,000	5.50	8.50	15.50	47.50	150.00	625.00
1927	37,981,000	.40	.60	.95	1.50	5.00	25.00
1927D	5,730,000	1.00	1.75	3.00	10.00	20.00	65.00
1927S	3,430,000	1.00	1.75	3.00	10.00	41.00	300.00
1928	23,411,000	.40	.60	.95	1.50	4.50	25.00
1928D	6,436,000	.75	1.00	2.25	4.50	8.00	30.00
1928S	6,936,000	.75	1.00	1.50	3.00	9.50	75.00
1929	36,446,000	.40	.50	.85	1.75	4.00	19.00
1929D	8,370,000	.60	.80	1.40	3.00	5.00	40.00
1929S	7,754,000	.55	.75	1.00	2.25	4.00	30.00
1930	22,849,000	.40	.50	.85	1.75	4.00	20.00
1930S	5,435,000	.50	.75	1.00	2.00	5.75	50.00
1931S	1,200,000	3.50	4.50	5.50	6.50	10.00	62.50
1934	20,213,003	.30	.45	.60	1.50	3.50	22.50
1934D	7,480,000	.45	.60	.85	1.50	5.00	32.00
1935	58,264,000	.30	.35	.45	.75	2.00	12.00
1935D	12,092,000	.35	.45	.60	1.75	3.50	22.50
1935S	10,300,000	.35	.40	.50	1.00	2.50	16.00
1936	119,001,420	.30	.35	.40	.75	1.50	11.00
1936 Proof	(4,420)						385.00
1936D	24,814,000	.30	.40	.50	1.00	2.00	12.00
1936S	14,930,000	.30	.40	.50	1.00	1.90	12.50
1937	79,485,769	.30	.35	.45	.75	1.50	11.00
1937 Proof	(5,769)						350.00
1937D	} 17,826,000	.30	.40	.55	1.00	1.75	12.00
1937D 3-Legged*		52.50	60.00	70.00	80.00	110.00	500.00
1937S	5,635,000	.40	.45	.55	1.00	1.75	12.00
1938D	} 7,020,000	.40	.45	.55	1.00	1.75	10.00
1938D, D over S					6.00	7.50	10.00	32.00

†Uncirculated pieces with full sharp details are worth considerably more.
*Beware of removed leg.

1937D "3-Legged" Variety

1938D, D over S Variety

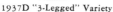

[94]

NICKEL FIVE-CENT PIECES
JEFFERSON TYPE 1938 to Date

This nickel was designed by Felix Schlag. He won an award of $1,000 in a competition with some 390 artists. It established the definite public approval of portrait and pictorial rather than symbolic devices on our coinage.

Designer Felix Schlag; weight 5 grams; composition: 1938-1942, 1946- , .750 copper, .250 nickel; 1942-1945, .560 copper, .350 silver, .090 manganese; diameter 21.2 mm; plain edge; mints: Philadelphia, Denver, San Francisco. Net weight 1942-1945: .05626 oz. pure silver.

Mint mark located at right of building.

VG-8 VERY GOOD—Second porch pillar from right nearly gone, other three still visible but weak.

F-12 FINE—Cheekbone worn flat. Hairlines and eyebrow faint. Second pillar weak, especially at bottom.

VF-20 VERY FINE—Second pillar plain and complete on both sides.

EF-40 EXTREMELY FINE—Cheekbone, hairlines, eyebrow slightly worn but well defined. Base of triangle above pillars visible but weak.

CHOICE UNCIRCULATED—No trace of wear. Barely noticeable blemishes.

	Quan. Minted	VG-8	F-12	VF-20	EF-40	MS-65	Proof
1938 .... (19,365)	19,515,365	$ .15	$ .25	$ .40	$ .55	$1.50	$27.50
1938D..................	5,376,000	1.10	1.35	1.50	2.25	6.00	
1938S..................	4,105,000	2.00	2.25	3.00	3.50	7.50	
1939 .... (12,535)	120,627,535	.15	.25	.35	.50	1.40	22.50
1939 Doubled MONTICELLO and FIVE CENTS			10.00	25.00	50.00		
1939D..................	3,514,000	4.00	4.50	5.50	9.00	50.00	
1939S..................	6,630,000	.70	.90	1.25	2.30	13.00	
1940 .... (14,158)	176,499,158			.20	.35	.85	22.50
1940D..................	43,540,000			.25	.40	1.50	
1940S..................	39,690,000			.30	.60	2.00	
1941 .... (18,720)	203,283,720			.15	.30	1.00	22.50
1941D..................	53,432,000			.20	.35	1.40	
1941S†.................	43,445,000			.25	.45	1.50	
1942 .... (29,600)	49,818,600			.25	.40	1.75	22.50
1942D..................	13,938,000	.40	.85	1.25	2.00	13.00	

†Large and small mint mark varieties, see page 59.

Wartime Alloy Variety 1942-1945

On October 8, 1942, the wartime five-cent piece composed of copper (56%), silver (35%) and manganese (9%) was introduced to eliminate nickel, a critical war material. The mint mark was made larger and placed above the dome of Monticello. The letter P for the Philadelphia Mint was used for the first time on this piece to indicate the change of alloy.

	Quan. Minted	VG-8	F-12	VF-20	EF-40	MS-65	Proof
1942P......... (27,600)	57,900,600	.50	.75	1.50	3.00	13.00	60.00
1942S..................	32,900,000	.40	.55	.80	1.40	6.50	
1943P, 3 over 2......⎫							
1943P...............⎬	271,165,000	.40	.50	.60	1.25	2.25	
1943D..................	15,294,000	.75	1.15	1.50	2.00	3.50	
1943S..................	104,060,000	.40	.50	.60	1.25	2.65	
1944P*.................	119,150,000	.40	.50	.60	1.25	2.25	
1944D..................	32,309,000	.40	.50	.80	1.25	3.25	
1944S..................	21,640,000	.50	.65	.85	1.25	3.00	
1945P..................	119,408,100	.40	.50	.60	1.25	2.50	
1945D..................	37,158,000	.40	.50	.60	1.25	2.25	
1945S..................	58,939,000	.40	.50	.60	1.00	2.00	

*1944 nickels without mint marks are counterfeits.

NICKEL FIVE-CENT PIECES

Prewar composition and mint mark style resumed 1946-1964

	Quan. Minted	VF-20	EF-40	MS-65	Proof
1946	161,116,000		$ .20	$ .60	
1946D	45,292,200	$ .20	.30	.75	
1946S	13,560,000	.30	.45	1.25	
1947	95,000,000		.20	.35	
1947D	37,822,000		.25	1.00	
1947S	24,720,000	.25	.40	1.25	
1948	89,348,000		.20	.50	
1948D	44,734,000	.25	.50	1.10	
1948S	11,300,000	.30	.50	1.75	
1949	60,652,000	.15	.25	.75	
1949D ⎫				———	
1949D, D over S* ⎬	36,498,000				
1949S	9,716,000	.40	.75	2.75	
1950 ...... (51,386)	9,847,386	.40	.70	1.75	$35.00
1950D	2,630,030	8.00	9.00	11.00	
1951 ...... (57,500)	28,609,500	.20	.30	1.00	15.00
1951D	20,460,000	.20	.30	1.60	
1951S	7,776,000	.50	.90	3.00	
1952 ...... (81,980)	64,069,980		.20	.50	10.00
1952D	30,638,000	.30	.65	1.75	
1952S	20,572,000	.20	.30	.85	
1953 ...... (128,800)	46,772,800		.20	.30	8.00
1953D	59,878,600		.20	.50	
1953S	19,210,900	.20	.30	.55	
1954 ...... (233,300)	47,917,350		.15	.25	5.50
1954D	117,183,060		.15	.25	
1954S ⎫		.15	.20	.30	
1954S, S over D ⎬	29,384,000	12.00	27.50	55.00	
1955 ...... (378,200)	8,266,200	.50	.60	1.50	3.25
1955D ⎫			.15	.25	
1955D, D over S* ⎬	74,464,100	6.00	12.00	25.00	

1943, 3 over 2

1954S, S over D

1955D, D over S

	Quan. Minted	VF-20	EF-40	MS-65	Proof
1956 ...... (669,384)	35,885,384		.15	.25	2.00
1956D	67,222,940		.15	.25	
1957 ...... (1,247,952)	39,655,952		.15	.25	1.25
1957D	136,828,900		.15	.20	
1958 ...... (875,652)	17,963,652	.15	.20	.35	1.75
1958D	168,249,120		.15	.20	
1959 ...... (1,149,291)	28,397,291		.15	.30	1.25
1959D	160,738,240			.15	
1960 ...... (1,691,602)	57,107,602			.15	1.15
1960D	192,582,180			.15	
1961 ...... (3,028,144)	76,668,244			.15	1.00
1961D	229,342,760			.15	
1962 ...... (3,218,019)	100,602,019			.15	1.00
1962D	280,195,720			.15	
1963 ...... (3,075,645)	178,851,645			.10	1.00

*Varieties exist.

NICKEL FIVE-CENT PIECES

The designer's initials FS were added below the bust starting in 1966, and dies were further remodeled to strengthen the design in 1971, 1972 and the reverse in 1977. Mint mark position was moved to the obverse starting in 1968.

Quan. Minted	MS-65	Proof
1963D 276,829,460	$ .10	
1964 (3,950,762)		
..... 1,028,622,762	.10	$1.00
1964D ... 1,787,297,160	.10	
1965 136,131,380	.10	
1966 156,208,283	.10	
1967 107,325,800	.10	
1968D 91,227,880	.10	
1968S (3,041,506)		
..... 103,437,510	.10	.65
1969D 202,807,500	.10	
1969S (2,934,631)		
..... 123,009,631	.10	.75
1970D 515,485,380	.10	
1970S (2,632,810)		
..... 241,464,814	.10	.75
1971 106,884,000	.10	
1971D 316,144,800	.10	
1971S Proof only*		
..... (3,220,733)		2.75
1972 202,036,000	.10	
1972D 351,694,600	.10	
1972S Proof only		
..... (3,260,996)		3.00

Quan. Minted	MS-65	Proof
1973 384,396,000	$ .10	
1973D 261,405,000	.10	
1973S Proof only		
..... (2,760,339)		$ 2.75
1974 601,752,000	.10	
1974D 277,373,000	.10	
1974S Proof only		
..... (2,612,568)		5.00
1975 181,772,000	.10	
1975D 401,875,300	.10	
1975S Proof only		
..... (2,845,450)		4.00
1976 367,124,000	.10	
1976D 563,964,147	.10	
1976S Proof only		
..... (4,149,730)		2.50
1977 585,376,000	.10	
1977D 297,313,422	.10	
1977S Proof only		2.50
..... (3,251,152)		
1978	.10	
1978D	.10	
1978S Proof only		2.50

*1971 proof nickels without mint mark were made in error. See pages 59-60.

SILVER THREE-CENT PIECES 1851-1873

This smallest of United States silver coins was authorized by Congress March 3, 1851. The first three-cent silver pieces had no lines bordering the six-pointed star. From 1854 through 1858 there were three lines, while issues of the last fifteen years show only two lines. Issues from 1854 through 1873 have an olive sprig over the III and a bundle of three arrows beneath.

1851-1853 — Designer James B. Longacre; weight .80 gram; composition: .750 silver, .250 copper; diameter 14 mm; plain edge; mints: Philadelphia, New Orleans.

1854-1873 — Weight .75 gram; composition: .900 silver, .100 copper; diameter 14 mm; plain edge. All coined at Philadelphia Mint.

mint mark
o

G-4 GOOD—*Star worn smooth. Legend and date readable.*
VG-8 VERY GOOD—*Outline of shield defined. Legend and date clear.*
F-12 FINE—*Only star points worn smooth.*
VF-20 VERY FINE—*Only partial wear on star ridges.*
EF-40 EXTREMELY FINE—*Ridges on star points show plainly.*
MS-60 UNCIRCULATED—*No trace of wear. Light blemishes.*

Variety 1 — 1851-1853

Quan. Minted	G-4	VG-8	F-12	VF-20	EF-40	MS-60	Proof
1851 Var. 1.... 5,447,400	$8.50	$12.00	$15.00	$26.50	$45.00	$225.00	——
1851O.......... 720,000	12.25	18.50	27.50	40.00	70.00	300.00	
1852 18,663,500	8.50	11.00	14.00	25.00	45.00	220.00	
1853 11,400,000	8.50	11.00	14.00	25.00	45.00	220.00	

SILVER THREE-CENT PIECES

Variety 2
1854-1858
Three
Outlines
to Star

Variety 3
1859-1873
Two
Outlines
to Star

Well struck specimens command higher prices.

	Quan. Minted	G-4	VG-8	F-12	VF-20	EF-40	MS-60	Proof
1854 Var. 2.....	671,000	$13.50	$17.50	$24.00	$40.00	$85.00	$600.00	——
1855	139,000	15.00	22.00	32.00	50.00	135.90	775.00	$2,800
1856	1,458,000	10.50	15.00	22.00	35.00	80.00	600.00	2,500
1857	1,042,000	10.50	15.00	22.00	35.00	80.00	600.00	2,400
1858	1,604,000	10.50	15.00	22.00	35.00	80.00	600.00	1,500
1859 Var. 3.....	365,000	11.50	15.00	21.00	32.00	55.00	225.00	400.00
1860 ... (1,000)	287,000	11.50	15.00	21.00	32.00	55.00	225.00	400.00
1861 ... (1,000)	498,000	11.50	15.00	21.00	32.00	55.00	225.00	400.00
1862, 2 over 1	⎰ 343,550	17.00	24.00	32.00	62.50	120.00	300.00	
1862 .... (550)	⎱	11.50	15.00	21.00	32.00	55.00	225.00	400.00
1863, 3 over 2	⎰ 21,460	....						1,000
1863 .... (460)	⎱						450.00	475.00
1864 .... (470)	12,470	....					475.00	475.00
1865 .... (500)	8,500	....					550	475.00
1866 .... (725)	22,725	....					525.00	440.00
1867 .... (625)	4,625	....	Circulated coins			....	500.00	440.00
1868 .... (600)	4,100	....	1863 to 1872 are			....	500.00	440.00
1869, 9 over 8	⎰ 5,100	....	rarely encountered.				——	
1869 .... (600)	⎱	....	They were melted			....	500.00	440.00
1870 ... (1,000)	4,000	....	or exported.			....	500.00	425.00
1871 .... (960)	4,360	....					500.00	425.00
1872 .... (950)	1,950	....					525.00	425.00
1873 .... (600)		600 (Closed 3 only)						525.00

HALF DIMES 1794-1873

The half dime types present the same general characteristics as larger United States silver coins. Authorized by the Act of April 2, 1792, they were not coined until February, 1795, although dated 1794. At first the weight was 20.8 grains, and fineness 892.4. By the Act of January 18, 1837 the weight was slightly reduced to 20 5/8 grains and the fineness changed to .900. Finally the weight was reduced to 19.2 grains by the Act of February 21, 1853. Both half dimes and dimes offer many varieties in the early dates.

FLOWING HAIR TYPE 1794-1795

Designer Robert Scot; weight 1.35 grams; composition: .8924 silver, .1076 copper; approx. diameter 16.5 mm; reeded edge. All coined at Philadelphia Mint.

AG-3 ABOUT GOOD—*Details clear enough to identify.*

G-4 GOOD—*Eagle, wreath, bust outlined but lack details.*

VG-8 VERY GOOD—*Some details remain on face. All lettering readable.*

F-12 FINE—*Hair ends show. Hair at top smooth.*

VF-20 VERY FINE—*Hairlines at top show. Hair about ear defined.*

EF-40 EXTREMELY FINE—*Hair above forehead and at neck well defined but shows some wear.*

MS-60 UNCIRCULATED—*No trace of wear. Light blemishes.*

	Quan. Minted	AG-3	G-4	VG-8	F-12	VF-20	EF-40	MS-60
1794	⎰ 86,416	$160.00	$275.00	$400.00	$550.00	$1,100	$1,750	$6,750
1795	⎱	140.00	260.00	325.00	450.00	800.00	1,200	4,500

HALF DIMES

DRAPED BUST TYPE, SMALL EAGLE REVERSE 1796-1797

AG-3 ABOUT GOOD—*Details clear enough to identify.*
G-4 GOOD—*Date, stars, LIBERTY readable. Bust outlined but no details.*
VG-8 VERY GOOD—*Some details show.*
F-12 FINE—*Hair and drapery lines worn, but visible.*
VF-20 VERY FINE—*Only left of drapery indistinct.*
EF-40 EXTREMELY FINE—*All hairlines show details.*
MS-60 UNCIRCULATED—*No trace of wear. Light blemishes.*

	Quan. Minted	AG-3	G-4	VG-8	F-12	VF-20	EF-40	MS-60
1796, 6 over 5		$225.00	$450.00	$625.00	$800.00	$1,350	$2,250	$7,000
1796 Nor. dt.	10,230	150.00	325.00	425.00	550.00	800.00	1,200	6,000
1796 LIKERTY		150.00	325.00	425.00	600.00	925.00	1,600	7,200
1797, 15 Stars		140.00	300.00	385.00	525.00	775.00	1,200	5,600
1797, 16 stars	44,527	140.00	300.00	385.00	525.00	775.00	1,300	5,700
1797, 13 stars		140.00	300.00	385.00	525.00	775.00	1,350	6,000

DRAPED BUST TYPE, HERALDIC EAGLE REVERSE 1800-1805

1800 LIBEKTY

		AG-3	G-4	VG-8	F-12	VF-20	EF-40	MS-60
1800 All kinds	24,000	115.00	200.00	265.00	400.00	600.00	1,000	5,000
1800 LIBEKTY		115.00	200.00	265.00	400.00	600.00	1,000	5,200
1801	33,910	120.00	220.00	290.00	475.00	675.00	1,100	5,500
1802	13,010	1,200	2,250	3,750	6,750	11,500	23,000	——
1803 Large 8	37,850	115.00	200.00	265.00	400.00	600.00	1,000	5,500
1803 Small 8		115.00	200.00	265.00	400.00	600.00	1,000	5,500
1805	15,600	175.00	300.00	450.00	675.00	1,100	1,600	——

CAPPED BUST TYPE 1829-1837

Designer William Kneass; weight 1.35 grams; composition: .8924 silver, .1076 copper; approx. diameter 15.5 mm; reeded edge. All coined at Philadelphia Mint.

G-4 GOOD—*Bust outlined, no detail. Date and legend readable.*
VG-8 VERY GOOD—*Complete legend and date plain. At least 3 letters of LIBERTY show clearly.*
F-12 FINE—*All letters in LIBERTY show.*
VF-20 VERY FINE—*Full rims. Ear and shoulder clasp show plainly.*
EF-40 EXTREMELY FINE—*Ear very distinct, eyebrow and hair well defined.*
MS-60 UNCIRCULATED—*No trace of wear. Light blemishes.*

	Quan. Minted	G-4	VG-8	F-12	VF-20	EF-40	MS-60
1829	1,230,000	17.00	20.00	25.00	35.00	70.00	475.00
1830	1,240,000	17.00	20.00	25.00	35.00	70.00	450.00
1831	1,242,700	17.00	20.00	25.00	35.00	70.00	450.00
1832	965,000	17.00	20.00	25.00	35.00	70.00	450.00
1833	1,370,000	17.00	20.00	25.00	35.00	70.00	450.00
1834	1,480,000	17.00	20.00	25.00	35.00	70.00	450.00
1835 All kinds	2,760,000						
1835 Lg. date and 5c		17.00	20.00	25.00	35.00	70.00	450.00
1835 Lg. date, sm. 5c		17.00	20.00	25.00	35.00	70.00	450.00
1835 Sm. date, lg. 5c		17.00	20.00	25.00	35.00	70.00	450.00
1835 Sm. date and 5c		17.00	20.00	25.00	35.00	70.00	450.00
1836 Small 5c	1,900,000	17.00	20.00	25.00	35.00	70.00	450.00
1836 Large 5c		17.00	20.00	25.00	35.00	70.00	450.00
1837 Small 5c	2,276,000	28.00	42.50	55.00	100.00	185.00	1,000
1837 Large 5c		17.00	20.00	25.00	35.00	70.00	450.00

HALF DIMES

LIBERTY SEATED TYPE 1837-1873
Variety 1 — No Stars on Obverse 1837-1838

Designer Christian Gobrecht; weight 1.34 grams; composition: .900 silver, .100 copper; diameter 15.5 mm; reeded edge; mints: Philadelphia, New Orleans.

G-4 GOOD—*LIBERTY on shield smooth. Date and letters readable.*
VG-8 VERY GOOD—*At least 3 letters in LIBERTY are visible.*
F-12 FINE—*Entire LIBERTY visible, weak spots.*
VF-20 VERY FINE—*Entire LIBERTY strong and even.*
EF-40 EXTREMELY FINE—*LIBERTY and scroll edges distinct.*
MS-60 UNCIRCULATED—*No trace of wear. Light blemishes.*

	Quan. Minted	G-4	VG-8	F-12	VF-20	EF-40	MS-60
1837 Sm. date	inc. above	$42.50	$60.00	$75.00	$105.00	$220.00	$900.00
1837 Lg. date		40.00	55.00	70.00	95.00	200.00	825.00
1838O No stars	70,000	50.00	70.00	110.00	180.00	325.00	2,700

No Drapery from Elbow 1837-1840

Drapery from Elbow Starting 1840

From 1838 through 1859 mint mark is located above bow on reverse. Large, medium or small mint mark varieties occur for several dates.

Variety 2 — Stars on Obverse 1838-1853

	Quan. Minted	G-4	VG-8	F-12	VF-20	EF-40	MS-60
1838 No drpy	2,255,000	7.00	8.00	12.00	25.00	50.00	400.00
1838 Small stars						—	—
1839 No drpy	1,069,150	7.00	8.00	12.00	25.00	50.00	390.00
1839O No drpy	1,034,039	9.00	12.50	17.50	30.00	60.00	500.00
1840 No drapery. All kinds	1,344,085	7.00	8.00	12.00	25.00	50.00	400.00
1840O No drapery All kinds	935,000	7.50	11.00	17.50	35.00	70.00	525.00
1840 Drapery		7.25	10.00	15.00	30.00	75.00	550.00
1840O Drapery		10.00	15.00	30.00	65.00	125.00	—
1841	1,150,000	7.00	8.00	11.00	22.00	45.00	325.00
1841O	815,000	9.00	12.00	20.00	32.50	65.00	650.00
1842	815,000	7.00	8.00	11.00	22.00	45.00	325.00
1842O	350,000	9.00	15.00	27.50	45.00	85.00	950.00
1843	1,165,000	7.00	8.00	11.00	22.00	45.00	325.00
1844	430,000	7.00	8.00	11.00	22.00	45.00	325.00
1844O	220,000	15.00	25.00	40.00	85.00	250.00	—
1845	1,564,000	7.00	8.00	11.00	22.00	45.00	325.00
1846	27,000	60.00	85.00	125.00	200.00	350.00	—
1847	1,274,000	7.00	8.00	11.00	22.00	45.00	325.00
1848 Med. date	668,000	7.00	8.00	11.00	22.00	45.00	350.00
1848 Lg. date		7.50	9.00	14.00	30.00	65.00	500.00
1848O	600,000	10.00	17.50	25.00	45.00	75.00	600.00
1849, 9 over 6	1,309,000	8.00	12.00	17.50	25.00	60.00	400.00
1849, 9 over 8		9.00	14.00	20.00	30.00	75.00	425.00
1849 Nor. date		7.00	8.00	11.00	22.00	45.00	325.00
1849O	140,000	25.00	40.00	65.00	125.00	265.00	—
1850	955,000	7.00	8.00	11.00	22.00	45.00	325.00
1850O	690,000	10.00	15.00	22.00	35.00	65.00	700.00
1851	781,000	7.00	8.00	11.00	22.00	45.00	325.00
1851O	860,000	10.00	15.00	22.00	35.00	65.00	550.00
1852	1,000,500	7.00	8.00	11.00	22.00	45.00	325.00
1852O	260,000	15.00	27.50	40.00	60.00	100.00	850.00
1853 No arrows	135,000	14.00	24.00	37.50	50.00	95.00	525.00
1853O No arrows	160,000	90.00	115.00	170.00	250.00	450.00	—

HALF DIMES

Variety 3 — Arrows at Date 1853-1855

Weight 1.24 grams; composition: .900 silver, .100 copper; diameter 15.5 mm; reeded edge; mints: Philadelphia, New Orleans, San Francisco.

As on the dimes, quarters and halves, arrows were placed at the sides of the date for a short period starting in 1853. They were placed there to denote the reduction of weight under the terms of the Act of February 21, 1853.

	Quan. Minted	G-4	VG-8	F-12	VF-20	EF-40	MS-60	Proof
1853	13,210,020	$6.00	$ 7.50	$ 9.50	$20.00	$37.50	$400.00	
1853O.	2,200,000	6.00	7.50	9.50	21.00	40.00	450.00	
1854	5,740,000	5.50	7.50	9.50	17.50	36.00	400.00	
1854O.	1,560,000	7.00	8.50	11.00	23.00	45.00	475.00	
1855	1,750,000	5.50	7.50	9.50	21.00	42.50	400.00	$2,250
1855O.	600,000	9.50	12.50	17.50	30.00	75.00	550.00	

Variety 2 Resumed 1856-1859

		G-4	VG-8	F-12	VF-20	EF-40	MS-60	Proof
1856	4,880,000	5.75	8.00	10.00	20.00	32.50	300.00	1,400
1856O.	1,100,000	6.50	8.50	10.50	21.00	40.00	400.00	
1857	7,280,000	5.75	8.00	10.00	20.00	32.50	300.00	1,000
1857O.	1,380,000	6.50	8.50	10.50	21.00	40.00	400.00	

1858 over Inverted Date

		G-4	VG-8	F-12	VF-20	EF-40	MS-60	Proof
1858		5.75	8.00	10.00	20.00	32.50	300.00	750.00
1858 over inverted date	3,500,000	30.00	35.00	67.50	110.00	200.00	675.00	
1858O.	1,660,000	6.50	8.50	10.50	21.00	40.00	400.00	
1859O.	560,000	10.00	17.50	22.50	32.50	60.00	450.00	

New die 1859 Philadelphia Mint. Stars hollow in center. Arms slimmer.

		G-4	VG-8	F-12	VF-20	EF-40	MS-60	Proof
1859	340,000	10.00	17.50	25.00	40.00	65.00	400.00	500.00

In the years 1859 and 1860 interesting half dime patterns were made which do not bear our nation's identity. These are transitional pieces, not made for circulation, but struck at the time the inscription UNITED STATES OF AMERICA was being transferred from the reverse to the obverse.

1859 Obv. of 59, rev. of 60.		7,250
1860 Obv. of 59, rev. of 60		
(With stars) 100.	2,000	

Variety 4 — Legend on Obverse 1860-1873

		G-4	VG-8	F-12	VF-20	EF-40	MS-60	Proof
1860 Legend (1,000)	799,000	5.50	6.50	9.00	14.00	30.00	225.00	300.00
1860O.	1,060,000	5.50	6.50	10.00	15.00	35.00	250.00	

HALF DIMES

	Quan. Minted	G-4	VG-8	F-12	VF-20	EF-40	MS-60	Proof
1861 . (1,000)	3,361,000	$5.25	$6.50	$8.00	$12.00	$25.00	$250.00	$300.00
1862 . . . (550)	1,492,550	5.25	6.50	8.00	12.00	25.00	250.00	300.00
1863 . . . (460)	18,460	32.50	45.00	62.50	85.00	145.00	500.00	425.00
1863S	100,000	14.00	17.50	22.50	40.00	90.00	575.00	
1864 . . . (470)	48,470	125.00	150.00	180.00	225.00	310.00	900.00	550.00
1864S	90,000	22.50	30.00	45.00	60.00	115.00	950.00	
1865 . . . (500)	13,500	50.00	60.00	80.00	110.00	175.00	575.00	400.00
1865S	120,000	12.50	17.50	25.00	45.00	70.00	650.00	
1866 . . . (725)	10,725	45.00	60.00	75.00	100.00	160.00	650.00	400.00
1866S	120,000	12.50	17.50	22.50	40.00	65.00	675.00	
1867 . . . (625)	8,625	65.00	85.00	100.00	150.00	225.00	675.00	400.00
1867S	120,000	12.50	17.50	22.50	45.00	75.00	675.00	
1868 . . . (600)	89,200	15.00	20.00	30.00	50.00	90.00	400.00	300.00
1868S	280,000	7.50	10.00	15.00	22.50	40.00	325.00	
1869 . . . (600)	208,600	7.00	9.00	12.00	20.00	30.00	300.00	300.00
1869S	230,000	7.50	10.00	15.00	22.50	40.00	375.00	
1870 . (1,000)	536,000	5.50	8.00	10.00	17.50	35.00	275.00	300.00
1871 . . . (960)	1,873,960	5.50	8.00	10.00	15.00	30.00	250.00	300.00
1871S	161,000	15.00	20.00	30.00	50.00	75.00	400.00	
1872 . . . (950)	2,947,950	5.50	8.00	10.00	15.00	30.00	250.00	300.00

Mint mark below bow 1860-1869, 1872-1873.

Mint mark above bow 1871-1872.

1872 All kinds . .	837,000							
1872S mm. above bow . .		5.50	8.00	10.00	15.00	30.00	250.00	
1872S mm. below bow . .		5.50	8.00	10.00	15.00	30.00	250.00	
1873 (Closed 3 only)								
(600)	712,600	5.50	8.00	10.00	15.00	30.00	250.00	300.00
1873S (Closed 3 only)								
. . . .	324,000	5.50	8.00	10.00	15.00	30.00	250.00	

BIBLIOGRAPHY

Newlin, H. P. *The Early Half-Dimes of the United States.* Philadelphia, 1883 (reprinted 1933).
Valentine, D. W. *The United States Half Dimes.* New York, 1931.
Breen, Walter. *United States Half Dimes: A Supplement.* New York, 1958.

DIMES — 1796 to Date

The designs of the dimes, first coined in 1796, follow closely those of the half dimes up through the Liberty seated type. The dimes in each instance weigh twice as much as the half dimes.

BIBLIOGRAPHY

Kosoff, A. *United States Dimes from 1796.* New York, 1945.
Ahwash, Kamal M. *Encyclopedia of United States Liberty Seated Dimes 1837-1891.* Kamal Press, 1977.

DRAPED BUST TYPE, SMALL EAGLE REVERSE 1796-1797

AG-3 ABOUT GOOD—*Details clear enough to identify.*

G-4 GOOD—*Date readable. Bust outlined, but no detail.*

VG-8 VERY GOOD—*All but deepest drapery folds worn smooth. Hairlines nearly gone and curls lack detail.*

F-12 FINE—*All drapery lines visible. Hair partly worn.*

VF-20 VERY FINE—*Only left side of drapery is indistinct.*

EF-40 EXTREMELY FINE—*Hair well outlined and shows details.*

MS-60 UNCIRCULATED—*No trace of wear. Light blemishes.*

Designer Robert Scot; weight 2.70 grams; composition: .8924 silver, .1076 copper; approx. diameter 19 mm; reeded edge. All coined at Philadelphia Mint.

DIMES

1797, 16 Stars   1797, 13 Stars

Quan. Minted	AG-3	G-4	VG-8	F-12	VF-20	EF-40	MS-60
1796 22,135	$250.00	$450.00	$575.00	$950.00	$1,600	$2,500	$7,000
1797 16 stars } 25,261	225.00	425.00	550.00	850.00	1,400	2,400	7,000
1797 13 stars }	225.00	425.00	550.00	850.00	1,400	2,400	7,000

DRAPED BUST TYPE, HERALDIC EAGLE REVERSE 1798-1807

	AG-3	G-4	VG-8	F-12	VF-20	EF-40	MS-60
1798 All kinds 27,550							
1798 over 97, 16 stars on rev.........	115.00	190.00	260.00	380.00	550.00	900.00	4,400
1798 over 97, 13 stars on rev.		700.00	1,200	2,000	——		
1798	115.00	190.00	260.00	380.00	550.00	900.00	4,500
1798 Small 8	150.00	275.00	350.00	750.00	1,300	1,750	
1800 21,760	110.00	160.00	210.00	260.00	425.00	700.00	4,000
1801 34,640	110.00	165.00	250.00	350.00	550.00	850.00	4,250
1802 10,975	125.00	200.00	260.00	400.00	700.00	1,100	4,500
1803 33,040	110.00	165.00	250.00	350.00	550.00	800.00	4,250
1804 All kinds 8,265							
1804 13 stars on rev.	250.00	400.00	700.00	1,050	2,000	3,000	——
1804 14 stars on rev.	225.00	375.00	600.00	950.00	1,750	2,750	4,500
1805 4 ber. } 120,780	75.00	150.00	215.00	275.00	400.00	700.00	3,500
1805 5 ber. }	75.00	150.00	215.00	275.00	400.00	700.00	3,500
1807 165,000	70.00	150.00	210.00	265.00	385.00	665.00	3,250

CAPPED BUST TYPE 1809-1837

AG-3 ABOUT GOOD—*Details clear enough to identify.*
G-4 GOOD—*Date, letters and stars discernible. Bust outlined, no details.*
VG-8 VERY GOOD—*Legends and date plain. Minimum of 3 letters in LIBERTY.*
F-12 FINE—*Full LIBERTY. Ear and shoulder clasp visible. Part of rim shows both sides.*
VF-20 VERY FINE—*LIBERTY distinct. Full rim. Ear and clasp plain and distinct.*
EF-40 EXTREMELY FINE—*LIBERTY sharp. Ear distinct. Hair above eye well defined.*
MS-60 UNCIRCULATED—*No trace of wear. Light blemishes.*

Designer John Reich; weight 2.70 grams; composition: .8924 silver, .1076 copper; approx. diameter 18.8 mm; reeded edge. All coined at Philadelphia Mint.

Variety 1 —
Large Size 1809-1828

1809 51,065	45.00	65.00	100.00	150.00	250.00	400.00	3,600
1811 over 9.... 65,180	27.50	42.50	57.50	80.00	150.00	300.00	3,000

[103]

DIMES

1814 Small Date   1814 Large Date

	Quan. Minted	G-4	VG-8	F-12	VF-20	EF-40	MS-60
1814 Sm. date .. ⎱	421,500	$28.50	$35.00	$50.00	$90.00	$220.00	$2,100
1814 Lg. date... ⎰		27.50	32.00	45.00	80.00	200.00	2,000
1814 STATESOFAMERICA							
One word		30.00	35.00	60.00	100.00	300.00	2,500

1820 Large 0   1821 Small Date   1821 Large Date

1820 Lg. 0..... ⎱	942,587	22.50	30.00	40.00	60.00	135.00	1,700
1820 Sm. 0 .... ⎰		22.50	30.00	40.00	60.00	135.00	1,700
1821 Sm. date ⎱	1,186,512	22.50	30.00	40.00	65.00	145.00	1,700
1821 Lg. date ⎰		22.50	30.00	40.00	60.00	135.00	1,700
1822 100,000		60.00	80.00	135.00	275.00	525.00	3,300

1823, 3 over 2   Small E's   Large E's

1823, 3 over 2, All kinds 440,000							
1823, 3 over 2, sm. E's		22.50	30.00	40.00	70.00	140.00	2,150
1823, 3 over 2, lg. E's		22.50	30.00	40.00	70.00	140.00	2,150

1824, 4 over 2   1828 Large Date   1828 Small Date

1824, 4 over 2 .. ⎱	510,000	30.00	40.00	60.00	100.00	200.00	2,350
1825 .... ⎰		22.00	30.00	40.00	80.00	200.00	1,800
1827 1,215,000		20.00	28.00	35.00	60.00	160.00	2,000
1828 Both vars 125,000							
1828 Lg. date, curl base 2 ..		30.00	45.00	70.00	125.00	250.00	2,000

Variety 2 — Reduced Size 1828-1837

New mint equipment was used to make the small date 1828 dimes and subsequent issues. Unlike earlier coinage, these have beaded borders and a uniform diameter. Large date has curl base knob 2; small date has square base knob 2.

1829 Small 10c   Large 10c   1830, 30 over 29

DIMES

	Quan. Minted	G-4	F-12	VF-20	EF-40	MS-60
1828 Small date, sq. base 2		$25.00	$40.00	$70.00	$150.00	$1,400
1829 Curl base 2				—		
1829 Small 10c		15.00	25.00	40.00	85.00	1,000
1829 Medium 10c	770,000	15.00	25.00	40.00	85.00	1,000
1829 Large 10c		20.00	35.00	60.00	100.00	1,000
1830, 30 over 29			150.00	250.00	400.00	1,700
1830 Large 10c	510,000	15.00	25.00	40.00	85.00	1,000
1830 Small 10c		15.00	25.00	40.00	85.00	1,000
1831	771,350	15.00	25.00	40.00	85.00	1,000
1832	522,500	15.00	25.00	40.00	85.00	1,000
1833	485,000	15.00	25.00	40.00	85.00	1,000
1833 Last 3 high		15.00	25.00	40.00	85.00	1,000
1834 Small 4	635,000	15.00	25.00	40.00	85.00	1,000
1834 Large 4		15.00	25.00	40.00	85.00	1,000
1835	1,410,000	15.00	25.00	40.00	85.00	1,000
1836	1,190,000	15.00	25.00	40.00	85.00	1,000
1837 All kinds	1,042,000	15.00	25.00	40.00	85.00	1,000

LIBERTY SEATED TYPE 1837-1891

Variety 1 — No Stars on Obverse 1837-1838

Designer Christian Gobrecht; weight 2.67 grams; composition: .900 silver, .100 copper; diameter 17.9 mm; reeded edge; mints: Philadelphia, New Orleans.

No Drapery from Elbow
No Stars on Obverse

G-4 GOOD—*LIBERTY on shield smooth. Date and letters readable.*

VG-8 VERY GOOD—*At least 3 letters in LIBERTY are visible.*

F-12 FINE—*Entire LIBERTY visible, weak spots.*

VF-20 VERY FINE—*Entire LIBERTY strong and even.*

EF-40 EXTREMELY FINE—*LIBERTY and scroll edges distinct.*

MS-60 UNCIRCULATED—*No trace of wear. Light blemishes.*

Mint marks on Liberty seated dimes are placed on the reverse within, or below, the wreath. Size of mint mark varies on many dates.

		G-4	F-12	VF-20	EF-40	MS-60
1837 Small date . . .	incl. above	35.00	75.00	140.00	275.00	1,600
1837 Large date . . .		35.00	75.00	140.00	275.00	1,500
1838O	406,034	35.00	100.00	200.00	375.00	2,500

Variety 2 — Stars on Obverse 1838-1853

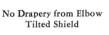
No Drapery from Elbow
Tilted Shield

1838 Small Stars   1838 Large Stars

		G-4	F-12	VF-20	EF-40	MS-60
1838 Small stars		15.00	30.00	50.00	85.00	650.00
1838 Large stars	1,992,500	8.00	12.50	20.00	50.00	550.00
1838 Partial drapery		15.00	32.50	55.00	90.00	625.00
1839	1,053,115	5.50	10.00	18.00	45.00	575.00
1839O	1,323,000	6.50	14.00	27.50	55.00	625.00
1840 All kinds	1,358,580	5.50	10.00	18.00	40.00	550.00
1840O	1,175,000	7.00	15.00	30.00	55.00	650.00
1841 Proof, see page 106.						

DIMES

Drapery from Elbow
Upright Shield

	Quan. Minted	G-4	F-12	VF-20	EF-40	MS-60	Proof
1840		$12.50	$25.00	$40.00	$100.00	$1,000	
1841	1,622,500	4.75	9.00	18.00	35.00	400.00	——*
1841O	2,007,500	7.00	15.00	25.00	50.00	525.00	
1842	1,887,500	4.75	9.00	18.00	35.00	425.00	
1842O	2,020,000	4.75	10.00	20.00	50.00	550.00	
1843	1,370,000	4.75	9.00	18.00	35.00	400.00	
1843O	150,000	30.00	80.00	225.00	600.00	——	
1844	72,500	30.00	80.00	160.00	375.00	1,500	
1845	1,755,000	4.75	9.00	18.00	35.00	400.00	
1845O	230,000	15.00	40.00	125.00	500.00	——	
1846	31,300	35.00	70.00	120.00	300.00	1,300	
1847	245,000	7.50	20.00	35.00	65.00	500.00	
1848	451,500	5.00	11.00	22.50	45.00	400.00	
1849	839,000	4.75	9.00	18.00	35.00	400.00	
1849O	300,000	10.00	20.00	50.00	100.00	850.00	
1850	1,931,500	4.75	9.00	17.00	32.50	400.00	
1850O	510,000	8.00	15.00	40.00	75.00	575.00	
1851	1,026,500	4.75	9.00	17.00	32.50	400.00	
1851O	400,000	8.00	15.00	40.00	75.00	600.00	
1852	1,535,500	4.75	9.00	17.00	32.50	400.00	
1852O	430,000	8.00	15.00	40.00	100.00	700.00	
1853 No arrows	95,000	25.00	45.00	75.00	150.00	750.00	

*Termed "no drapery" because excessive polishing of the proof die removed most of the drapery and reduced the size of the stars. Unique 1973 M.A.N.A. sale $52,000.

Variety 3 — Arrows at Date 1853-1855

Weight 2.49 grams; composition: .900 silver, .100 copper; diameter 17.9 mm, reeded edge; mints: Philadelphia, New Orleans. Also San Francisco and Carson City after 1855.

Arrows at Date   Small Date, Arrows Removed

1853 With arrows	12,078,010	5.00	10.00	22.00	45.00	450.00	
1853O	1,100,000	6.50	12.50	30.00	65.00	600.00	
1854	4,470,000	5.00	10.00	20.00	45.00	450.00	
1854O	1,770,000	6.00	12.00	25.00	60.00	500.00	
1855	2,075,000	5.00	10.00	20.00	45.00	450.00	$2,100

Variety 2 Resumed 1856-1860

1856 Sm. date	5,780,000	4.00	7.50	14.00	30.00	375.00	1,000
1856 Lg. date		4.25	8.00	15.00	35.00	475.00	
1856O	1,180,000	4.25	8.00	18.00	40.00	550.00	
1856S	70,000	35.00	80.00	150.00	275.00	——	
1857	5,580,000	4.00	7.50	14.00	30.00	375.00	900.00
1857O	1,540,000	4.00	7.75	15.00	32.50	450.00	

DIMES

	Quan. Minted	G-4	F-12	VF-20	EF-40	MS-60	Proof
1858	1,540,000	$4.00	$7.50	$14.00	$30.00	$375.00	$700.00
1858O	290,000	5.50	10.00	22.50	45.00	525.00	
1858S	60,000	25.00	60.00	115.00	275.00	——	
1859	430,000	4.00	7.50	14.00	30.00	400.00	500.00
1859O	480,000	4.00	7.75	15.00	32.00	450.00	
1859S	60,000	22.00	55.00	110.00	200.00	2,200	
1860S	140,000	10.00	30.00	65.00	125.00	950.00	

In 1859 an interesting pattern dime was made which does not bear our nation's identity. It is a "transitional" piece, not made for circulation, but struck at the time the inscription UNITED STATES OF AMERICA was being transferred from the reverse to the obverse.

1859 5,500

Variety 4 — Legend on Obverse 1860-1873

		G-4	F-12	VF-20	EF-40	MS-60	Proof
1860 ...... (1,000)	607,000	4.00	7.50	12.50	25.00	225.00	325.00
1860O	40,000	325.00	700.00	1,050	2,000	——	
1861* ...... (1,000)	1,884,000	4.00	7.50	12.50	25.00	215.00	325.00
1861S	172,500	15.00	35.00	70.00	150.00	1,000	
1862 .... (550)	847,550	4.00	7.50	12.50	25.00	215.00	325.00
1862S	180,750	10.00	25.00	60.00	120.00	900.00	
1863 .... (460)	14,460	45.00	85.00	110.00	175.00	600.00	375.00
1863S	157,500	12.00	30.00	65.00	150.00	700.00	
1864 .... (470)	11,470	47.50	90.00	125.00	200.00	600.00	375.00
1864S	230,000	10.00	25.00	50.00	125.00	950.00	
1865 .... (500)	10,500	52.50	100.00	140.00	200.00	650.00	385.00
1865S	175,000	10.00	25.00	50.00	125.00	950.00	
1866 .... (725)	8,725	50.00	90.00	150.00	210.00	700.00	375.00
1866S	135,000	12.50	27.50	55.00	125.00	950.00	
1867 .... (625)	6,625	50.00	90.00	150.00	225.00	700.00	375.00
1867S	140,000	12.50	27.50	55.00	125.00	950.00	
1868 .... (600)	464,600	4.00	7.50	17.50	35.00	500.00	325.00
1868S	260,000	8.00	17.50	40.00	75.00	390.00	
1869 .... (600)	256,000	4.00	7.50	17.50	35.00	350.00	325.00
1869S	450,000	7.00	15.00	30.00	70.00	390.00	
1870 .... (1,000)	471,500	4.00	7.50	17.50	35.00	275.00	300.00
1870S	50,000	50.00	100.00	150.00	275.00	1,000	
1871 .... (960)	907,710	4.00	7.50	12.50	25.00	225.00	300.00
1871CC	20,100	135.00	350.00	750.00	1,400	——	
1871S	320,000	10.00	25.00	50.00	110.00	675.00	
1872 .... (950)	2,396,450	4.00	7.50	12.50	25.00	225.00	300.00
1872CC	35,480	100.00	225.00	400.00	825.00	2,750	
1872S	190,000	11.00	25.00	45.00	85.00	450.00	
1873 All kinds	1,568,600						
1873 Closed 3 (600)		4.00	7.50	12.50	25.00	225.00	325.00
1873 Open 3		5.00	15.00	25.00	50.00	350.00	
1873CC (Unique)	12,400					——	

*Dies modified slightly during 1861. First variety with only five vertical lines in top of shield is scarcer than the later variety.

DIMES

Variety 5 — Arrows at Date 1873-1874

Weight 2.50 grams; composition: .900 silver, .100 copper; diameter 17.9 mm; reeded edge; mints: Philadelphia, New Orleans, San Francisco, Carson City.

In 1873 the dime was increased in weight to 2.50 grams. Arrows at date in 1873 and 1874 indicate this change.

	Quan. Minted	G-4	F-12	VF-20	EF-40	MS-60	Proof
1873 .... (800)	2,378,500	$11.00	$27.50	$45.00	$90.00	$550.00	$750.00
1873CC	18,791	300.00	600.00	800.00	1,500	——	
1873S	455,000	16.00	32.50	60.00	100.00	625.00	
1874 .... (700)	2,940,000	11.00	27.50	45.00	90.00	550.00	750.00
1874CC	10,817	125.00	350.00	650.00	1,250	——	
1874S	240,000	19.00	45.00	80.00	125.00	650.00	

Variety 4 Resumed 1875-1891

	Quan. Minted	G-4	F-12	VF-20	EF-40	MS-60	Proof
1875 .... (700)	10,350,700	4.00	6.50	12.00	22.50	200.00	300.00
1875CC Below bow							
All kinds	4,645,000	4.50	8.50	16.00	25.00	225.00	
1875CC Above bow		4.00	6.50	12.00	22.50	235.00	
1875S Below bow							
All kinds	9,070,000	4.00	6.50	12.00	35.00	200.00	
1875S Above bow		4.00	6.50	12.00	30.00	200.00	
1876 ... (1,150)	11,461,150	4.00	6.50	12.00	22.50	200.00	300.00
1876CC	8,270,000	4.00	6.50	12.00	22.50	250.00	
1876S	10,420,000	4.00	6.50	12.00	22.50	215.00	
1877 .... (510)	7,310,510	4.00	6.50	12.00	22.50	200.00	325.00
1877CC	7,700,000	4.00	6.50	12.00	22.50	225.00	
1877S	2,340,000	4.00	6.50	12.00	22.50	215.00	
1878 .... (800)	1,678,000	4.00	6.50	12.00	22.50	215.00	300.00
1878CC	200,000	17.50	35.00	50.00	100.00	425.00	
1879 ... (1,100)	15,100	40.00	70.00	110.00	160.00	450.00	350.00
1880 ... (1,355)	37,355	35.00	60.00	95.00	130.00	425.00	350.00
1881 .... (975)	24,975	37.50	65.00	100.00	140.00	425.00	350.00
1882 ... (1,100)	3,911,100	4.00	6.50	12.00	22.50	215.00	300.00
1883 ... (1,039)	7,675,712	4.00	6.50	12.00	22.50	215.00	300.00
1884 .... (875)	3,366,380	4.00	6.50	12.00	22.50	215.00	300.00
1884S	564,969	11.00	20.00	40.00	60.00	350.00	
1885 .... (930)	2,533,427	4.00	6.50	12.00	22.50	215.00	300.00
1885S	43,690	82.50	135.00	260.00	425.00	1,500	
1886 .... (886)	6,377,570	4.00	6.50	12.00	22.50	200.00	275.00
1886S	206,524	11.00	20.00	35.00	50.00	300.00	
1887 .... (710)	11,283,939	4.00	6.50	12.00	22.50	200.00	275.00
1887S	4,454,450	4.00	6.50	12.00	22.50	215.00	
1888 .... (832)	5,496,487	4.00	6.50	12.00	22.50	200.00	275.00
1888S	1,720,000	4.00	6.50	12.00	22.50	225.00	
1889 .... (711)	7,380,711	4.00	6.50	12.00	22.50	200.00	275.00
1889S	972,678	11.00	20.00	50.00	90.00	325.00	
1890 .... (590)	9,911,541	4.75	6.50	12.00	22.50	200.00	300.00
1890S	1,423,076	4.00	9.00	15.00	25.00	240.00	
1891 .... (600)	15,310,600	4.00	6.50	12.00	22.50	200.00	300.00
1891O	4,540,000	4.00	6.50	20.00	35.00	250.00	
1891O O over S............					——	——	
1891S	3,196,116	4.00	6.50	12.00	26.00	235.00	

DIMES

BARBER or LIBERTY HEAD TYPE 1892-1916

Designed by Charles E. Barber, Chief Engraver of the Mint. He also designed the 25 and 50-cent pieces. His initial B is at the truncation of the neck.

G-4 GOOD—*Date and letters plain. LIBERTY is obliterated.*
VG-8 VERY GOOD—*At least 3 letters visible in LIBERTY.*
F-12 FINE—*All letters in LIBERTY visible, though some are weak.*
VF-20 VERY FINE—*All letters of LIBERTY evenly plain.*
EF-40 EXTREMELY FINE—*All letters in LIBERTY are sharp, distinct. Headband edges are distinct.*
MS-60 UNCIRCULATED—*No trace of wear. Light blemishes.*

Mint mark location is on the reverse below the wreath.

Designer Charles E. Barber; weight 2.50 grams; composition: .900 silver, .100 copper; diameter 17.9 mm; reeded edge; mints: Philadelphia, Denver, New Orleans, San Francisco. Net weight: .07234 oz. pure silver.

	Quan. Minted	G-4	VG-8	F-12	VF-20	EF-40	MS-60	Proof
1892 . (1,245)	12,121,245	$1.75	$3.00	$5.00	$8.50	$22.00	$120.00	$300.00
1892O	3,841,700	3.50	5.50	9.00	12.00	27.50	140.00	
1892S	990,710	19.00	30.00	42.50	57.50	80.00	240.00	
1893, 3 over 2	} 3,340,792					—	—	—
1893 . . . (792)		3.50	5.50	9.00	12.00	25.00	130.00	300.00
1893O	1,760,000	9.00	12.50	20.00	30.00	45.00	150.00	
1893S	2,491,401	5.50	7.00	13.00	20.00	32.00	135.00	
1894 . . . (972)	1,330,972	6.00	8.50	14.00	22.50	35.00	165.00	300.00
1894O	720,000	25.00	40.00	67.50	90.00	135.00	425.00	
1894S	24					1974 Private Sale		$97,000
1895 . . . (880)	690,880	25.00	40.00	67.50	90.00	140.00	400.00	400.00
1895O	440,000	60.00	85.00	130.00	180.00	300.00	950.00	
1895S	1,120,000	12.00	18.00	25.00	35.00	60.00	250.00	
1896 . . . (762)	2,000,762	4.25	6.50	11.00	20.00	30.00	135.00	300.00
1896O	610,000	30.00	42.50	65.00	87.00	135.00	375.00	
1896S	575,056	30.00	42.50	65.00	87.00	140.00	450.00	
1897 . . . (731)	10,869,264	1.00	2.25	4.25	8.00	20.00	120.00	300.00
1897O	666,000	22.50	35.00	55.00	75.00	120.00	335.00	
1897S	1,342,844	6.50	11.00	18.00	35.00	55.00	250.00	
1898 . . . (735)	16,320,735	1.00	1.75	3.50	7.50	19.00	120.00	300.00
1898O	2,130,000	3.50	6.00	12.50	22.50	50.00	175.00	
1898S	1,702,507	3.50	6.00	10.00	18.00	40.00	175.00	
1899 . . . (846)	19,580,846	1.00	1.50	3.00	7.00	18.00	120.00	300.00
1899O	2,650,000	3.25	6.00	11.00	20.00	45.00	160.00	
1899S	1,867,493	4.00	6.25	11.00	17.00	45.00	140.00	
1900 . . . (912)	17,600,912	1.00	1.50	3.00	7.00	20.00	120.00	300.00
1900O	2,010,000	4.00	6.50	12.50	25.00	45.00	175.00	
1900S	5,168,270	2.00	3.50	6.00	9.00	20.00	135.00	
1901 . . . (813)	18,860,478	1.00	1.50	3.00	7.00	19.00	120.00	300.00
1901O	5,620,000	1.65	3.00	6.50	13.00	35.00	215.00	
1901S	593,022	22.50	45.00	80.00	100.00	160.00	700.00	
1902 . . . (777)	21,380,777	1.00	1.50	2.50	7.00	19.00	120.00	300.00
1902O	4,500,000	1.50	2.50	6.00	12.00	27.50	140.00	
1902S	2,070,000	3.25	6.00	10.00	22.50	45.00	165.00	
1903 . . . (755)	19,500,755	1.00	1.50	2.50	7.00	19.00	120.00	300.00
1903O	8,180,000	1.25	2.00	5.00	8.50	22.50	135.00	
1903S	613,300	19.00	27.50	37.50	65.00	100.00	350.00	
1904 . . . (670)	14,601,027	1.00	1.50	2.50	7.00	19.00	120.00	300.00
1904S	800,000	12.50	20.00	27.50	42.50	70.00	325.00	
1905 . . . (727)	14,552,350	1.00	1.50	2.50	7.00	19.00	120.00	300.00

DIMES

	Quan. Minted	G-4	VG-8	F-12	VF-20	EF-40	MS-60	Proof
1905O*	3,400,000	$1.50	$3.25	$7.00	$14.00	$27.50	$140.00	
1905S	6,855,199	1.00	2.00	4.50	9.00	20.00	135.00	
1906 ... (675)	19,958,406	1.00	1.50	2.50	6.50	17.50	120.00	$300.00
1906D	4,060,000	1.25	2.50	4.50	9.00	20.00	130.00	
1906O	2,610,000	2.00	4.25	9.00	17.50	25.00	140.00	
1906S	3,136,640	1.50	2.75	5.50	10.00	22.50	130.00	
1907 ... (575)	22,220,575	1.00	1.50	2.50	6.50	17.50	120.00	310.00
1907D	4,080,000	1.25	2.25	6.00	9.50	20.00	125.00	
1907O	5,058,000	1.25	2.25	6.00	9.50	20.00	130.00	
1907S	3,178,470	1.25	2.25	6.00	9.50	20.00	125.00	
1908 ... (545)	10,600,545	1.00	1.50	2.50	6.50	17.50	120.00	310.00
1908D	7,490,000	1.00	1.50	2.50	6.50	17.50	120.00	
1908O	1,789,000	3.00	6.00	8.50	16.50	27.50	145.00	
1908S	3,220,000	1.50	2.50	5.00	9.50	20.00	135.00	
1909 ... (650)	10,240,650	1.00	1.50	2.50	6.50	17.50	120.00	310.00
1909D	954,000	3.25	5.50	12.00	22.50	40.00	175.00	
1909O	2,287,000	2.00	3.50	8.00	14.00	27.50	150.00	
1909S	1,000,000	4.00	6.50	15.00	25.00	42.50	175.00	
1910 ... (551)	11,520,551	1.00	1.50	2.50	6.50	17.50	120.00	310.00
1910D	3,490,000	1.25	2.00	3.00	8.00	20.00	120.00	
1910S	1,240,000	2.25	4.00	6.00	12.00	27.00	145.00	
1911 ... (543)	18,870,543	1.00	1.50	2.50	6.50	17.50	120.00	310.00
1911D	11,209,000	1.00	1.50	2.50	6.50	17.50	120.00	
1911S	3,520,000	1.25	2.00	3.50	8.50	20.00	120.00	
1912 ... (700)	19,350,000	1.00	1.50	2.50	6.50	17.50	120.00	310.00
1912D	11,760,000	1.00	1.50	2.50	6.50	17.50	120.00	
1912S	3,420,000	1.25	2.00	4.50	9.00	20.00	130.00	
1913 ... (622)	19,760,622	1.00	1.50	2.50	6.50	17.50	120.00	310.00
1913S	510,000	8.00	13.00	28.00	45.00	90.00	375.00	
1914 ... (425)	17,360,655	1.00	1.50	2.50	6.50	17.50	120.00	350.00
1914D	11,908,000	1.00	1.50	2.50	6.50	17.50	120.00	
1914S	2,100,000	1.50	3.00	4.00	8.50	21.00	140.00	
1915 ... (450)	5,620,450	1.00	1.50	2.50	6.50	17.50	120.00	350.00
1915S	960,000	2.00	3.00	6.00	11.00	22.50	150.00	
1916	18,490,000	1.00	1.50	2.50	6.50	17.50	120.00	
1916S	5,820,000	1.00	1.50	2.50	6.50	17.50	120.00	

*Normal and "microscopic" mint mark varieties, see page 59.

WINGED LIBERTY HEAD or "MERCURY" TYPE 1916-1945

Although this coin is commonly called the "Mercury Dime," the main device is in fact a representation of Liberty. The wings crowning her cap are intended to symbolize liberty of thought. The designer's initials AW are right of neck.

Mint mark location.

Designer Adolph A. Weinman. Standards same as previous issue; mints: Philadelphia, Denver, San Francisco.

G-4 GOOD—*Letters and date clear. Lines and bands in fasces are obliterated.*
VG-8 VERY GOOD—*One-half of sticks discernible in fasces.*
F-12 FINE—*All sticks in fasces are defined. Diagonal bands worn nearly flat.*
VF-20 VERY FINE—*The two crossing diagonal bands must show.*
EF-40 EXTREMELY FINE—*Diagonal bands show only slight wear. Braids and hair before ear show clearly.*
MS-60 UNCIRCULATED—*No trace of wear. Light blemishes.*
MS-65—*CHOICE UNCIRCULATED—No trace of wear. Barely noticeable blemishes.*

DIMES

Uncirculated values shown are for average pieces with minimum blemishes, those with sharp strikes and split bands on reverse are worth much more.

	Quan. Minted	G-4	VG-8	F-12	VF-20	EF-40	MS-60	Proof
1916	22,180,080	$ .75	$1.00	$1.50	$2.25	$6.00	$30.00	
1916D	264,000	155.00	200.00	300.00	400.00	625.00	2,250	
1916S	10,450,000	1.65	2.75	4.75	6.00	9.00	40.00	
1917	55,230,000	.65	.90	1.35	1.75	4.00	26.00	
1917D	9,402,000	1.65	3.75	6.75	10.00	22.00	140.00	
1917S	27,330,000	.75	1.20	1.75	3.00	7.00	55.00	
1918	26,680,000	.75	1.20	3.25	6.50	15.00	65.00	
1918D	22,674,800	.80	1.25	3.50	6.75	16.00	120.00	
1918S	19,300,000	.75	1.10	2.25	5.50	13.00	95.00	
1919	35,740,000	.65	1.00	1.50	3.00	7.50	45.00	
1919D	9,939,000	1.75	2.50	5.50	14.00	30.00	185.00	
1919S	8,850,000	1.75	2.50	5.50	14.00	30.00	210.00	
1920	59,030,000	.65	1.00	1.25	1.60	3.75	30.00	
1920D	19,171,000	.75	1.50	2.50	4.25	9.00	90.00	
1920S	13,820,000	.70	1.10	1.75	3.50	9.00	85.00	
1921	1,230,000	16.00	25.00	45.00	85.00	285.00	1,450	
1921D	1,080,000	27.50	37.50	60.00	110.00	275.00	1,300	
1923*	50,130,000	.65	.85	1.00	1.35	3.25	30.00	
1923S	6,440,000	.80	1.20	3.25	6.00	20.00	175.00	
1924	24,010,000	.65	.85	1.00	1.35	4.75	45.00	
1924D	6,810,000	.75	1.50	2.65	5.00	16.50	185.00	
1924S	7,120,000	.70	1.25	2.25	4.75	14.00	185.00	
1925	25,610,000	.65	1.00	1.25	1.60	4.75	47.50	
1925D	5,117,000	1.90	3.75	7.50	17.50	55.00	385.00	
1925S	5,850,000	.75	1.25	1.85	6.00	16.00	200.00	
1926	32,160,000	.65	.85	1.00	1.35	4.00	35.00	
1926D	6,828,000	.75	1.35	2.25	4.25	15.00	110.00	
1926S	1,520,000	5.75	8.00	11.50	23.00	70.00	750.00	
1927	28,080,000	.65	.90	1.10	1.35	3.50	25.00	
1927D	4,812,000	1.00	2.35	5.00	16.00	30.00	350.00	
1927S	4,770.000	.75	1.15	1.75	5.00	13.50	200.00	
1928	19,480,000	.65	.90	1.10	1.25	2.75	26.00	
1928D	4,161,000	1.25	1.60	3.25	10.00	28.00	165.00	
1928S†	7,400,000	.70	1.00	1.25	3.50	11.00	100.00	
1929	25,970,000	.65	.85	1.00	1.25	2.35	22.00	
1929D	5,034,000	.75	1.00	2.30	3.00	4.75	29.00	
1929S	4,730,000	.65	.90	1.25	2.00	4.00	45.00	
1930*	6,770,000	.65	.90	1.25	2.00	4.00	40.00	
1930S	1,843,000	2.50	3.00	4.00	5.00	10.00	130.00	
1931	3,150,000	.75	1.00	1.50	3.00	5.25	62.50	
1931D	1,260,000	6.50	7.50	9.00	14.00	20.00	130.00	
1931S	1,800,000	2.50	2.50	3.00	4.25	8.50	140.00	
1934	24,080,000	.60	.75	.90	1.25	2.00	18.00	
1934D†	6,772,000	.65	.85	1.20	1.75	4.75	50.00	
1935	58,830,000	.50	.75	.90	1.10	1.50	7.50	
1935D	10,477,000	.50	.75	1.00	2.00	6.50	110.00	
1935S	15,840,000	.50	.75	.90	1.25	2.00	21.00	
1936 . (4,130)								
. . . .	87,504,130	.50	.65	.85	1.00	1.25	5.00	$160.00
1936D	16,132,000	.50	.65	.85	1.25	4.00	50.00	
1936S	9,210,000	.50	.65	.85	1.25	2.00	26.00	
1937 . (5,756)								
. . . .	56,865,756		.50	.75	1.00	1.25	4.00	125.00

*Dimes dated 1923D and 1930D are counterfeit. †Large and small mint mark varieties, see page 59.

DIMES

	Quan. Minted	VG-8	F-12	VF-20	EF-40	MS-65	Proof
1937D	14,146,000	$.65	$.85	$1.10	$1.50	$35.00	
1937S	9,740,000	.65	.85	1.10	1.50	21.00	
1938 ..... (8,728)	22,198,728	.50	.65	.75	1.00	9.00	$110.00
1938D	5,537,000	.75	1.00	1.25	2.00	20.00	
1938S	8,090,000	.60	.75	1.10	1.75	15.00	
1939 ..... (9,321)	67,749,321	.50	.65	.75	1.00	6.50	85.00
1939D	24,394,000	.50	.75	1.00	1.25	8.50	
1939S	10,540,000	.60	.75	1.00	2.50	30.00	
1940 ..... (11,827)	65,361,827	.50	.65	.75	1.00	4.25	80.00
1940D	21,198,000	.50	.75	1.00	1.25	10.00	
1940S	21,560,000	.50	.65	.75	1.00	7.00	
1941 ..... (16,557)	175,106,557	.50	.65	.75	1.00	4.00	80.00
1941D	45,634,000	.50	.65	.75	1.00	7.00	
1941S*	43,090,000	.50	.65	.75	1.00	7.50	

1942, 2 over 1

1942D, 2 over 1

	Quan. Minted	VG-8	F-12	VF-20	EF-40	MS-65	Proof
1942, 2 over 1 ...	205,432,329	140.00	160.00	200.00	300.00	2,400	
1942 ..... (22,329)		.50	.65	.75	1.00	3.50	80.00
1942D, 2 over 1..	60,740,000	160.00	185.00	260.00	475.00	2,750	
1942D		.50	.65	.75	1.00	5.00	
1942S	49,300,000	.50	.65	.75	1.00	7.00	
1943	191,710,000	.50	.65	.75	1.00	4.00	
1943D	71,949,000	.50	.65	.75	1.00	4.00	
1943S	60,400,000	.50	.65	.75	1.00	4.50	
1944	231,410,000	.50	.65	.75	1.00	4.00	
1944D	62,224,000	.50	.65	.75	1.00	4.00	
1944S	49,490,000	.50	.65	.75	1.00	4.25	
1945	159,130,000	.50	.65	.75	1.00	3.75	
1945D	40,245,000	.50	.65	.75	1.00	4.00	
1945S Normal S .	41,920,000	.50	.65	.75	1.00	4.00	
1945S Micro S* ..		.65	.85	1.00	2.00	16.00	

*Large and small mint mark varieties, see page 59.

ROOSEVELT TYPE 1946 to Date

John R. Sinnock (whose initials JS are at the truncation of the neck) designed this dime showing a portrait of Franklin D. Roosevelt. The design has heavier lettering and a more modernistic character than preceding types.

Mint mark on
reverse 1946-1964.

Mint mark on
obverse starting 1968.

Designer John R. Sinnock. Standards same as previous issue.

F-12 FINE—*Flame worn smooth. Horizontal lines on torch do not show. All vertical lines will show.*
VF-20 VERY FINE—*Hair above ear slightly worn. All vertical lines on torch plain.*
EF-40 EXTREMELY FINE—*All lines of torch, flame and hair very plain.*
MS-65 CHOICE UNCIRCULATED—*No trace of wear. Barely noticeable blemishes.*

DIMES

	Quan. Minted	VF-20	EF-40	MS-65	Proof
1946	255,250,000	$ .60	$ .75	$1.00	
1946D	61,043,500	.60	.75	1.00	
1946S	27,900,000	.60	.75	1.25	
1947	121,520,000	.60	.75	1.15	
1947D	46,835,000	.60	.75	1.50	
1947S	34,840,000	.60	.75	2.00	
1948	74,950,000	.60	.75	2.25	
1948D	52,841,000	.60	.75	1.50	
1948S	35,520,000	.60	.75	1.75	
1949	30,940,000	.75	1.50	12.00	
1949D	26,034,000	.60	.75	5.00	
1949S	13,510,000	1.25	3.50	15.00	
1950 (51,386)	50,181,500	.60	.75	2.50	$25.00
1950D	46,803,000	.60	.75	2.50	
1950S	20,440,000	.75	1.50	10.00	
1951 (57,500)	103,937,602	.60	.75	2.00	15.00
1951D	56,529,000	.60	.75	1.25	
1951S	31,630,000	.70	1.25	8.00	
1952 (81,980)	99,122,073	.60	.75	1.00	10.00
1952D	122,100,000	.60	.75	1.65	
1952S	44,419,500	.60	.75	3.00	
1953 (128,800)	53,618,920	.60	.75	1.15	8.00
1953D	136,433,000	....	.60	.75	
1953S	39,180,000	....	.60	.75	
1954 (233,300)	114,243,503	....	.60	.75	4.00
1954D	106,397,000	....	.60	.75	
1954S	22,860,000	....	.60	.75	
1955 (378,200)	12,828,381	.65	.85	1.50	3.25
1955D	13,959,000	.60	.75	.85	
1955S	18,510,000	....	.60	.75	
1956 (669,384)	109,309,384	....	.60	.75	1.75
1956D	108,015,100	....	.60	.75	
1957 (1,247,952)	161,407,952	....	.60	.75	1.25
1957D	113,354,330	....	.60	.75	
1958 (875,652)	32,785,652	....	.60	.75	2.00
1958D	136,564,600	....	.60	.75	
1959 (1,149,291)	86,929,291	....	.60	.75	1.25
1959D	164,919,790	....	.60	.75	
1960 (1,691,602)	72,081,602	....	.60	.75	1.25
1960D	200,160,400	....	.60	.75	
1961 (3,028,244)	96,758,244	....	.60	.75	1.00
1961D	209,146,550	....	.60	.75	
1962 (3,218,019)	75,668,019	....	.60	.75	1.00
1962D	334,948,380	....	.60	.75	
1963 (3,075,645)	126,725,645	....	.60	.75	1.00
1963D	421,476,530	....	.60	.75	
1964 (3,950,762)	933,310,762	....	.60	.75	1.00
1964D	1,357,517,180	....	.60	.75	

Clad Coinage

Weight 2.27 grams; composition: outer layers of copper nickel (.750 copper, .250 nickel) bonded to inner core of pure copper; diameter 17.9 mm; reeded edge.

	Quan. Minted	MS-65	Proof
1965	1,652,140,570	.20	
1966	1,382,734,540	.20	

DIMES

Quan. Minted	MS-65	Proof		Quan. Minted	MS-65	Proof
1967 2,244,007,320	$.20		1973D 455,032,426	$.20	
1968 424,470,400	.20		1973S Proof... (2,760,339)		$2.00
1968D 480,748,280	.20		1974 470,248,000	.20	
1968S Proof* .. (3,041,506)		$1.25	1974D 571,083,000	.20	
1969 145,790,000	.20		1974S Proof ... (2,612,568)		2.50
1969D 563,323,870	.20		1975 585,673,900	.20	
1969S Proof... (2,934,631)		1.25	1975D 313,705,300	.20	
1970 345,570,000	.20		1975S Proof* .. (2,845,450)		2.75
1970D 754,942,100	.20		1976 568,760,000	.20	
1970S Proof* .. (2,632,810)		2.75	1976D 695,222,774	.20	
1971 162,690,000	.20		1976S Proof... (4,149,730)		2.25
1971D 377,914,240	.20		1977 796,930,000	.20	
1971S Proof... (3,220,733)		1.50	1977D 376,607,228	.20	
1972 431,540,000	.20		1977S Proof... (3,251,152)		2.25
1972D 330,290,000	.20		1978	.20	
1972S Proof... (3,260,996)		1.50	1978D	.20	
1973 315,670,000	.20		1978S Proof.............		2.25

*Varieties of 1968, 1970 and 1975 proof dimes without S mint mark were made in error. See pages 59-60.

TWENTY-CENT PIECES — 1875-1878

This short-lived coin was authorized by the Act of March 3, 1875. Soon after

the appearance of the first twenty-cent pieces, the people complained about the similarity in design and size to the quarter-dollar. The eagle is very similar to that used on the Trade Dollar. The edge of the coin is plain. Most of the 1876CC coins were melted at the mint and never released. Mint mark is on the reverse below the eagle.

Designer William Barber; weight 5 grams; composition: .900 silver, .100 copper; diameter 22 mm; plain edge; mints: Philadelphia, Carson City, San Francisco.

G-4 GOOD—*LIBERTY on shield obliterated. Letters and date legible.*
VG-8 VERY GOOD—*One or two letters in LIBERTY may show. Other details will be bold.*
F-12 FINE—*At least 3 letters of LIBERTY show.*
VF-20 VERY FINE—*LIBERTY completely readable, but partly weak.*
EF-40 EXTREMELY FINE—*LIBERTY sharp. Only slight wear on high points of coin.*
MS-60 UNCIRCULATED—*No trace of wear. Light blemishes.*

Quan. Minted	G-4	VG-8	F-12	VF-20	EF-40	MS-60	Proof
1875 ... (1,200) 39,700	$50.00	$60.00	$75.00	$110.00	$190.00	$1,000	$1,250
1875CC 133,290	50.00	60.00	75.00	110.00	190.00	1,000	
1875S 1,155,000	40.00	50.00	60.00	95.00	165.00	900.00	
1876 ... (1,150) 15,900	70.00	80.00	110.00	150.00	250.00	1,100	1,450
1876CC 10,000						50,000	
1877 ..... (510) 510							1,500
1878 ..... (600) 600							1,450

QUARTER DOLLARS — 1796 to Date

Authorized in 1792, this denomination was not issued until four years later. The first coinage, dated 1796, follows the pattern of the early half-dimes and dimes by the absence of a mark of value. In 1804 the value "25c" was added to the reverse. Figures were used until 1838 when the term "QUAR. DOL." appeared. It was not until 1892 that the value was spelled out entirely.

The first type weighed 104 grains which remained standard until modified to 103⅛ grains by the Act of January 18, 1837. As with the dime and half dime, the weight was reduced and arrows placed at the date in 1853, and rays were placed in the field of the reverse during that year only.

The law of 1873 also affected the quarter, for the weight was slightly increased and arrows again placed at the date.

Proofs of some dates prior to 1856 are known to exist, and all are rare.

BIBLIOGRAPHY

Browning, A. W. *The Early Quarter Dollars of the United States 1796-1838.* New York, 1925.
Cline, J. H. *Standing Liberty Quarters.* 1976.
Duphorne, R. *The Early Quarter Dollars of The United States.* 1975.
Haseltine, J. W. *Type Table of United States Dollars, Half Dollars and Quarter Dollars.* Philadelphia, 1881 (reprinted 1927, 1968).
Kelman, Keith N. *Standing Liberty Quarters.* 1976.

DRAPED BUST TYPE, SMALL EAGLE REVERSE 1796

Designer Robert Scot; weight 6.74 grams; composition: .8924 silver, .1076 copper; approx. diameter 27.5 mm; reeded edge. All coined at Philadelphia.

AG-3 ABOUT GOOD—*Details clear enough to identify.*

G-4 GOOD—*Date readable. Bust outlined, but no detail.*

VG-8 VERY GOOD—*All but deepest drapery folds worn smooth. Hairlines nearly gone and curls lack detail.*

F-12 FINE—*All drapery lines visible. Hair partly worn.*

VF-20 VERY FINE—*Only left side of drapery is indistinct.*

EF-40 EXTREMELY FINE—*Hair well outlined and detailed.*

MS-60 UNCIRCULATED—*No trace of wear. Light blemishes.*

	Quan. Minted	AG-3	G-4	VG-8	F-12	VF-20	EF-40	MS-60
1796	6,146	$750.00	$1,300	$1,900	$3,100	$4,500	$7,250	$18,000

DRAPED BUST TYPE, HERALDIC EAGLE REVERSE 1804-1807

	Quan. Minted	AG-3	G-4	VG-8	F-12	VF-20	EF-40	MS-60
1804	6,738	150.00	225.00	325.00	600.00	1,250	3,000	——
1805	121,395	70.00	100.00	130.00	225.00	425.00	900.00	4,250
1806 6 over 5	206,124	70.00	100.00	130.00	225.00	450.00	950.00	5,500
1806		60.00	90.00	120.00	220.00	400.00	850.00	4,500
1807	220,643	60.00	90.00	120.00	220.00	400.00	850.00	3,750

QUARTER DOLLARS
CAPPED BUST TYPE 1815-1838
Variety 1 — Large Size 1815-1828

AG-3 ABOUT GOOD—*Details clear enough to identify.*
G-4 GOOD—*Date, letters and stars readable. Hair under headband smooth. Cap lines worn smooth.*
VG-8 VERY GOOD—*Rim well defined. Main details visible. Full LIBERTY on cap. Hair above eye nearly smooth.*
F-12 FINE—*All hairlines show but drapery has only part details. Shoulder clasp distinct.*
VF-20 VERY FINE—*All details show, but some wear. Clasp and ear sharp.*
EF-40 EXTREMELY FINE—*All details show distinctly. Hair well outlined.*
MS-60 UNCIRCULATED—*No trace of wear. Light blemishes.*

Designer John Reich; weight 6.74 grams; composition: .8924 silver, .1076 copper; approx. diameter 27 mm; reeded edge. All coined at Philadelphia.

	Quan. Minted	AG-3	G-4	VG-8	F-12	VF-20	EF-40	MS-60
1815	89,235	$25.00	$45.00	$55.00	$75.00	$200.00	$400.00	$3,100
1818 8 over 5 ⎫		25.00	45.00	55.00	75.00	200.00	350.00	3,000
1818 Normal ⎬	361,174							
date . . . . ⎭		25.00	45.00	55.00	75.00	160.00	325.00	2,600
1819 Small 9 ⎱	144,000	25.00	45.00	55.00	75.00	150.00	325.00	2,600
1819 Large 9 ⎰		25.00	45.00	55.00	75.00	150.00	325.00	2,600

1820 Small 0

1820 Large 0

1822, 25 over 50c

	Quan. Minted	AG-3	G-4	VG-8	F-12	VF-20	EF-40	MS-60
1820 Small 0 ⎱	127,444	25.00	40.00	50.00	75.00	150.00	325.00	2,600
1820 Large 0 ⎰		25.00	40.00	50.00	75.00	150.00	325.00	2,600
1821	216,851	25.00	40.00	50.00	75.00	150.00	325.00	2,600
1822 All kinds . .	64,080	25.00	40.00	50.00	75.00	150.00	350.00	2,700
1822, 25 over 50c		150.00	200.00	300.00	400.00	800.00	1,200	3,700
1823, 3 over 2 . .	17,800	800.00	1,500	3,000	5,000	7,500	10,000	——

1825 over 22 (wide date)

1825 over 23 (close date)

	Quan. Minted	AG-3	G-4	VG-8	F-12	VF-20	EF-40	MS-60
1824 over 2 . . ⎫		30.00	45.00	60.00	100.00	175.00	350.00	3,100
1825 over 22 ⎬	168,000	22.00	40.00	50.00	70.00	140.00	325.00	3,000
1825 over 23 ⎬		22.00	40.00	50.00	70.00	140.00	325.00	2,800
1825 over 24 ⎭		22.00	40.00	50.00	70.00	140.00	325.00	2,800
1827 Original (Curled base 2 in 25c) 4,000 Minted								40,000
1827 Restrike (Square base 2 in 25c)								14,500
1828 All kds . . .	102,000	22.00	40.00	50.00	70.00	140.00	325.00	3,000
1828, 25 over 50c		50.00	80.00	110.00	175.00	300.00	525.00	3,300

QUARTER DOLLARS

Variety 2 — Reduced Size, No Motto on Reverse 1831-1838

G-4 GOOD—*Bust well defined. Hair under headband smooth. Date, letters, stars readable. Scant rims.*
VG-8 VERY GOOD—*Details apparent but worn on high spots. Rims strong. Full LIBERTY.*
F-12 FINE—*All hairlines visible. Drapery partly worn. Shoulder clasp distinct.*
VF-20 VERY FINE—*Only top spots worn. Clasp sharp. Ear distinct.*
EF-40 EXTREMELY FINE—*Hair details and clasp are bold and clear.*
MS-60 UNCIRCULATED—*No trace of wear. Light blemishes.*

Designer William Kneass; weight 6.74 grams; composition: .8924 silver, .1076 copper; diameter 24.3 mm; reeded edge. All coined at Philadelphia.

| 1831 | | Small Letters | | | Large Letters | | |
Quan. Minted		G-4	VG-8	F-12	VF-20	EF-40	MS-60
1831 Small letters...	} 398,000	$35.00	$40.00	$50.00	$85.00	$160.00	$1,500
1831 Large letters ..		35.00	40.00	50.00	85.00	160.00	1,500
1832	320,000	35.00	40.00	50.00	85.00	160.00	1,500
1833	156,000	40.00	50.00	70.00	100.00	200.00	1,650
1834	286,000	35.00	40.00	50.00	85.00	160.00	1,500
1835	1,952,000	35.00	40.00	50.00	85.00	160.00	1,500
1836	472,000	35.00	40.00	50.00	85.00	160.00	1,500
1837	252,400	35.00	40.00	50.00	85.00	160.00	1,500
1838 Both types	832,000	35.00	40.00	50.00	85.00	160.00	1,500

LIBERTY SEATED TYPE 1838-1891
Variety 1 — No Motto Above Eagle 1838-1853

G-4 GOOD—*Scant rim. LIBERTY on shield worn off. Date and letters readable.*
VG-8 VERY GOOD—*Rim fairly defined, at least 3 letters in LIBERTY evident.*
F-12 FINE—*LIBERTY complete, but partly weak.*
VF-20 VERY FINE—*LIBERTY strong.*
EF-40 EXTREMELY FINE—*Complete LIBERTY and edges of scroll. Clasp shows plainly.*
MS-60 UNCIRCULATED—*No trace of wear. Light blemishes.*

Designer Christian Gobrecht; weight 6.68 grams; composition: .900 silver, .100 copper; diameter 24.3 mm; reeded edge; mints: Philadelphia, New Orleans.

No Drapery from Elbow   Drapery from Elbow

Mint mark location is on the reverse below the eagle.

1838 No drapery.... incl. above	11.00	16.50	25.00	50.00	135.00	1,600
1839 No drapery....... 491,146	11.00	16.50	25.00	50.00	135.00	1,650
1840O No drapery						
All kinds........ 425,200	11.00	16.50	25.00	50.00	135.00	1,750
1840 Drapery.......... 188,127	12.00	15.00	20.00	50.00	100.00	850.00
1840O Drapery	12.00	15.00	20.00	50.00	100.00	850.00
1841 120,000	15.00	20.00	30.00	50.00	100.00	700.00
1841O................ 452,000	8.50	12.50	20.00	55.00	125.00	700.00

QUARTER DOLLARS

	Quan. Minted	G-4	VG-8	F-12	VF-20	EF-40	MS-60
1842 Small date	88,000					Proofs Only	——
1842 Large date		$40.00	$60.00	$95.00	$175.00	$250.00	$950.00
1842O Small date ...	769,000	90.00	160.00	250.00	400.00	600.00	1,200
1842O Large date ...		9.00	12.00	15.00	25.00	55.00	750.00
1843	645,600	9.00	12.00	15.00	25.00	55.00	500.00
1843O	968,000	10.00	14.00	20.00	40.00	90.00	700.00
1844	421,200	9.00	12.50	18.00	27.50	60.00	500.00
1844O	740,000	9.00	12.00	15.00	25.00	70.00	775.00
1845	922,000	9.00	12.00	15.00	25.00	55.00	500.00
1846	510,000	9.00	12.00	15.00	25.00	50.00	500.00
1847	734,000	9.00	12.00	15.00	25.00	50.00	500.00
1847O	368,000	15.00	20.00	30.00	70.00	100.00	800.00
1848	146,000	15.00	20.00	27.50	50.00	100.00	700.00
1849	340,000	9.00	12.00	15.00	25.00	70.00	500.00
1849O	†incl. below	110.00	175.00	275.00	500.00	900.00	3,000
1850	190,800	9.00	12.00	15.00	25.00	70.00	600.00
1850O	412,000	15.00	20.00	30.00	50.00	100.00	650.00
1851	160,000	9.00	12.00	15.00	25.00	75.00	600.00
1851O	88,000	75.00	110.00	175.00	275.00	700.00	1,400
1852	177,060	15.00	25.00	35.00	50.00	90.00	650.00
1852O	96,000	175.00	235.00	350.00	525.00	900.00	2,250
1853* Recut date, no arrows or rays..........	44,200	100.00	135.00	200.00	275.00	450.00	1,750

†Coinage for 1849O included with 1850O
*Beware of altered 1858.

Variety 2 — Arrows at Date, Rays Around Edge 1853 Only

Weight 6.22 grams; composition: .900 silver, .100 copper; diameter 24.3 mm; reeded edge; mints: Philadelphia, New Orleans, San Francisco, Carson City.

The reduction in weight is indicated by the arrows at the date. Rays were added on the reverse side in the field around the eagle. The arrows were retained through 1855, but the rays were omitted after 1853.

	Quan. Minted	G-4	VG-8	F-12	VF-20	EF-40	MS-60
1853	15,210,000	10.00	13.50	18.00	35.00	100.00	1,300
1853, 3 over 4				300.00	450.00	800.00	——
1853O	1,332,000	11.00	15.00	20.00	40.00	125.00	1,400

Variety 3 — Arrows at Date, No Rays 1854-1855

	Quan. Minted	G-4	VG-8	F-12	VF-20	EF-40	MS-60
1854	12,380,000	7.50	10.00	13.00	30.00	70.00	750.00
1854O	1,484,000	8.00	11.00	14.00	32.00	75.00	800.00
1854O Large O ...							
1855	2,857,000	8.00	11.00	14.00	32.00	75.00	800.00
1855O	176,000	45.00	65.00	95.00	175.00	325.00	1,450
1855S	396,400	45.00	65.00	95.00	160.00	300.00	1,400

QUARTER DOLLARS
Variety 1 Resumed 1856-1865

	Quan. Minted	G-4	VG-8	F-12	VF-20	EF-40	MS-60	Proof
1856	7,264,000	$8.00	$10.00	$14.00	$20.00	$35.00	$450.00	$1,400
1856O	968,000	9.00	11.50	16.00	25.00	50.00	600.00	
1856S	} 286,000	21.00	30.00	45.00	100.00	190.00	1,250	
1856S, S over S		25.00	50.00	100.00	250.00	350.00	——	
1857	9,644,000	8.00	10.00	14.00	20.00	35.00	450.00	1,250
1857O	1,180,000	9.00	11.50	16.00	25.00	50.00	550.00	
1857S	82,000	27.50	42.50	65.00	150.00	250.00	1,750	
1858	7,368,000	8.00	10.00	14.00	20.00	45.00	500.00	950.00
1858O	520,000	9.00	11.50	16.00	25.00	55.00	600.00	
1858S	121,000	30.00	35.00	50.00	110.00	170.00	1,000	
1859	1,344,000	8.00	10.00	14.00	20.00	35.00	450.00	600.00
1859O	260,000	10.00	14.00	20.00	30.00	60.00	700.00	
1859S	80,000	40.00	60.00	100.00	200.00	350.00	1,350	
1860 ... (1,000)	805,400	8.00	10.00	14.00	20.00	35.00	450.00	600.00
1860O	388,000	10.00	14.00	20.00	30.00	60.00	600.00	
1860S	56,000	50.00	75.00	125.00	275.00	400.00	1,250	
1861 ... (1,000)	4,854,600	8.00	10.00	14.00	20.00	35.00	450.00	600.00
1861S	96,000	23.00	30.00	45.00	90.00	225.00	1,400	
1862 .... (550)	932,550	8.00	10.00	14.00	20.00	35.00	450.00	600.00
1862S	67,000	25.00	35.00	50.00	100.00	225.00	1,400	
1863 .... (460)	192,060	16.00	20.00	30.00	45.00	85.00	600.00	650.00
1864 .... (470)	94,070	25.00	35.00	50.00	80.00	135.00	750.00	650.00
1864S	20,000	100.00	175.00	250.00	375.00	800.00	3,250	
1865 .... (500)	59,300	32.50	45.00	65.00	85.00	150.00	750.00	650.00
1865S	41,000	30.00	37.50	60.00	125.00	250.00	2,250	
1866 Transitional piece (Unique)								——

The 1866 proof quarter, half and dollar without motto are not mentioned in the Director's Report, and were not issued for circulation.

Variety 4 — Motto Above Eagle 1866-1873

The motto IN GOD WE TRUST was added to the reverse side in 1866. As on the half dollar and silver dollar the motto has been retained since that time.

1866 .... (725)	17,525	50.00	65.00	110.00	170.00	250.00	700.00	525.00
1866S	28,000	40.00	50.00	110.00	135.00	275.00	1,750	
1867 .... (625)	20,625	45.00	55.00	105.00	150.00	250.00	675.00	525.00
1867S	48,000	32.50	45.00	75.00	100.00	175.00	1,500	
1868 .... (600)	30,000	35.00	50.00	80.00	100.00	175.00	600.00	525.00
1868S	96,000	25.00	35.00	65.00	90.00	135.00	925.00	
1869 .... (600)	16,600	50.00	70.00	110.00	175.00	250.00	800.00	525.00
1869S	76,000	25.00	35.00	60.00	80.00	150.00	1,200	
1870 ... (1,000)	87,400	25.00	32.50	47.50	75.00	125.00	600.00	500.00
1870CC	8,340	300.00	450.00	800.00	1,100	2,000	3,500	
1871 .... (960)	119,160	10.00	14.00	20.00	35.00	65.00	500.00	450.00
1871CC	10,890	225.00	350.00	600.00	850.00	1,500	——	
1871S	30,900	65.00	125.00	175.00	250.00	400.00	1,500	

QUARTER DOLLARS

	Quan. Minted	G-4	VG-8	F-12	VF-20	EF-40	MS-60	Proof
1872 ... (950)	182,950	$8.50	$12.50	$17.50	$30.00	$60.00	$400.00	$450.00
1872CC	22,850	170.00	240.00	350.00	550.00	900.00	3,500	
1872S.............	83,000	75.00	150.00	250.00	325.00	500.00	1,750	
1873 Cl. 3(600)	212,600	30.00	50.00	90.00	175.00	275.00	675.00	450.00
1873 Open 3...		10.00	20.00	30.00	50.00	100.00	500.00	
1873CC	4,000			James Stack Sale 1976			$85,000	

Variety 5 — Arrows at Date 1873-1874

Weight 6.25 grams; composition: .900 silver, .100 copper; diameter 24.3 mm; reeded edge; mints: Philadelphia, San Francisco, Carson City.

Arrows were placed at the date in the years 1873 and 1874 to denote the change of weight from 6.22 to 6.25 grams.

1873 ... (540)	1,271,700	19.00	24.00	30.00	70.00	150.00	725.00	1,000
1873CC	12,462	400.00	500.00	750.00	950.00	1,500	3,750	
1873S...........	156,000	20.00	25.00	40.00	80.00	150.00	750.00	
1874 ... (700)	471,900	19.00	24.00	30.00	65.00	150.00	725.00	1,000
1874S...........	392,000	20.00	25.00	40.00	80.00	150.00	750.00	

Variety 4 Resumed 1875-1891

1875 ... (700)	4,293,500	7.00	9.00	11.00	20.00	40.00	350.00	450.00
1875CC	140,000	20.00	30.00	60.00	85.00	175.00	900.00	
1875S...........	680,000	9.00	12.00	20.00	35.00	65.00	425.00	
1876 . (1,150)	17,817,150	7.00	9.00	11.00	20.00	45.00	375.00	450.00
1876CC	4,944,000	8.00	11.00	15.00	30.00	60.00	450.00	
1876S...........	8,596,000	7.00	9.00	11.00	20.00	45.00	375.00	
1877 ... (510)	10,911,710	7.00	9.00	11.00	20.00	45.00	350.00	475.00
1877CC	4,192,000	8.00	11.00	15.00	30.00	60.00	450.00	
1877S...........	8,996,000	7.00	9.00	11.00	20.00	45.00	350.00	
1877S over horizontal S		—	—	100.00	135.00	225.00	700.00	
1878 ... (800)	2,260,800	7.00	9.00	11.00	20.00	45.00	350.00	450.00
1878CC	996,000	9.00	11.00	15.00	25.00	55.00	500.00	
1878S...........	140,000	50.00	75.00	125.00	175.00	250.00	1,500	
1879 . (1,100)	14,700	50.00	57.50	80.00	110.00	180.00	550.00	525.00
1880 . (1,355)	14,955	50.00	57.50	80.00	110.00	180.00	550.00	500.00

QUARTER DOLLARS

	Quan. Minted	G-4	VG-8	F-12	VF-20	EF-40	MS-60	Proof
1881 ... (975)	12,975	$50.00	$57.50	$80.00	$110.00	$180.00	$600.00	$525.00
1882 . (1,100)	16,300	45.00	50.00	75.00	100.00	160.00	600.00	525.00
1883 . (1,039)	15,439	45.00	50.00	75.00	100.00	160.00	600.00	525.00
1884 ... (875)	8,875	60.00	70.00	90.00	125.00	215.00	700.00	525.00
1885 ... (930)	14,530	45.00	50.00	75.00	100.00	160.00	600.00	525.00
1886 ... (886)	5,886	65.00	75.00	100.00	150.00	235.00	750.00	525.00
1887 ... (710)	10,710	55.00	65.00	85.00	110.00	200.00	600.00	525.00
1888 ... (832)	10,833	55.00	65.00	85.00	110.00	200.00	600.00	525.00
1888S	1,216,000	7.00	9.00	11.00	20.00	40.00	350.00	
1889 ... (711)	12,711	50.00	60.00	80.00	110.00	175.00	550.00	525.00
1890 ... (590)	80,590	30.00	40.00	52.50	70.00	120.00	500.00	500.00
1891 ... (600)	3,920,600	7.00	9.00	11.00	20.00	40.00	350.00	500.00
1891O	68,000	110.00	125.00	200.00	300.00	500.00	2,800	
1891S	2,216,000	8.00	10.00	13.00	24.00	40.00	375.00	

BARBER or LIBERTY HEAD TYPE 1892-1916

Like other silver coins of this type the quarter dollars minted from 1892 to 1916 were designed by Charles E. Barber. His initial B is found at the truncation of the neck of Liberty. There are two varieties of the 1892 reverse: 1) Eagle's wing covers only half of E. 2) Eagle's wing covers most of E.

Designer Charles E. Barber; weight 6.25 grams; composition: .900 silver, .100 copper; diameter 24.3 mm; reeded edge; mints: Philadelphia, Denver, New Orleans, San Francisco. Net weight: .18084 oz. pure silver.

G-4 GOOD—Date and legends readable. LIBERTY worn off headband.

VG-8 VERY GOOD—Minimum of 3 letters in LIBERTY readable.

F-12 FINE—LIBERTY completely readable but not sharp.

VF-20 VERY FINE—All letters in LIBERTY evenly plain.

EF-40 EXTREMELY FINE—LIBERTY bold, and its ribbon distinct.

MS-60 UNCIRCULATED—No trace of wear. Light blemishes.

Mint mark location is on the reverse below the eagle.

1892 . (1,245)	8,237,245	2.00	4.00	8.00	20.00	50.00	260.00	460.00
1892O	2,640,000	4.50	6.75	12.00	25.00	55.00	300.00	
1892S	964,079	12.00	17.50	27.50	45.00	80.00	350.00	
1893 ... (792)	5,444,815	2.00	4.00	8.00	20.00	52.50	270.00	460.00
1893O	3,396,000	2.50	6.00	12.00	25.00	55.00	275.00	
1893S	1,454,535	5.75	9.25	16.00	32.50	65.00	300.00	
1894 ... (972)	3,432,972	2.00	4.00	8.00	21.00	52.50	270.00	460.00
1894O	2,852,000	2.75	6.00	12.00	24.00	55.00	275.00	
1894S	2,648,821	2.25	5.50	12.00	24.00	55.00	290.00	
1895 ... (880)	4,440,880	2.00	4.00	8.00	20.00	52.50	270.00	460.00
1895O	2,816,000	2.25	5.50	12.00	25.00	55.00	300.00	
1895S	1,764,681	4.50	7.50	13.50	30.00	57.50	285.00	
1896 ... (762)	3,874,762	2.00	4.00	8.00	20.00	52.50	265.00	460.00
1896O	1,484,000	4.00	7.50	15.00	30.00	75.00	475.00	
1896S	188,039	120.00	180.00	270.00	375.00	635.00	2,250	
1897 ... (731)	8,140,731	2.00	4.00	8.00	20.00	50.00	260.00	460.00
1897O	1,414,800	6.00	9.00	17.00	32.50	70.00	450.00	
1897S	542,229	11.00	15.00	25.00	45.00	85.00	425.00	
1898 ... (735)	11,100,735	2.00	4.00	8.00	20.00	50.00	260.00	460.00

QUARTER DOLLARS

	Quan. Minted	G-4	VG-8	F-12	VF-20	EF-40	MS-60	Proof
1898O	1,868,000	$3.00	$6.00	$12.00	$27.50	$55.00	$300.00	
1898S	1,020,592	4.50	7.50	10.00	25.00	55.00	400.00	
1899 ... (846)	12,624,846	2.00	4.00	8.00	20.00	50.00	260.00	450.00
1899O	2,644,000	2.00	4.50	10.00	25.00	55.00	300.00	
1899S	708,000	7.50	12.00	18.00	35.00	62.50	335.00	
1900 ... (912)	10,016,912	2.00	4.00	8.00	20.00	50.00	260.00	450.00
1900O	3,416,000	4.00	8.00	13.50	25.00	55.00	325.00	
1900S	1,858,585	2.00	4.00	8.00	21.00	52.50	300.00	
1901 ... (813)	8,892,813	2.00	4.00	8.00	20.00	50.00	260.00	450.00
1901O	1,612,000	9.00	15.00	30.00	62.50	115.00	490.00	
1901S	72,664	400.00	500.00	625.00	775.00	1,150	4,500	
1902 ... (777)	12,197,744	2.00	4.00	8.00	20.00	50.00	260.00	450.00
1902O	4,748,000	2.00	4.00	8.00	20.00	55.00	300.00	
1902S	1,524,612	5.75	9.00	14.00	30.00	65.00	350.00	
1903 ... (755)	9,670,064	2.00	4.00	8.00	20.00	50.00	260.00	450.00
1903O	3,500,000	2.50	4.50	10.00	25.00	60.00	325.00	
1903S	1,036,000	5.50	9.50	16.00	35.00	70.00	420.00	
1904 ... (670)	9,588,813	2.00	4.00	8.00	20.00	50.00	260.00	450.00
1904O	2,456,000	4.00	8.00	15.00	32.50	75.00	400.00	
1905 ... (727)	4,968,250	2.00	4.00	8.00	20.00	50.00	260.00	450.00
1905O	1,230,000	5.00	9.00	16.00	32.00	67.50	360.00	
1905S	1,884,000	3.50	5.00	9.00	23.00	55.00	300.00	
1906 ... (675)	3,656,435	2.00	4.00	8.00	20.00	50.00	260.00	450.00
1906D	3,280,000	2.00	4.00	8.00	23.00	55.00	270.00	
1906O	2,056,000	3.50	5.00	9.00	23.00	57.50	300.00	
1907 ... (575)	7,192,575	2.00	4.00	8.00	20.00	50.00	260.00	450.00
1907D	2,484,000	2.00	4.00	8.00	21.00	55.00	265.00	
1907O	4,560,000	2.00	4.00	8.00	21.00	55.00	300.00	
1907S	1,360,000	2.50	5.00	8.00	21.00	55.00	285.00	
1908 ... (545)	4,232,545	2.00	4.00	8.00	20.00	50.00	260.00	450.00
1908D	5,788,000	2.00	4.00	8.00	20.00	50.00	260.00	
1908O	6,244,000	2.00	4.00	8.00	20.00	50.00	285.00	
1908S	784,000	6.00	10.00	15.00	27.50	60.00	435.00	
1909 ... (650)	9,268,650	2.00	4.00	8.00	20.00	50.00	260.00	450.00
1909D	5,114,000	2.00	4.00	8.00	20.00	50.00	260.00	
1909O	712,000	11.00	16.00	32.00	55.00	120.00	600.00	
1909S	1,348,000	2.25	4.00	8.00	20.00	50.00	300.00	
1910 ... (551)	2,244,551	2.00	4.00	8.00	20.00	50.00	260.00	450.00
1910D	1,500,000	2.25	4.00	8.00	20.00	55.00	275.00	
1911 ... (543)	3,720,543	2.00	4.00	8.00	20.00	50.00	260.00	450.00
1911D	933,600	3.00	5.00	10.00	24.00	57.50	285.00	
1911S	988,000	2.25	5.00	10.00	24.00	57.50	285.00	
1912 ... (700)	4,400,700	2.00	4.00	8.00	20.00	50.00	260.00	450.00
1912S	708,000	3.00	5.00	10.00	25.00	57.50	380.00	
1913 ... (613)	484,613	7.00	12.00	25.00	70.00	170.00	850.00	700.00
1913D	1,450,800	2.50	4.00	9.00	20.00	55.00	390.00	
1913S	40,000	150.00	225.00	350.00	500.00	850.00	2,750	
1914 ... (380)	6,244,610	2.00	4.00	8.00	20.00	50.00	260.00	575.00
1914D	3,046,000	2.00	4.00	8.00	20.00	50.00	260.00	
1914S	264,000	10.00	15.00	22.50	57.50	125.00	550.00	
1915 ... (450)	3,480,450	2.00	4.00	8.00	20.00	50.00	260.00	575.00
1915D	3,694,000	2.00	4.00	8.00	20.00	50.00	260.00	
1915S	704,000	3.00	5.00	9.50	25.00	55.00	300.00	
1916	1,788,000	2.00	4.00	8.00	20.00	50.00	260.00	
1916D	6,540,888	2.00	4.00	8.00	20.00	50.00	260.00	

QUARTER DOLLARS
STANDING LIBERTY TYPE 1916-1930

This type quarter was designed by Hermon A. MacNeil. The left arm of Liberty is upraised bearing a shield in the attitude of protection, from which the cover is being drawn. The right hand bears the olive branch of peace. The designer's initial M is located above and to the right of the date.

There was a modification in 1917 because of public resentment to Liberty's exposed breast. The reverse has a new arrangement of the stars and the eagle is higher.

In 1925 a depression was made in the pedestal on which Liberty stands and which bears the date. On the first issues the dates wore off easily because they were too high and were not protected by other features of the coin. The new "recessed" dates proved more durable as a result of this change.

No proof coins of this type were officially issued, but a specimen of the first variety, dated 1917, with matte proof features is known to exist.

G-4 GOOD—*Date and lettering readable. Top of date worn. Liberty's right leg and toes worn off. Left leg and drapery lines show much wear.*

VG-8 VERY GOOD—*Distinct date. Toes show faintly. Drapery lines visible above her left leg.*

F-12 FINE—*High curve of right leg flat from thigh to ankle. Left leg shows only slight wear. Drapery lines over right thigh seen only at sides of leg.*

VF-20 VERY FINE—*Garment line across right leg will be worn but show at sides.*

EF-40 EXTREMELY FINE—*Flattened only at high spots. Her toes are sharp. Drapery lines across right leg are evident.*

MS-60 UNCIRCULATED—*No trace of wear. Light blemishes.*

(Some modifications must be made for grading variety 2.)

Designer Hermon A. MacNeil. Standards same as previous issue; mints: Philadelphia, Denver, San Francisco.

Uncirculated pieces with fully struck head of Liberty are worth more than prices listed below.

Variety 1

	Quan. Minted	G-4	VG-8	F-12	VF-20	EF-40	MS-60
1916	52,000	$335.00	$425.00	$575.00	$775.00	$975.00	$1,750
1917 Variety 1	8,740,000	7.50	9.00	12.00	20.00	50.00	250.00
1917D Variety 1	1,509,200	8.00	9.50	13.00	24.00	60.00	260.00
1917S Variety 1	1,952,000	8.00	9.50	13.00	24.00	60.00	275.00

1918S, 8 over 7

Variety 2

Mint mark position is on obverse at left of date.

	Quan. Minted	G-4	VG-8	F-12	VF-20	EF-40	MS-60
1917 Variety 2	13,880,000	6.00	8.00	11.50	17.00	30.00	130.00
1917D Variety 2	6,224,400	11.00	13.00	20.00	25.00	37.50	145.00
1917S Variety 2	5,552,000	12.50	16.00	22.50	27.50	40.00	145.00
1918	14,240,000	6.00	8.00	11.50	16.00	35.00	125.00
1918D	7,380,000	10.50	12.00	16.00	24.00	40.00	150.00
1918S Norm. date	11,072,000	6.00	8.00	11.50	18.00	35.00	140.00
1918S 8 over 7		235.00	340.00	550.00	725.00	1,150	6,000
1919	11,324,000	9.50	12.00	17.00	24.00	34.00	130.00

QUARTER DOLLARS

	Quan. Minted	G-4	VG-8	F-12	VF-20	EF-40	MS-60
1919D	1,944,000	$28.00	$36.00	$50.00	$65.00	$115.00	$385.00
1919S	1,836,000	35.00	45.00	60.00	75.00	125.00	390.00
1920	27,860,000	4.25	5.50	8.00	10.00	22.00	125.00
1920D	3,586,400	13.00	17.00	22.00	32.00	60.00	175.00
1920S	6,380,000	8.50	11.50	14.00	21.00	30.00	150.00
1921	1,916,000	25.00	35.00	50.00	65.00	90.00	375.00
1923	9,716,000	4.00	5.00	7.00	9.00	18.00	125.00
1923S	1,360,000	47.50	58.00	75.00	100.00	135.00	425.00
1924	10,920,000	4.00	5.00	7.00	10.00	20.00	125.00
1924D	3,112,000	13.00	18.00	21.00	28.00	37.50	135.00
1924S	2,860,000	10.00	12.00	16.00	27.00	35.00	160.00

Recessed Date Style 1925-1930

	Quan. Minted	G-4	VG-8	F-12	VF-20	EF-40	MS-60
1925	12,280,000	1.50	2.00	3.00	7.00	20.00	115.00
1926	11,316,000	1.50	2.00	3.00	7.00	20.00	115.00
1926D	1,716,000	2.00	3.50	6.00	12.50	27.00	115.00
1926S	2,700,000	2.00	3.00	5.00	10.00	30.00	225.00
1927	11,912,000	1.50	2.00	3.00	7.00	20.00	100.00
1927D	976,000	2.25	4.00	8.50	15.00	31.00	125.00
1927S	396,000	5.00	7.50	15.00	50.00	140.00	1,000
1928	6,336,000	1.50	2.00	3.00	7.00	20.00	100.00
1928D	1,627,600	1.50	2.00	3.00	7.00	21.00	100.00
1928S*	2,644,000	1.50	2.00	3.00	7.00	20.00	100.00
1929	11,140,000	1.50	2.00	3.00	7.00	20.00	100.00
1929D	1,358,000	1.75	2.25	3.25	7.50	22.50	125.00
1929S	1,764,000	1.50	2.00	3.00	7.00	20.00	100.00
1930	5,632,000	1.50	2.00	3.00	7.00	20.00	100.00
1930S	1,556,000	1.50	2.00	3.00	7.00	20.00	100.00

*Large and small mint mark varieties, see page 59.

WASHINGTON TYPE 1932 to Date

G-4 GOOD—*Letters and date flat, but separated from rim. No hairlines near face.*
VG-8 VERY GOOD—*Wing tips outlined. Rims are fine and even. Tops of letters at rim are flattened.*
F-12 FINE—*Hairlines about ear are visible. Tiny feathers on eagle's breast are faintly visible.*
EF-40 EXTREMELY FINE—*Hairlines sharp. Wear spots confined to top of eagle's legs and center of breast.*
MS-60 UNCIRCULATED—*No trace of wear. Light blemishes.*
MS-65 CHOICE UNCIRCULATED—*No trace of wear. Barely noticeable blemishes.*

This type was intended to be a commemorative issue marking the two-hundredth anniversary of Washington's birth. John Flanagan, a New York sculptor, was the designer. The initials JF are found at the base of the neck. Mint mark is reverse below wreath, 1932 to 1964.

	Quan. Minted	G-4	VG-8	F-12	EF-40	MS-60	Proof
1932	5,404,000	$1.50	$1.75	$2.00	$5.00	$33.00	
1932D	436,800	37.50	45.00	55.00	95.00	650.00	
1932S	408,000	37.50	42.50	50.00	70.00	250.00	
1934 Light motto	} 31,912,052	1.50	1.75	2.50	6.00	19.00	
1934 Hvy. motto		1.50	1.75	2.00	4.00	18.00	
1934 Doubled die					75.00	175.00	
1934D	3,527,200	1.50	2.25	5.00	15.00	120.00	
1935	32,484,000	1.50	1.75	2.00	3.50	15.00	
1935D	5,780,000	1.50	1.75	2.50	9.00	120.00	
1935S	5,660,000	1.50	1.75	2.50	9.00	70.00	

QUARTER DOLLARS

	Quan. Minted	G-4	VG-8	F-12	EF-40	MS-65	Proof
1936 ..... (3,837)	41,303,837	$1.50	$1.75	$2.00	$3.00	$15.00	$485.00
1936D............	5,374,000	1.50	2.00	4.00	30.00	300.00	
1936S............	3,828,000	1.50	1.75	2.50	9.00	65.00	
1937 ..... (5,542)	19,701,542	....	1.50	1.75	3.00	22.00	100.00
1937D............	7,189,600	....	1.50	2.00	5.00	30.00	
1937S............	1,652,000	5.00	6.00	8.00	20.00	90.00	
1938 ..... (8,045)	9,480,045	....	1.50	2.00	10.00	50.00	95.00
1938S............	2,832,000	2.00	3.00	4.00	12.00	45.00	
1939 ..... (8,795)	33,548,795	....	1.50	1.75	3.00	10.00	50.00
1939D............	7,092,000	....	1.50	1.75	3.00	23.00	
1939S............	2,628,000	2.00	2.50	3.50	10.00	50.00	
1940 .... (11,246)	35,715,246	....	1.50	1.75	3.00	10.00	32.50
1940D............	2,797,600	1.50	2.00	3.50	12.00	50.00	
1940S............	8,244,000	....	1.50	1.75	3.00	25.00	
1941 .... (15,287)	79,047,287	....		1.50	2.00	5.00	27.50
1941D............	16,714,800	....		1.50	2.50	17.50	
1941S*..........	16,080,000	....		1.50	2.25	14.00	
1942 .... (21,123)	102,117,123	....			1.50	4.00	27.50
1942D............	17,487,200	....		1.50	2.50	17.50	
1942S............	19,384,000	....	1.50	2.50	4.50	40.00	
1943	99,700,000	....			1.50	3.75	
1943D............	16,095,600	....		1.50	2.50	9.00	
1943S............	21,700,000	....		1.50	2.50	14.00	
1943S Doubled die obverse						———	
1944	104,956,000	....			1.50	4.00	
1944D............	14,600,800	....			1.50	5.00	
1944S............	12,560,000	....		1.50	2.50	8.00	
1945	74,372,000	....			1.50	2.50	
1945D............	12,341,600	....			1.50	5.50	
1945S............	17,004,001	....			1.50	3.50	
1946	53,436,000	....			1.50	3.25	
1946D............	9,072,800	....			1.50	7.00	
1946S............	4,204,000	....		1.50	2.00	5.50	
1947	22,556,000	....			1.50	2.75	
1947D............	15,338,400	....			1.50	3.00	
1947S............	5,532,000	....		1.50	2.00	4.00	
1948	35,196,000	....			1.50	2.25	
1948D............	16,766,800	....			1.50	3.00	
1948S............	15,960,000	....			1.50	2.75	
1949	9,312,000	....		1.50	3.00	16.00	
1949D............	10,068,400	....		1.50	2.25	8.00	
1950 .... (51,386)	24,971,512	....			1.50	2.50	25.00
1950D.........	} 21,075,600	....			1.50	4.00	
1950 D, D over S						———	
1950S.........	} 10,284,004	....			1.50	6.00	
1950S, S over D						———	
1951 .... (57,500)	43,505,602	....			1.50	2.00	21.00
1951D............	35,354,800	....			1.50	2.75	
1951S............	9,048,000	....		1.50	2.50	10.00	
1952 .... (81,980)	38,862,073	....			1.50	2.00	15.00
1952D............	49,795,200	....			1.50	2.00	
1952S............	13,707,800	....			1.50	4.75	
1953 ... (128,800)	18,664,920	....			1.50	2.75	7.50
1953D............	56,112,400	....			1.50	2.00	
1953S............	14,016,000	....			1.50	3.25	

*Large and small mint mark varieties, see page 59.

QUARTER DOLLARS

	Quan. Minted	F-12	EF-40	MS-65	Proof
1954 . . . . (233,300)	54,645,503	. . . .	$1.50	$2.00	$4.25
1954D.	46,305,500	. . . .	1.50	2.00	
1954S.	11,834,722	. . . .	1.50	2.50	
1955 . . . . (378,200)	18,558,381	. . . .	1.50	2.00	3.50
1955D.	3,182,400	$2.00	2.50	4.00	
1956 . . . . (669,384)	44,813,384	. . . .		1.75	2.25
1956D.	32,334,500	. . . .		1.75	
1957 . . . . (1,247,952)	47,779,952	. . . .		1.75	2.00
1957D.	77,924,160	. . . .		1.75	
1958 . . . . (875,652)	7,235,652	. . . .	1.50	2.25	2.50
1958D.	78,124,900	. . . .		1.75	
1959 . . . . (1,149,291)	25,533,291	. . . .		1.75	2.00
1959D.	62,054,232	. . . .		1.75	
1960 . . . . (1,691,602)	30,855,602	. . . .		1.75	2.00
1960D.	63,000,324	. . . .		1.75	
1961 . . . . (3,028,244)	40,064,244	. . . .		1.75	2.00
1961D.	83,656,928	. . . .		1.75	
1962 . . . . (3,218,019)	39,374,019	. . . .		1.75	2.00
1962D.	127,554,756	. . . .		1.75	
1963 . . . . (3,075,645)	77,391,645	. . . .		1.75	2.00
1963D.	135,288,184	. . . .		1.75	
1964 . . . . (3,950,762)	564,341,347	. . . .		1.75	2.00
1964D.	704,135,528	. . . .		1.75	

Clad Coinage — 1965 to Date

Weight 5.67 grams; composition: outer layers of copper nickel (.750 copper, .250 nickel) bonded to inner core of pure copper; diameter 24.3 mm; reeded edge.

Proof coins from 1937 through 1972 were made from special dies with high relief and minor detail differences. Some of the circulation coins of 1956-1964 and 1969D-1972D were also made from dies with these same features. A variety of the 1964D quarter occurs with the modified reverse normally found only on the clad coins.

Starting in 1968 mint mark is on obverse at right of ribbon.

	Quan. Minted	MS-65	Proof
1965	1,819,717,540	$ .50	
1966	821,101,500	.50	
1967	1,524,031,848	.50	
1968	220,731,500	.50	
1968D	101,534,000	.65	
1968S Proof . .	(3,041,506)		$1.50
1969	176,212,000	.50	
1969D	114,372,000	.75	
1969S Proof . .	(2,934,631)		1.50
1970	136,420,000	.50	
1970D	417,341,364	.50	
1970S Proof . .	(2,632,810)		2.50
1971	109,284,000	.50	
1971D	258,634,428	.50	
1971S Proof . .	(3,220,733)		1.50

	Quan. Minted	MS-65	Proof
1972	215,048,000	$ .50	
1972D	311,067,732	.50	
1972S Proof . .	(3,260,996)		$1.25
1973	346,924,000	.50	
1973D	232,977,400	.50	
1973S Proof . .	(2,760,339)		1.50
1974	801,456,000	.50	
1974D	353,160,300	.50	
1974S Proof . .	(2,612,568)		2.00
Eagle Reverse Resumed (Dies slightly modified to lower relief)			
1977	468,556,000	.50	
1977D	256,524,978	.50	
1977S Proof . .	(3,251,152)		2.00
1978		.50	
1978D		.50	
1978S Proof			2.00

QUARTER DOLLARS
BICENTENNIAL COINAGE DATED 1776-1976

Few events have equaled the national significance of the Bicentennial of the United States. In October of 1973, the Treasury announced an open contest for the selection of suitable designs for the reverses of the quarter, half dollar and dollar, with $5,000 to be awarded to each winner. Twelve semifinalists were chosen, and from these the symbolic entry of Jack L. Ahr was selected for the quarter reverse. It features a Colonial drummer facing left, with a victory torch encircled by thirteen stars at the upper left. Except for a dual dating, 1776-1976, the obverse remained unchanged. Pieces with this dual dating were coined during 1975 and 1976. They were struck for general circulation and included in all the Mint's offerings of proof and uncirculated sets.

Designers John Flanagan and Jack L. Ahr. Silver issue: weight 5.75 grams; composition: outer layers of .800 silver, .200 copper bonded to inner core of .210 silver, .790 copper. Copper-nickel issue: weight 5.67 grams; composition: outer layers of .750 copper, .250 nickel bonded to inner core of pure copper. Diameter 24.3 mm; reeded edge. Net weight of silver issues: .07396 oz. pure silver.

	Quan. Minted	MS-65	Proof
1976 Copper-nickel clad	809,784,016	$ .50	
1976D Copper-nickel clad	860,118,839	.50	
1976S Copper-nickel clad	(7,059,099)		$2.50
1976S Silver clad	*11,000,000	2.00	
1976S Silver clad	(*4,000,000)		5.00

*Approximate mintage. Not all released.

HALF DOLLARS — 1794 to Date

The half dollar, authorized by the Act of April 2, 1792, was not minted until December, 1794. The early types of this series have been extensively collected by die varieties, of which many exist for most dates. Valuations given below are in each case for the most common variety, scarcer ones as listed by Beistle and Overton (see bibliography below) generally command higher prices.

The weight of the half dollar was 208 grains and its fineness .8924 when first issued. This standard was not changed until 1837 when the law of January 18, 1837 specified 206¼ grains, .900 fine.

Arrows at the date in 1853 indicate the reduction of weight to 192 grains, in conformity with the Act of February 21, 1853. During that year only, rays were added to the field on the reverse side. Arrows remained in 1854 and 1855.

In 1873 the weight was raised by law to 192.9 grains and arrows were again placed at the date, to be removed in 1875.

BIBLIOGRAPHY

Beistle, M. L. *Register of United States Half Dollar Die Varieties and Sub-Varieties.* Shippensburg, Pa., 1929.

Haseltine, J. W. *Type Table of United States Dollars, Half Dollars and Quarter Dollars.* Philadelphia, 1881 (reprinted 1927, 1968).

Overton, Al C. *Early Half Dollar Die Varieties 1794-1836.* Colorado Springs, 1967. Revised edition, 1970.

HALF DOLLARS
FLOWING HAIR TYPE 1794-1795

AG-3 ABOUT GOOD—*Clear enough to identify.*

G-4 GOOD—*Date and letters sufficient to be readable. Main devices outlined, but lack details.*

VG-8 VERY GOOD—*Major details discernible. Letters well formed but worn.*

F-12 FINE—*Hair ends distinguishable. Top hairlines show, but otherwise worn smooth.*

VF-20 VERY FINE—*Hair in'center shows some detail. Other details more bold.*

EF-40 EXTREMELY FINE—*Hair above head and down neck detailed, with slight wear.*

Designer Robert Scot; weight 13.48 grams; composition: .8924 silver, .1076 copper; approx. diameter 32.5 mm; edge: FIFTY CENTS OR HALF A DOLLAR with decorations between words.

1794

3 Leaves under Wings

	Quan. Minted	AG-3	G-4	VG-8	F-12	VF-20	EF-40
1794	23,464	$200.00	$375.00	$550.00	$775.00	$1,400	$2,400
1795 All kinds	299,680	140.00	250.00	325.00	450.00	750.00	1,300
1795 Recut date		160.00	275.00	400.00	600.00	900.00	1,750
1795 3 leaves under each wing.		200.00	420.00	625.00	900.00	1,500	2,500

Varieties of 1795 are known with final S in STATES over D, with A in STATES over E, and with Y in LIBERTY over a star.

DRAPED BUST TYPE, SMALL EAGLE REVERSE 1796-1797

Grading same as above for About Good to Fine.

VF-20 VERY FINE—*Right side of drapery slightly worn. Left side to curls is smooth.*

EF-40 EXTREMELY FINE—*All lines in drapery on bust will show distinctly around to hair curls.*

1796, 15 Stars

1796, 16 Stars

1796, 15 stars	⎫	1,650	2,900	4,250	6,000	9,000	13,000
1796, 16 stars	⎬ 3,918	1,650	2,900	4,250	6,250	9,250	13,500
1797, 15 stars	⎭	1,650	2,900	4,250	6,250	9,250	14,000

HALF DOLLARS
DRAPED BUST TYPE, HERALDIC EAGLE REVERSE 1801-1807

	Quan. Minted	G-4	VG-8	F-12	VF-20	EF-40	MS-60
1801	30,289	$115.00	$165.00	$275.00	$500.00	$900.00	$5,000
1802	29,890	95.00	150.00	250.00	400.00	700.00	4,250
1803 Small 3	} 188,234	90.00	140.00	200.00	300.00	600.00	4,250
1803 Large 3		65.00	90.00	140.00	225.00	500.00	3,750

1805, 5 over 4   1806, 6 over 5

1805, 5 over 4	} 211,722	80.00	115.00	175.00	300.00	500.00	3,750
1805 Normal date....		50.00	65.00	100.00	190.00	450.00	3,650

Knobbed Top 6, Large Stars   Branch Stem through Claw

Pointed Top 6   Branch Stem Not through Claw

1806 All kinds 839,576							
1806, 6 over 5		55.00	85.00	125.00	215.00	525.00	3,750
1806, 6 over inverted 6........		65.00	105.00	150.00	265.00	500.00	4,000
1806 Knobbed 6, large stars (traces of overdate)		50.00	60.00	90.00	175.00	400.00	4,000
1806 Knobbed 6, small stars ...		50.00	60.00	90.00	175.00	400.00	4,000
1806 Knobbed 6, stem not through claw		Rare					
1806 Pointed 6, stem through claw*		50.00	60.00	90.00	175.00	400.00	4,000
1806 Pointed 6, stem not through claw		50.00	60.00	90.00	175.00	400.00	4,000
1807 301,076		50.00	60.00	90.00	175.00	400.00	4,000

*One variety shows E in STATES over A.

HALF DOLLARS
CAPPED BUST TYPE, Lettered Edge 1807-1836

John Reich designed this Turban Head concept of Liberty. The head of Liberty facing left was used on all U.S. coin denominations for the next thirty years. Reich was the first artist to consistently include the denomination on our gold and silver coins. He was from Germany and a bondman freed from servitude by a mint official.

G-4 GOOD—*Date and letters readable. Bust worn smooth with outline distinct*

VG-8 VERY GOOD—*LIBERTY visible but faint. Legends distinguishable. Clasp at shoulder visible. Curl above it nearly smooth.*

F-12 FINE—*Clasp and adjacent curl clearly outlined with slight details.*

VF-20 VERY FINE—*Clasp at shoulder clear. Curl has wear only on highest point. Hair over brow distinguishable.*

EF-40 EXTREMELY FINE—*Clasp and adjacent curl fairly sharp. Brow and hair above distinct. Curls well defined.*

MS-60 UNCIRCULATED—*No trace of wear. Light blemishes.*

Designer John Reich; weight 13.48 grams; composition: .8924 silver, .1076 copper; approx. diameter 32.5 mm; edge varieties, 1807-1814: FIFTY CENTS OR HALF A DOLLAR; 1814-1831: star added between DOLLAR and FIFTY; 1832-1836: vertical lines added between words.

First style 1807-1808

1807 Small Stars   1807 Large Stars   1807, 50 over 20

	Quan. Minted	G-4	VG-8	F-12	VF-20	EF-40	MS-60
1807 Small stars....		$30.00	$40.00	$50.00	$100.00	$200.00	$950.00
1807 Large stars....	750,500	25.00	32.50	45.00	85.00	135.00	850.00
1807 Same, 50 over 20.....		25.00	32.50	45.00	85.00	135.00	900.00
1808, 8 over 7	1,368,600	22.50	30.00	42.50	65.00	100.00	700.00
1808		21.00	27.00	37.50	55.00	100.00	675.00

Remodeled Portrait and Eagle 1809-1834

1809 Experimental edge, xxxx between words.

1809 Experimental edge, IIIII between words.

HALF DOLLARS

	Quan. Minted	G-4	VG-8	F-12	VF-20	EF-40	MS-60
1809 Normal	} 1,405,810	$22.50	$27.50	$32.50	$40.00	$100.00	$575.00
1809 xxxx edge....		25.00	40.00	47.50	65.00	125.00	650.00
1809 IIIIIII edge....		23.00	30.00	42.50	55.00	115.00	625.00
1810	1,276,276	20.00	26.00	35.00	45.00	75.00	600.00

"Punctuated" Date 18.11   1811 Small 8   1811 Large 8

	Quan. Minted	G-4	VG-8	F-12	VF-20	EF-40	MS-60
1811 (18.11) 11 over 10....	} 1,203,644	24.00	35.00	60.00	90.00	130.00	600.00
1811 Small 8		18.00	24.00	30.00	40.00	65.00	500.00
1811 Large 8		18.00	24.00	30.00	40.00	70.00	525.00
1812, 2 over 1 small 8	} 1,628,059	22.50	32.50	60.00	95.00	125.00	550.00
1812, 2 over 1 large 8.......		75.00	100.00	150.00	200.00	500.00	——
1812		18.00	24.00	30.00	40.00	70.00	525.00

1812, 2 over 1, Small 8   1812, 2 over 1, Large 8   1813, 50 C. over UNI

	Quan. Minted	G-4	VG-8	F-12	VF-20	EF-40	MS-60
1813	} 1,241,903	18.00	25.00	30.00	40.00	70.00	525.00
1813, 50C over UNI.........		30.00	40.00	65.00	100.00	150.00	600.00
1814, 4 over 3	} 1,039,075	22.00	35.00	45.00	65.00	110.00	525.00
1814 E over A in STATES......		18.00	25.00	30.00	50.00	110.00	535.00
1814 Normal		20.00	26.00	32.00	42.50	75.00	500.00

1814, 4 over 3   1814 E over A in STATES

HALF DOLLARS

1817, 7 over 3

1817, 7 over 4

1817 Punctuated Date

	Quan. Minted	G-4	VG-8	F-12	VF-20	EF-40	MS-60
1815, 5 over 2	47,150	$200.00	$250.00	$400.00	$500.00	$750.00	$2,750.00
1817, 7 over 3 ..... ⎫		24.00	35.00	50.00	70.00	125.00	675.00
1817, 7 over 4 ..... ⎬ 1,215,567		V. Rare		——	——	——	
1817 dated 181.7... ⎪		24.00	35.00	50.00	70.00	120.00	550.00
1817 Normal ...... ⎭		17.00	22.00	27.50	37.50	60.00	500.00

1818, 1st 8 Small, 2nd 8 over 7

1819 Small 9 over 8

1818, 1st 8 Large, 2nd 8 over 7

1819 Large 9 over 8

1818, 8 over 7 small 8....... ⎫		17.00	22.00	27.50	37.50	60.00	500.00
1818, 8 over 7 ..... large 8....... ⎬ 1,960,322		17.00	22.00	27.50	37.50	60.00	500.00
1818 Normal ...... ⎭		17.00	22.00	27.50	37.50	60.00	500.00
1819 Sm. 9 over 8.. ⎫		19.00	24.00	30.00	40.00	65.00	525.00
1819 Lg. 9 over 8.. ⎬ 2,208,000		19.00	24.00	30.00	40.00	65.00	525.00
1819 Normal ...... ⎭		19.00	24.00	30.00	40.00	65.00	525.00

1820, 20 over 19
Square Base 2

1820, 20 over 19
Curl Base 2

Curl Base, No Knob 2,
Small Date

Square Base, Knob 2,
Large Date

Square Base, No Knob 2,
Large Date

1822, 2 over 1

HALF DOLLARS

	Quan. Minted	G-4	VG-8	F-12	VF-20	EF-40	MS-60
1820, 20 over 19 square 2......		$20.00	$28.00	$38.00	$47.50	$75.00	$525.00
1820, 20 over 19 curl 2		20.00	28.00	38.00	47.50	75.00	525.00
1820 Curl base 2, .. small date....	751,122	20.00	28.00	38.00	47.50	75.00	575.00
1820 Sq. base knob 2, large date		20.00	28.00	38.00	47.50	75.00	550.00
1820 Sq. base no knob 2, lg. date		20.00	28.00	38.00	47.50	75.00	550.00
1821	1,305,797	18.00	22.00	30.00	40.00	50.00	500.00
1822, 2 over 1		40.00	55.00	80.00	100.00	170.00	650.00
1822	1,559,573	18.00	22.00	30.00	40.00	50.00	500.00

1823 Broken 3

1823 Patched 3

1823 Ugly 3

1823 Broken 3.....		40.00	55.00	80.00	100.00	150.00	550.00
1823 Patched 3	1,694,200	40.00	55.00	80.00	100.00	150.00	550.00
1823 Ugly 3		18.00	22.00	30.00	40.00	50.00	525.00
1823 Normal		16.00	20.00	25.00	35.00	45.00	450.00

"Various Dates" (probably 4 over 2 over 0)

1824, 4 over 1

1824, 4 over 4

1824, 4 over 4

1824 over various dates.........		18.00	22.00	30.00	40.00	50.00	450.00
1824, 4 over 1	3,504,954	18.00	22.00	30.00	40.00	50.00	475.00
1824, 4 over 4 (2 var.).......		18.00	22.00	30.00	40.00	50.00	525.00
1824 Normal		16.00	20.00	25.00	35.00	45.00	500.00
1825	2,943,166	16.00	20.00	25.00	35.00	45.00	475.00
1826	4,004,180	16.00	20.00	25.00	35.00	45.00	475.00
1827, 7 over 6		20.00	25.00	35.00	45.00	65.00	500.00
1827 Curl base 2...	5,493,400	20.00	25.00	35.00	45.00	65.00	500.00
1827 Sq. base 2		16.00	20.00	25.00	35.00	45.00	475.00

1828 Curl Base, Knob 2

1828 Square Base 2, Large 8's

1828 Square Base 2, Small 8's

HALF DOLLARS

1828 Large Letters

1828 Small Letters

	Quan. Minted	G-4	VG-8	F-12	VF-20	EF-40	MS-60
1828 All kinds	3,075,200						
1828 Curl base no knob 2		$16.00	$20.00	$25.00	$35.00	$45.00	$450.00
1828 Curl base knob 2		35.00	45.00	60.00	85.00	100.00	600.00
1828 Sq. base 2, lg. 8's		18.00	22.00	28.00	40.00	60.00	475.00
1828 Sq. base 2, sm. 8's, lg. let.		16.00	20.00	25.00	35.00	45.00	470.00
1828 Sq. base 2, sm. 8's & let.		20.00	35.00	40.00	75.00	125.00	500.00
1829, 9 over 7	} 3,712,156	16.00	20.00	25.00	35.00	45.00	480.00
1829		16.00	20.00	25.00	35.00	45.00	475.00

1832 Large Letters Reverse

Raised segment lines to right, 1830.

Raised segment lines to left, 1830-1831.

Adopted edge 1830-1836.

1830 Large 0	} 4,764,800	16.00	20.00	25.00	35.00	45.00	450.00
1830 Small 0		16.00	20.00	25.00	35.00	45.00	450.00
1831	5,873,660	16.00	20.00	25.00	35.00	45.00	450.00
1832 Normal	} 4,797,000	16.00	20.00	25.00	35.00	45.00	450.00
1832 Large letters		16.00	20.00	25.00	35.00	50.00	500.00
1833	5,206,000	16.00	20.00	25.00	35.00	45.00	450.00

1830 Small 0

1834 Large Date

1834 Small Date

1834 Lg. Letters Reverse

1834 Sm. Letters Reverse

1836, 50 over 00

Portrait Modified Slightly 1834-1836

1834 Small date stars, letters	} 6,412,004	16.00	20.00	25.00	35.00	45.00	450.00
1834 Large date, small letters		16.00	20.00	25.00	35.00	45.00	475.00
1834 Lg. date & let		16.00	20.00	25.00	35.00	45.00	475.00
1835	5,352,000	16.00	20.00	25.00	35.00	45.00	450.00
1836	} 6,545,000	16.00	20.00	25.00	35.00	45.00	450.00
1836, 50 over 00		30.00	40.00	50.00	75.00	110.00	600.00

HALF DOLLARS

Variety 2 — Reeded Edge, Reverse "50 CENTS" 1836-1837

Designer Christian Gobrecht; weight 13.36 grams; composition: .900 silver, .100 copper; diameter 30 mm; reeded edge; mints: Philadelphia, New Orleans.

G-4 GOOD—*LIBERTY discernible on headband.*

VG-8 VERY GOOD—*Minimum of 3 letters in LIBERTY must be clear.*

F-12 FINE—*LIBERTY complete.*

VF-20 VERY FINE—*LIBERTY is sharp. Shoulder clasp is clear.*

EF-40 EXTREMELY FINE—*LIBERTY sharp and strong. Hair details show.*

MS-60 UNCIRCULATED—*No trace of wear. Light blemishes.*

	Quan. Minted	G-4	VG-8	F-12	VF-20	EF-40	MS-60
1836	1,200	$225.00	$325.00	$425.00	$825.00	$1,450	$3,400
1837	3,629,820	26.00	35.00	50.00	75.00	150.00	950.00

Variety 3 — Reeded Edge, Reverse "HALF DOL." 1838-1839

1838-O

The 1838O was the first branch mint half dollar, though not mentioned in the Director's report. The New Orleans chief coiner stated that only 20 were struck. In 1838-39 the mint mark appears on the obverse; thereafter it is on the reverse through 1915.

1838	3,546,000	26.00	35.00	50.00	75.00	150.00	950.00
1838O	(20)	James Stack Sale 1975					50,000
1839 All kinds	3,334,500	26.00	35.00	50.00	75.00	150.00	950.00
1839 Small letters reverse					—	—	
1839O	178,976	75.00	100.00	150.00	225.00	350.00	2,500

LIBERTY SEATED TYPE 1839-1891

Variety 1 — No Motto Above Eagle 1839-1853

Designer Christian Gobrecht; weight 13.36 grams; composition: .900 silver, .100 copper; diameter 30.6 mm; reeded edge; mints: Philadelphia, New Orleans.

G-4 GOOD—*Scant rim. LIBERTY on shield worn off. Date and letters readable.*

VG-8 VERY GOOD—*Rim fairly defined. At least 3 letters in LIBERTY are evident.*

F-12 FINE—*LIBERTY complete, but weak.*

VF-20 VERY FINE—*LIBERTY mostly sharp.*

EF-40 EXTREMELY FINE—*LIBERTY entirely sharp. Scroll edges and clasp distinct.*

MS-60 UNCIRCULATED—*No trace of wear. Light blemishes.*

1839 No drapery from elbow	35.00	50.00	80.00	125.00	325.00	5,000

HALF DOLLARS

**Modified obverse, drapery from elbow. Small letters in legend
1839-1841.**

Drapery from Elbow
Starting 1839

Small Letters in
Legend 1839-41

1840 (only) With
Medium Letters, Large Eagle
(Style of 1838)

	Quan. Minted	G-4	VG-8	F-12	VF-20	EF-40	MS-60
1839		$14.00	$16.00	$25.00	$40.00	$75.00	$500.00
1840 Sm. letters ...	1,435,008	12.00	14.00	22.00	35.00	70.00	475.00
1840 Med. letters		25.00	37.50	60.00	100.00	200.00	575.00
1840O.............	855,100	12.00	14.00	22.00	35.00	70.00	500.00
1841	310,000	15.00	18.00	28.00	45.00	85.00	500.00
1841O................	401,000	12.00	14.00	22.00	35.00	85.00	575.00

Modified reverse with large letters in legend 1842-1853.

Small Date

Medium Date

Large Letter Reverse

1842 Sm. date	2,012,764	12.00	14.00	22.00	35.00	75.00	575.00
1842 Med. date		12.00	14.00	22.00	35.00	75.00	475.00
1842O Small date and letters							
All kinds........	957,000	150.00	200.00	300.00	500.00	900.00	——
1842O Med. date, lg. letters....		12.00	14.00	22.00	35.00	70.00	500.00
1843	3,844,000	12.00	14.00	22.00	35.00	70.00	450.00
1843O...............	2,268,000	12.00	14.00	22.00	35.00	70.00	500.00
1844	1,766,000	12.00	14.00	22.00	35.00	70.00	450.00
1844O.............	2,005,000	12.00	14.00	22.00	35.00	70.00	500.00
1844O Double date		30.00	45.00	75.00	175.00	325.00	650.00
1845	589,000	12.00	14.00	22.00	35.00	70.00	500.00
1845O.............	2,094,000	12.00	14.00	22.00	35.00	70.00	575.00
1845O No drapery		25.00	40.00	50.00	75.00	165.00	650.00

HALF DOLLARS

In 1846 date size was again enlarged. The 1846 medium date is approximately the size of the 1842 medium date shown above. Tall date is similar to 1853.

	Quan. Minted	G-4	VG-8	F-12	VF-20	EF-40	MS-60
1846 Med. dt. All	2,210,000	$12.00	$14.00	$22.00	$35.00	$70.00	$450.00
1846 Tall date		12.00	14.00	22.00	35.00	70.00	500.00
1846 over horizontal 6 (error)..		40.00	60.00	85.00	135.00	175.00	700.00
1846O Med. date...	2,304,000	12.00	14.00	22.00	35.00	70.00	475.00
1846O Tall date.....		27.50	40.00	60.00	100.00	175.00	750.00
1847, 7 over 6	1,156,000	—	—	—	—	—	—
1847 Normal date..		12.00	14.00	22.00	35.00	70.00	450.00
1847O.............	2,584,000	12.00	14.00	22.00	35.00	70.00	500.00
1848	580,000	20.00	27.50	40.00	60.00	85.00	700.00
1848O.............	3,180,000	12.00	14.00	22.00	35.00	70.00	475.00
1849	1,252,000	12.00	14.00	22.00	35.00	70.00	450.00
1849O.............	2,310,000	12.00	14.00	22.00	35.00	70.00	475.00
1850	227,000	30.00	40.00	65.00	90.00	160.00	625.00
1850O.............	2,456,000	12.00	14.00	22.00	35.00	70.00	550.00
1851	200,750	30.00	40.00	65.00	90.00	160.00	750.00
1851O.............	402,000	12.00	14.00	22.00	35.00	70.00	600.00
1852	77,130	60.00	75.00	125.00	225.00	375.00	1,000
1852O.............	144,000	30.00	40.00	65.00	90.00	160.00	750.00
1853O (Clarke Sale, 1975)		—	—	24,000	—		

Variety 2 — Arrows at Date, Rays Around Eagle 1853 Only

Weight 12.44 grams; composition: .900 silver, .100 copper; diameter 30.6 mm; reeded edge; mints: Philadelphia, New Orleans, San Francisco.

1853	3,532,708	14.00	20.00	35.00	80.00	250.00	2,200
1853O All kinds	1,328,000	14.00	20.00	35.00	80.00	250.00	2,300

Variety 3 — Arrows at Date, No Rays 1854-1855

1854	2,982,000	12.00	14.00	22.00	35.00	75.00	700.00
1854O.............	5,240,000	12.00	14.00	22.00	35.00	75.00	700.00
1855 over 1854	759,500		75.00	125.00	275.00	500.00	1,500
1855 Normal date..		12.00	14.00	22.00	35.00	75.00	725.00
1855O.............	3,688,000	12.00	14.00	22.00	35.00	75.00	750.00
1855S...............	129,950	100.00	125.00	200.00	400.00	550.00	2,750

Variety 1 Resumed 1856-1866

1856	938,000	11.00	13.00	20.00	30.00	60.00	425.00
1856O.............	2,658,000	11.00	13.00	20.00	30.00	60.00	450.00
1856S.............	211,000	15.00	20.00	30.00	80.00	125.00	650.00
1857	1,988,000	11.00	13.00	20.00	30.00	60.00	450.00
1857O.............	818,000	11.00	13.00	20.00	30.00	60.00	500.00
1857S.............	158,000	18.00	25.00	40.00	85.00	140.00	700.00

HALF DOLLARS

	Quan. Minted	G-4	VG-8	F-12	VF-20	EF-40	MS-60	Proof
1858	4,226,000	$11.00	$13.00	$20.00	$30.00	$60.00	$400.00	$1,150
1858O	7,294,000	11.00	13.00	20.00	30.00	60.00	450.00	
1858S	476,000	13.00	18.00	25.00	40.00	85.00	600.00	
1859	748,000	11.00	13.00	20.00	30.00	60.00	425.00	800.00
1859O	2,834,000	11.00	13.00	20.00	30.00	60.00	500.00	
1859S	566,000	13.00	18.00	25.00	40.00	95.00	625.00	
1860 . (1,000)	303,700	11.00	13.00	20.00	30.00	75.00	475.00	650.00
1860O	1,290,000	11.00	13.00	20.00	30.00	60.00	425.00	
1860S	472,000	13.00	18.00	25.00	40.00	70.00	525.00	
1861 . (1,000)	2,888,400	11.00	13.00	20.00	30.00	60.00	450.00	650.00
1861O	2,532,633	11.00	13.00	20.00	30.00	60.00	475.00	

The 1861O quantity includes 330,000 struck under the United States government; 1,240,000 for the State of Louisiana after it seceded from the Union; and 962,633 after Louisiana joined the Confederate States of America. As all these 1861O coins were struck from U.S. dies it is impossible to distinguish one from another. They should not be confused with the very rare Confederate half dollar of 1861 (see p. 249) which has a distinctive reverse.

1861S	939,500	11.00	13.00	20.00	30.00	60.00	475.00	
1862 . . . (550)	253,550	15.00	20.00	25.00	50.00	100.00	600.00	650.00
1862S	1,352,000	11.00	13.00	20.00	30.00	60.00	450.00	
1863 . . . (460)	503,660	11.00	13.00	20.00	25.00	50.00	75.00	600.00	650.00
1863S	916,000	11.00	13.00	20.00	30.00	60.00	475.00	
1964 . . . (470)	379,570	11.00	13.00	20.00	30.00	75.00	450.00	650.00
1864S	658,000	11.00	13.00	20.00	30.00	60.00	475.00	
1865 . . . (500)	511,900	11.00	13.00	20.00	30.00	75.00	500.00	650.00
1865S	675,000	11.00	13.00	20.00	30.00	60.00	550.00	
1866S No motto		45.00	75.00	115.00	225.00	300.00	4,000	
1866 Transitional piece		(Unique — see quarter on page 119)						——

Variety 4 —
Motto "In God We Trust"
Added Above Eagle
1866-1873

1882

1866 . . . (725)	745,625	11.00	13.00	20.00	30.00	60.00	400.00	500.00
1866S All kinds . .	1,054,000	11.00	13.00	20.00	30.00	60.00	450.00	
1867 . . . (625)	449,925	11.00	13.00	20.00	30.00	75.00	425.00	500.00
1867S	1,196,000	11.00	13.00	20.00	30.00	60.00	425.00	
1868 . . . (600)	418,200	11.00	13.00	20.00	30.00	60.00	425.00	500.00
1868S	1,160,000	11.00	13.00	20.00	30.00	60.00	425.00	
1869 . . . (600)	795,900	11.00	13.00	20.00	30.00	60.00	425.00	500.00
1869S	656,000	11.00	13.00	20.00	30.00	60.00	425.00	
1870 . (1,000)	634,900	11.00	13.00	20.00	30.00	60.00	400.00	475.00
1870CC	54,617	125.00	225.00	350.00	600.00	1,000	——	
1870S	1,004,000	11.00	13.00	20.00	30.00	75.00	425.00	
1871 . . . (960)	1,204,560	11.00	13.00	20.00	30.00	65.00	400.00	475.00
1871CC	153,950	47.50	65.00	115.00	200.00	500.00	2,750	
1871S	2,178,000	11.00	13.00	20.00	30.00	65.00	400.00	

HALF DOLLARS

	Quan. Minted	G-4	VG-8	F-12	VF-20	EF-40	MS-60	Proof
1872 ... (950)	881,550	$11.00	$13.00	$20.00	$30.00	$60.00	$400.00	$500.00
1872CC	257,000	32.50	55.00	85.00	175.00	275.00	1,450	
1872S.........	580,000	11.00	13.00	20.00	30.00	65.00	450.00	
1873 Closed 3 . (600) ⎫ 1873 Open 3 ⎬	801,800	11.00	13.00	20.00	30.00	60.00	450.00	525.00
1873CC	122,500	50.00	75.00	135.00	235.00	350.00	2,250	
1873S No arrows	5,000			Unknown in any collection.				

<table>
<tr><td>

Variety 5 —
Arrows at Date
1873-1874

Arrows were placed at the date to denote a change in weight from 12.44 to 12.50 grams.

</td><td></td><td></td></tr>
</table>

Weight 12.50 grams; composition: .900 silver, .100 copper; diameter 30.6 mm; reeded edge; mints: Philadelphia, Carson City, San Francisco.

	Quan. Minted	G-4	VG-8	F-12	VF-20	EF-40	MS-60	Proof
1873 ... (550)	1,815,700	18.00	30.00	45.00	85.00	160.00	750.00	1,100
1873CC	214,560	32.50	55.00	100.00	175.00	250.00	1,450	
1873S.........	228,000	25.00	35.00	60.00	100.00	160.00	900.00	
1874 ... (700)	2,360,300	18.00	30.00	45.00	85.00	160.00	675.00	1,100
1874CC	59,000	45.00	75.00	175.00	250.00	500.00	1,700	
1874S.........	394,000	30.00	45.00	75.00	125.00	190.00	1,225	

Variety 4 Resumed 1875-1891

	Quan. Minted	G-4	VG-8	F-12	VF-20	EF-40	MS-60	Proof
1875 ... (700)	6,027,500	11.00	13.00	20.00	30.00	55.00	425.00	525.00
1875CC	1,008,000	12.50	17.00	25.00	45.00	70.00	525.00	
1875S........	3,200,000	11.00	13.00	20.00	30.00	55.00	400.00	
1876 . (1,150)	8,419,150	11.00	13.00	20.00	30.00	55.00	400.00	500.00
1876CC	1,956,000	11.50	14.00	22.00	35.00	60.00	685.00	
1876S........	4,528,000	11.00	13.00	20.00	30.00	55.00	400.00	
1877 ... (510)	8,304,510	11.00	13.00	20.00	30.00	55.00	400.00	550.00
1877CC	1,420,000	12.00	15.00	22.00	35.00	70.00	475.00	
1877S........	5,356,000	11.00	13.00	20.00	30.00	55.00	400.00	
1878 ... (800)	1,378,400	11.00	13.00	20.00	30.00	55.00	400.00	550.00
1878CC	62,000	125.00	175.00	250.00	400.00	650.00	2,250	
1878S..........	12,000	1,200	1,900	2,600	3,750	5,500	9,000	
1879 . (1,100)	5,900	80.00	100.00	125.00	175.00	225.00	600.00	550.00
1880 . (1,355)	9,755	75.00	90.00	115.00	160.00	200.00	575.00	550.00
1881 ... (975)	10,975	70.00	85.00	100.00	140.00	190.00	575.00	550.00
1882 . (1,100)	5,500	80.00	100.00	125.00	175.00	225.00	625.00	550.00
1883 . (1,039)	9,039	75.00	90.00	115.00	160.00	200.00	575.00	550.00
1884 ... (875)	5,275	80.00	100.00	125.00	175.00	225.00	650.00	575.00
1885 ... (930)	6,130	80.00	100.00	125.00	175.00	225.00	650.00	575.00
1886 ... (886)	5,886	85.00	110.00	125.00	175.00	225.00	650.00	575.00
1887 ... (710)	5,710	80.00	100.00	125.00	175.00	225.00	650.00	575.00
1888 ... (832)	12,833	70.00	85.00	100.00	140.00	190.00	575.00	550.00
1889 ... (711)	12,711	70.00	85.00	100.00	140.00	190.00	575.00	550.00
1890 ... (590)	12,590	70.00	85.00	100.00	140.00	190.00	575.00	550.00
1891 ... (600)	200,600	11.50	14.00	22.50	35.00	65.00	450.00	550.00

HALF DOLLARS
BARBER or LIBERTY HEAD TYPE 1892-1915

Like the dime and quarter dollar, this type was designed by Charles E. Barber, whose initial B is at the truncation of the neck.

G-4 GOOD—*Date and legends readable. LIBERTY worn off headband.*
VG-8 VERY GOOD—*Minimum of 3 letters readable in LIBERTY.*
F-12 FINE—*LIBERTY completely readable, but not sharp.*
VF-20 VERY FINE—*All letters in LIBERTY evenly plain.*
EF-40 EXTREMELY FINE—*LIBERTY bold, and its ribbon distinct.*
MS-60 UNCIRCULATED—*No trace of wear. Light blemishes.*

Designer Charles E. Barber; weight 12.50 grams; composition: .900 silver, .100 copper; diameter 30.6 mm; reeded edge; mints: Philadelphia, Denver, New Orleans, San Francisco.

Mint mark location on reverse below eagle.

	Quan. Minted	G-4	VG-8	F-12	VF-20	EF-40	MS-60	Proof
1892 . (1,245)	935,245	$8.00	$13.00	$25.00	$55.00	$135.00	$525.00	$650.00
1892O*	390,000	65.00	75.00	100.00	150.00	210.00	625.00	
1892S	1,029,028	55.00	70.00	100.00	140.00	195.00	625.00	
1893 . . . (792)	1,826,792	8.00	13.00	25.00	55.00	125.00	525.00	650.00
1893O	1,389,000	14.00	22.50	40.00	65.00	145.00	595.00	
1893S	740,000	40.00	65.00	95.00	140.00	190.00	650.00	
1894 . . . (972)	1,148,972	8.00	13.00	25.00	55.00	130.00	525.00	650.00
1894O	2,138,000	8.00	13.00	25.00	55.00	130.00	550.00	
1894S	4,048,690	5.00	9.00	22.00	50.00	125.00	525.00	
1895 . . . (880)	1,835,218	5.00	9.00	22.00	52.50	125.00	540.00	650.00
1895O	1,766,000	8.00	13.00	25.00	55.00	130.00	550.00	
1895S	1,108,086	13.00	21.00	35.00	65.00	140.00	550.00	
1896 . . . (762)	950,762	7.50	12.00	24.00	55.00	140.00	525.00	650.00
1896O	924,000	14.00	20.00	32.50	70.00	150.00	575.00	
1896S	1,140,948	35.00	50.00	70.00	100.00	160.00	650.00	
1897 . . . (731)	2,480,731	5.00	7.00	18.00	40.00	110.00	525.00	650.00
1897O	632,000	32.50	45.00	70.00	100.00	170.00	725.00	
1897S	933,900	40.00	55.00	80.00	115.00	175.00	675.00	
1898 . . . (735)	2,956,735	5.00	7.00	12.00	45.00	115.00	525.00	650.00
1898O	874,000	9.00	15.00	30.00	65.00	175.00	600.00	
1898S	2,358,550	6.00	9.00	16.00	50.00	115.00	575.00	
1899 . . . (846)	5,538,846	4.50	6.50	13.00	40.00	115.00	500.00	650.00
1899O	1,724,000	5.00	7.00	15.00	50.00	120.00	550.00	
1899S	1,686,411	8.00	12.00	20.00	50.00	115.00	600.00	
1900 . . . (912)	4,762,912	4.25	6.00	12.00	40.00	115.00	525.00	650.00
1900O	2,744,000	4.25	6.00	12.00	40.00	115.00	525.00	
1900S	2,560,322	5.25	8.00	13.00	40.00	115.00	550.00	
1901 . . . (813)	4,268,813	4.00	6.00	11.00	40.00	115.00	525.00	650.00
1901O	1,124,000	5.50	9.00	20.00	55.00	150.00	650.00	
1901S	847,044	10.00	18.00	50.00	115.00	225.00	1,250	
1902 . . . (777)	4,922,777	4.25	6.00	11.00	40.00	115.00	500.00	650.00
1902O	2,526,000	5.00	7.00	12.00	45.00	115.00	550.00	

*Normal and "microscopic" mint mark varieties, see page 59.

[140]

HALF DOLLARS

Quan. Minted	G-4	VG-8	F-12	VF-20	EF-40	MS-60	Proof
1902S 1,460,670	$4.25	$6.00	$12.00	$45.00	$115.00	$550.00	
1903 . . . (755) 2,278,755	3.75	5.50	11.00	40.00	115.00	500.00	$650.00
1903O 2,100,000	3.75	5.50	11.00	40.00	115.00	525.00	
1903S 1,920,722	4.50	7.00	13.00	42.00	120.00	600.00	
1904 . . . (670) 2,992,670	3.75	5.50	11.00	40.00	115.00	500.00	650.00
1904O 1,117,600	5.00	9.00	15.00	50.00	125.00	600.00	
1904S 553,038	10.00	18.00	35.00	85.00	155.00	750.00	
1905 . . . (727) 662,727	5.50	10.00	20.00	70.00	140.00	700.00	700.00
1905O 505,000	8.50	16.00	30.00	75.00	150.00	600.00	
1905S 2,494,000	3.75	5.50	11.00	40.00	115.00	525.00	
1906 . . . (675) 2,638,675	3.75	5.50	11.00	40.00	115.00	500.00	650.00
1906D 4,028,000	3.75	5.50	11.00	40.00	115.00	500.00	
1906O 2,446,000	3.75	5.50	11.00	40.00	115.00	525.00	
1906S 1,740,154	3.75	5.50	11.00	40.00	115.00	525.00	
1907 . . . (575) 2,598,575	3.75	5.50	11.00	40.00	115.00	500.00	650.00
1907D 3,856,000	3.75	5.50	11.00	40.00	115.00	500.00	
1907O 3,946,600	3.75	5.50	11.00	40.00	115.00	510.00	
1907S 1,250,000	3.75	5.50	11.00	40.00	115.00	510.00	
1908 . . . (545) 1,354,545	3.75	5.50	11.00	40.00	115.00	510.00	650.00
1908D 3,280,000	3.75	5.50	11.00	40.00	115.00	500.00	
1908O 5,360,000	3.75	5.50	11.00	40.00	115.00	510.00	
1908S 1,644,828	3.75	5.50	11.00	40.00	115.00	525.00	
1909 . . . (650) 2,368,650	3.75	5.50	11.00	40.00	115.00	500.00	650.00
1909O 925,400	3.75	5.50	11.00	42.00	120.00	575.00	
1909S 1,764,000	3.75	5.50	11.00	40.00	115.00	500.00	
1910 . . . (551) 418,551	6.50	13.00	25.00	60.00	135.00	625.00	675.00
1910S 1,948,000	3.75	5.50	11.00	40.00	115.00	525.00	
1911 . . . (543) 1,406,543	3.75	5.50	11.00	40.00	115.00	500.00	650.00
1911D 695,080	4.25	6.00	12.00	42.00	125.00	525.00	
1911S 1,272,000	3.75	5.50	11.00	40.00	115.00	510.00	
1912 . . . (700) 1,550,700	3.75	5.50	11.00	40.00	115.00	500.00	650.00
1912D 2,300,800	3.75	5.50	11.00	40.00	115.00	500.00	
1912S 1,370,000	3.75	5.50	11.00	40.00	115.00	500.00	
1913 . . . (627) 188,627	15.00	20.00	35.00	70.00	175.00	725.00	750.00
1913D 534,000	4.50	7.00	13.00	45.00	150.00	550.00	
1913S 604,000	4.50	7.00	13.00	45.00	120.00	575.00	
1914 . . . (380) 124,610	22.50	31.00	50.00	100.00	200.00	850.00	900.00
1914S 992,000	3.75	5.50	12.50	40.00	115.00	525.00	
1915 . . . (450) 138,450	17.50	24.00	45.00	90.00	175.00	750.00	850.00
1915D 1,170,400	3.75	5.50	11.00	40.00	115.00	500.00	
1915S 1,604,000	3.75	5.50	11.00	40.00	115.00	500.00	

LIBERTY WALKING TYPE 1916-1947

This type was designed by A. A. Weinman. The designer's monogram AW appears under the tip of the wing feathers. On the 1916 coins and some of the 1917 coins the mint mark is located on the obverse below the motto.

G-4 GOOD—*Rims are defined. Motto IN GOD WE TRUST readable.*

VG-8 VERY GOOD—*Motto is distinct. About half of skirt lines at left are clear.*

F-12 FINE—*All skirt lines evident, but worn in spots. Details in sandal below motto are clear.*

VF-20 VERY FINE—*Skirt lines sharp including leg area. Little wear on breast and right arm.*

EF-40 EXTREMELY FINE—*All skirt lines bold.*

MS-60 UNCIRCULATED—*No trace of wear. Light blemishes.*

Designer Adolph A. Weinman; weight 12.50 grams; composition: .900 silver, .100 copper; diameter 30.6 mm; reeded edge; mints: Philadelphia, Denver, San Francisco. Net weight: .36169 oz. pure silver.

HALF DOLLARS

Choice uncirculated, well struck specimens are worth 25-50% above values listed.

	Quan. Minted	G-4	VG-8	F-12	VF-20	EF-40	MS-60	Proof
1916	608,000	$12.00	$20.00	$35.00	$50.00	$85.00	$300.00	
1916D (Obv.)	1,014,400	7.50	11.00	18.50	35.00	60.00	260.00	
1916S (Obv.)	508,000	24.00	35.00	67.50	110.00	200.00	450.00	
1917	12,292,000	2.50	3.25	4.25	9.00	17.50	100.00	
1917D (Obv.)	765,400	6.50	9.00	20.00	50.00	90.00	350.00	
1917D. (Rev.)	1,940,000	3.50	4.50	10.50	27.50	70.00	400.00	
1917S (Obv.)	952,000	7.50	11.00	27.50	67.50	150.00	750.00	
1917S . (Rev.)	5,554,000	2.50	3.25	5.00	13.50	30.00	325.00	
1918	6,634,000	2.50	3.25	5.00	16.00	42.00	300.00	
1918D.......	3,853,040	3.00	4.00	7.50	25.00	65.00	500.00	
1918S.....	10,282,000	2.50	3.50	4.50	14.50	40.00	325.00	
1919	962,000	5.00	8.00	19.00	65.00	200.00	1,000	
1919D.......	1,165,000	4.75	6.75	20.00	80.00	225.00	1,500	
1919S.......	1,552,000	4.50	6.00	12.00	62.50	210.00	2,000	
1920	6,372,000	2.50	3.50	5.00	13.00	37.50	300.00	
1920D.......	1,551,000	3.50	5.50	11.00	55.00	130.00	1,200	
1920S........	4,624,000	3.00	4.00	7.00	27.00	70.00	1,200	
1921	246,000	38.00	50.00	85.00	195.00	400.00	1,850	
1921D........	208,000	65.00	85.00	125.00	200.00	475.00	2,000	
1921S........	548,000	10.00	20.00	35.00	120.00	700.00	6,000	
1923S.......	2,178,000	2.50	3.50	6.00	35.00	100.00	900.00	
1927S.......	2,392,000	2.50	3.50	5.00	14.50	50.00	600.00	
1928S†	1,940,000	2.50	3.50	5.00	14.50	55.00	750.00	
1929D.......	1,001,200	3.50	4.25	5.00	11.00	40.00	300.00	
1929S.......	1,902,000	2.75	3.50	4.50	7.50	30.00	325.00	
1933S........	1,786,000		3.25	4.25	11.00	35.00	500.00	
1934	6,964,000		3.00	3.50	4.00	7.75	40.00	
1934D†	2,361,400		3.00	3.50	5.50	19.00	275.00	
1934S.......	3,652,000		3.00	3.50	6.50	25.00	525.00	
1935	9,162,000		3.00	3.50	4.00	6.00	32.50	
1935D.......	3,003,800		3.00	3.50	5.50	17.50	250.00	
1935S........	3,854,000		3.00	3.50	6.50	21.00	325.00	
1936 . (3,901)	12,617,901		2.75	3.25	4.00	7.00	30.00	$525.00
1936D.......	4,252,400		2.75	3.25	4.75	10.00	125.00	
1936S.......	3,884,000		2.75	3.25	6.50	19.50	250.00	
1937 . (5,728)	9,527,728		2.75	3.25	4.25	6.25	32.50	250.00
1937D.......	1,676,000		2.75	3.75	8.00	22.50	250.00	
1937S........	2,090,000		2.75	3.25	5.00	16.00	225.00	
1938 . (8,152)	4,118,152		2.75	3.25	5.00	12.00	70.00	170.00
1938D........	491,600	24.00	27.00	30.00	35.00	70.00	375.00	
1939 . (8,808)	6,820,808		2.75	3.25	4.00	6.00	45.00	160.00
1939D.......	4,267,800		2.75	3.25	4.00	6.00	47.00	
1939S........	2,552,000		3.00	3.50	6.00	12.00	90.00	

†Large and small mint mark varieties, see page 59. Pieces dated 1928D are counterfeit.

HALF DOLLARS

	Quan. Minted	F-12	VF-20	EF-40	MS-60	Proof
1940 .... (11,279)	9,167,279	$3.00	$3.75	$5.00	$27.50	$145.00
1940S................	4,550,000	3.00	3.75	5.50	45.00	
1941* .... (15,412)	24,207,412	3.00	3.75	4.75	20.00	145.00
1941D................	11,248,400	3.00	3.75	5.00	35.00	
1941S................	8,098,000	3.00	5.00	8.00	87.50	
1942 .... (21,120)	47,839,120	3.00	3.75	5.00	20.00	145.00
1942D................	10,973,800	2.75	4.00	5.75	27.50	
1942S†...............	12,708,000	3.00	4.00	6.00	52.50	
1943.................	53,190,000	....	3.25	4.50	19.00	
1943D................	11,346,000	....	3.25	5.00	37.50	
1943S................	13,450,000	....	3.25	5.00	30.00	
1944.................	28,206,000	....	3.25	4.50	19.00	
1944D................	9,769,000	....	3.25	4.75	25.00	
1944S................	8,904,000	....	3.25	4.75	30.00	
1945.................	31,502,000	....	3.25	4.50	19.00	
1945D................	9,966,800	....	3.25	4.75	25.00	
1945S................	10,156,000	....	3.25	4.75	25.00	
1946	12,118,000	....	3.25	4.50	22.50	
1946D................	2,151,000	....	3.50	5.75	26.00	
1946S................	3,724,000	....	3.50	4.50	32.00	
1947	4,094,000	....	3.50	4.50	25.00	
1947D................	3,900,600	....	3.75	5.00	25.00	

*Proofs struck with or without designer's initials.
†Large and small mint mark varieties, see page 59.

FRANKLIN-LIBERTY BELL TYPE 1948-1963

The Benjamin Franklin half dollar and the Roosevelt dime were both designed by John R. Sinnock. His initials appear below the shoulder. The Liberty Bell is similar to that used by Sinnock on the 1926 Sesquicentennial commemorative half dollar modeled from a sketch by John Frederick Lewis.

VF-20 VERY FINE—*At least half of the lower and upper incused lines on the rim of the bell must show.*

EF-40 EXTREMELY FINE—*Wear spots appear at top of end curls and hair back of ears. On reverse, Liberty Bell will show wear at top.*

MS-60 UNCIRCULATED—*No trace of wear. Light blemishes.*

MS-65 CHOICE UNCIRCULATED—*No trace of wear. Barely noticeable blemishes.*

Mint mark location.

Choice, well struck uncirculated halves command higher prices.

1948	3,006,814	3.25	5.00	6.00	12.00	
1948D.................	4,028,600	3.00	3.25	5.00	10.00	
1949	5,614,000	3.00	3.25	7.00	36.50	
1949D.................	4,120,600	3.00	3.25	8.00	30.00	
1949S.................	3,744,000	3.00	3.25	9.50	50.00	
1950 .... (51,386)	7,793,509	3.00	3.25	8.00	23.00	95.00
1950D.................	8,031,600	3.00	3.25	6.00	20.00	
1951 .... (57,500)	16,859,602		3.00	5.00	15.00	70.00
1951D.................	9,475,200		3.25	8.00	24.00	
1951S.................	13,696,000		3.00	6.00	17.50	

HALF DOLLARS

	Quan. Minted	F-12	VF-20	EF-40	MS-65	Proof
1952 .... (81,980)	21,274,073		$3.00	$4.00	$11.00	$40.00
1952D.................	25,395,600		3.00	3.50	6.00	
1952S.................	5,526,000		3.00	7.25	24.00	
1953 ...... (128,800)	2,796,920	$3.25	5.00	7.00	17.50	30.00
1953D.................	20,900,400		3.00	3.50	6.00	
1953S.................	4,148,000		3.00	4.00	10.00	
1954 ...... (233,300)	13,421,503		3.00	3.25	4.50	14.00
1954D.................	25,445,580		3.00	3.25	4.50	
1954S.................	4,993,400		3.00	3.75	5.00	
1955 ...... (378,200)	2,876,381	5.25	7.50	8.00	10.00	18.00
1956 ...... (669,384)	4,701,384		3.00	3.50	4.75	7.00
1957 ... (1,247,952)	6,361,952		3.00	3.25	4.25	5.00
1957D.................	19,966,850		3.00	3.25	4.00	
1958 ...... (875,652)	4,917,652		3.00	3.25	4.25	7.00
1958D.................	23,962,412	....		3.00	4.00	
1959 ... (1,149,291)	7,349,291	....		3.00	3.75	5.00
1959D.................	13,053,750	....		3.00	3.75	
1960 ..... (1,691,602)	7,715,602	....		3.00	3.75	3.75
1960D.................	18,215,812	....		3.00	3.75	
1961 ..... (3,028,244)	11,318,244	....		3.00	3.75	3.75
1961D.................	20,276,442	....		3.00	3.75	
1962 ...... (3,218,019)	12,932,019	....		3.00	3.75	3.75
1962D.................	35,473,281	....		3.00	3.75	
1963 ...... (3,075,645)	25,239,645	....		3.00	3.50	3.75
1963D.................	67,069,292	....		3.00	3.50	

KENNEDY TYPE 1964 to Date

Gilroy Roberts, former Chief Engraver of the Mint, designed the obverse of this coin. His stylized initials are on the truncation of the forceful bust of President John F. Kennedy. The reverse, which uses the presidential coat of arms for the motif, is the work of Chief Engraver Frank Gasparro.

Designers Gilroy Roberts and Frank Gasparro. 1964: Standards same as previous issue; 1965-1970: weight 11.50 grams; composition: outer layers of .800 silver, .200 copper bonded to inner core of .210 silver, .790 copper; 1971: weight 11.34 grams; composition: outer layers of copper nickel (.750 copper, .250 nickel) bonded to inner core of pure copper; diameter 30.6 mm; reeded edge. Net weight: 1964 .36169 oz. pure silver. 1965-1970 .14792 oz. pure silver.

Silver Coinage 1964

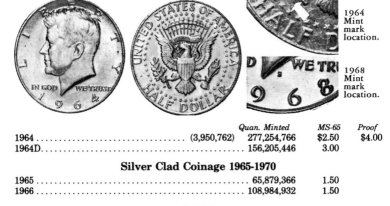

1964 Mint mark location.

1968 Mint mark location.

	Quan. Minted	MS-65	Proof
1964 .... (3,950,762)	277,254,766	$2.50	$4.00
1964D...	156,205,446	3.00	

Silver Clad Coinage 1965-1970

1965	65,879,366	1.50	
1966	108,984,932	1.50	

[144]

HALF DOLLARS

	Quan. Minted	MS-65	Proof
1967	295,046,978	$1.50	
1968D	246,951,930	1.50	
1968S Proof	(3,041,506)		$3.50
1969D	129,881,800	1.50	
1969S Proof	(2,934,631)		3.00
1970D	2,150,000	20.00	
1970S Proof	(2,632,810)		7.00

Copper-Nickel Clad Coinage — Modified Design 1971-

	Quan. Minted	MS-65	Proof
1971	155,164,000	1.00	
1971D	302,097,424	1.00	
1971S Proof	(3,220,733)		3.00
1972	153,180,000	1.00	
1972D	141,890,000	1.00	
1972S Proof	(3,260,996)		2.70
1973	64,964,000	1.00	
1973D	83,171,400	1.00	
1973S Proof	(2,760,339)		5.00
1974	201,596,000	1.00	
1974D	79,066,300	1.00	
1974S Proof	(2,612,568)		4.50
1977	43,598,000	1.00	
1977D	31,449,106	1.00	
1977S Proof	(3,251,152)		4.00
1978		1.00	
1978D		1.00	
1978S Proof			4.00

BICENTENNIAL COINAGE DATED 1776—1976

In an open contest for the selection of suitable designs for the special Bicentennial reverses of the quarter, half dollar and dollar, Seth G. Huntington's winning entry was featured on the half dollar. It shows Independence Hall in Philadelphia as the center device. The obverse was unchanged except for the dual dating 1776-1976. They were struck during 1975 and 1976 for general circulation as well as being included in proof and uncirculated sets.

Designers Gilroy Roberts and Seth Huntington. Silver clad: weight 11.50 grams; composition: outer layers of .800 silver, .200 copper bonded to inner core of .210 silver, .790 copper; copper-nickel clad: weight 11.34 grams; composition: outer layers of copper nickel (.750 copper, .250 nickel) bonded to inner core of pure copper; diameter 30.6 mm; reeded edge. Net weight: silver clad coinage .14792 oz. pure silver.

	Quan. Minted	MS-65	Proof
1976 Copper-nickel clad	234,308,000	1.00	
1976D Copper-nickel clad	287,565,248	1.00	
1976S Copper-nickel clad	(7,059,099)		3.00
1976S Silver clad	4,239,722	3.00	
1976S Silver clad	(3,295,714)		5.00

SILVER DOLLARS — 1794 to Date

The silver dollar was authorized by Congress April 2, 1792. Weight and fineness were specified at 416 grains and 892.4 fine. The first issues appeared in 1794 and until 1804 all silver dollars had the value stamped on the edge: HUNDRED CENTS, ONE DOLLAR OR UNIT. After a lapse in coinage of the silver dollar during the period 1804 to 1839, these coins had reeded edges and the value was placed on the reverse side.

The weight was changed by the law of January 18, 1837 to 412½ grains, fineness .900. The coinage was discontinued by the act of February 12, 1873 and reauthorized by the Act of February 28, 1878. The dollar was again discontinued after 1935 and since then only the copper-nickel pieces first authorized in 1971 have been coined for circulation.

ORIGIN OF THE DOLLAR

The word Dollar evolves from German Taler, the name given to the first large-sized European silver coin. Designed as a substitute for the gold Florin, the coin originated in the Tyrol in 1484. So popular did these large silver coins become during the 16th century that many other countries struck similar pieces, giving them names derived from taler. In the Netherlands the coin was called Rijksdaalder, in Denmark Rigsdaler, in Italy Tallero, in Poland Talar, in France Jocandale, in Russia Jefimok. All these names are abbreviations of "Joachimsthaler." Until the discovery of the great silver deposits in Mexican and South American mines, the mint with the greatest output of large silver coins was that of Joachimsthal in the Bohemian Erzgebirge.

The Spanish Dollar, or piece-of-eight, was widely used and familiar to everyone in the English-American colonies. It was only natural therefore that the word "dollar" was adopted officially as the standard monetary unit of the United States by Congress on July 6, 1785. The Continental dollar of 1776 is described on page 30.

FLOWING HAIR TYPE 1794-1795

AG-3 ABOUT GOOD—*Clear enough to identify.*
G-4 GOOD—*Date and letters readable. Main devices outlined, but lack details.*
VG-8 VERY GOOD—*Major details discernible. Letters well formed but worn.*
F-12 FINE—*Hair ends distinguishable. Top hairlines show, but otherwise worn smooth.*
VF-20 VERY FINE—*Hair in center shows some detail. Other details more bold.*
EF-40 EXTREMELY FINE—*Hair well defined but will show some wear.*
MS-60 UNCIRCULATED—*No trace of wear. Light blemishes.*

Designer Robert Scot; weight 26.96 grams; composition: .8924 silver, .1076 copper; approx. diameter 39-40 mm; edge: HUNDRED CENTS ONE DOLLAR OR UNIT with decorations between words.

	Quan. Minted	AG-3	G-4	VG-8	F-12	VF-20	EF-40	MS-60
1794	1,758	$1,600	$3,000	$4,400	$7,250	$12,250	$21,500	——

SILVER DOLLARS

Varieties listed are those most significant to collectors, but numerous minor variations may be found because each of the early dies was individually made. Values of variations not listed in this guide depend on collector interest and demand.

1795

Two Leaves Beneath
Each Wing (11 Varieties)

Three Leaves Beneath
Each Wing

	Quan. Minted	AG-3	G-4	VG-8	F-12	VF-20	EF-40	MS-60
1795 Two leaves...	} 160,295	$190.00	$365.00	$465.00	$600.00	$900.00	$1,750	$16,000
1795 Three leaves..		190.00	365.00	465.00	600.00	900.00	1,750	16,000

DRAPED BUST TYPE, SMALL EAGLE REVERSE 1795-1798

AG-3 ABOUT GOOD—*Clear enough to identify.*
G-4 GOOD—*Bust outlined, no detail. Date readable, some leaves evident.*
VG-8 VERY GOOD—*Drapery worn except deepest folds. Hairlines smooth.*
F-12 FINE—*All drapery lines distinguishable. Hairlines near cheek and neck show some detail.*
VF-20 VERY FINE—*Left side of drapery worn smooth.*
EF-40 EXTREMELY FINE—*Drapery shows distinctly. Hair well outlined and detailed.*
MS-60 UNCIRCULATED—*No trace of wear. Light blemishes.*

1795 (2 varieties)	42,738	175.00	340.00	425.00	550.00	800.00	1,500	15,000

[147]

SILVER DOLLARS

Small Date

Large Date

Small Letters

Large Letters

	Quan. Minted	AG-3	G-4	VG-8	F-12	VF-20	EF-40	MS-60
1796 Sm. date, sm. let. (3 vars.)								
All kinds	72,920	$170.00	$275.00	$350.00	$500.00	$725.00	$1,300	$11,000
1796 Sm. date lg. let		170.00	275.00	350.00	500.00	725.00	1,300	
1796 Lg. date sm. let		170.00	275.00	350.00	500.00	725.00	1,300	11,000
1797 9 stars left, 7 right								
Sm. let. All kinds	7,776	275.00	400.00	550.00	775.00	1,600	——	——
1797 9 stars 1., 7 r., lg. let		175.00	285.00	375.00	525.00	735.00	1,350	11,000
1797 10 stars left, 6 right		175.00	285.00	375.00	525.00	735.00	1,350	11,000
1798 15 stars on obverse		175.00	285.00	375.00	550.00	750.00	1,400	12,000
All kinds	327,536							
1798 13 stars on obverse		175,00	285.00	375.00	525.00	735.00	1,350	11,500

HERALDIC EAGLE REVERSE 1798-1804

G-4 GOOD—*Letters and date readable. E PLURIBUS UNUM obliterated.*

VG-8 VERY GOOD—*Motto partially readable. Only deepest drapery details visible. All other lines smooth.*

F-12 FINE—*All drapery lines distinguishable. Hairlines near cheek and neck show some detail.*

VF-20 VERY FINE—*Left side of drapery worn smooth.*

EF-40 EXTREMELY FINE—*Drapery is distinct. Hair well detailed.*

MS-60 UNCIRCULATED—*No trace of wear. Light blemishes.*

	Quan. Minted	G-4	VG-8	F-12	VF-20	EF-40	MS-60
1798 Large heraldic eagle, knob 9		235.00	300.00	425.00	550.00	850.00	6,250
1798 Lg. eagle, 10 arrows		230.00	290.00	415.00	535.00	800.00	6,000
1798 Close date		230.00	290.00	415.00	535.00	800.00	6,000
1798 Wide date, 13 arrows (11 var.)		230.00	290.00	415.00	535.00	800.00	6,000

1799 over 98, Stars 7 and 6

Stars 8 and 5

[148]

SILVER DOLLARS

	Quan. Minted	G-4	VG-8	F-12	VF-20	EF-40	MS-60
1799 9 over 8 rev. with 15 stars							
All kinds............ 423,515		$230.00	$290.00	$415.00	$525.00	$800.00	$6,000
1799 9 over 8 rev. with 13 stars...		230.00	290.00	415.00	525.00	800.00	6,000
1799 Irregular date, 15-star rev.		230.00	290.00	415.00	525.00	800.00	6,000
1799 Irregular date, 13-star rev. ...		230.00	290.00	415.00	525.00	800.00	6,000
1799 Normal date................		230.00	290.00	415.00	525.00	800.00	6,000
1799 Stars - 8 left, 5 right		230.00	290.00	415.00	525.00	800.00	6,000
1800 All kinds............ 220,920		230.00	290.00	415.00	525.00	800.00	6,000
1800 Very wide date, low 8.......		230.00	290.00	415.00	525.00	800.00	6,000
1800 "Dotted date" from die breaks		230.00	290.00	415.00	525.00	800.00	6,000
1800 Only 12 arrows.............		230.00	290.00	415.00	525.00	800.00	6,000
1800 Only 10 arrows.............		230.00	290.00	415.00	525.00	800.00	6,000
1800 AMERICAI (2 varieties).......		230.00	290.00	415.00	525.00	800.00	6,000
1801 (4 varieties) 54,454		230.00	290.00	415.00	525.00	800.00	6,000
1801 Proof restrike (rev. struck							
from first die of 1804 dollar) .						(Proof)	——

1802 over 1

		G-4	VG-8	F-12	VF-20	EF-40	MS-60
1802 2 over 1, narrow date ..		230	290	415	525	800	6,000
1802 2 over 1, wide date	41,650	230	290	415	525	800	6,000
1802 Narrow normal date ...		230	290	415	525	800	6,000
1802 Wide normal date......		230	290	415	525	800	6,000
1802 Proof restrike						(Proof)	——

Small 3

Large 3

		G-4	VG-8	F-12	VF-20	EF-40	MS-60
1803 Large 3 (1 variety).....	85,634	230	290	415	525	800	6,000
1803 Small 3 (5 varieties)....		230	290	415	525	800	6,000
1803 Proof restrike						(Proof)	——

THE 1804 DOLLAR

This piece is one of the most publicized rarities in the United States series. There are specimens known as originals (class 1), of which eight are known, and restrikes (class 2), of which seven are known.

Numismatists have found that the 1804 "original" dollars were struck at the mint between 1834 and 1835, for use in presentation proof sets. The first known specimen, a proof, was obtained from a mint officer by Mr. Stickney on May 9, 1843, in exchange for an "Immune Columbia" piece in gold. Later, in 1859, the pieces known as restrikes were made at the mint to supply the needs of collectors who wanted specimens of these dollars.

Evidence that these pieces were struck during the later period is based on the fact that the 1804 dollars differ from issues of 1803 or earlier and conform more closely to those struck after 1836, their edges or borders having beaded segments and raised rim, not elongated denticles such as are found on the earlier dates.

SILVER DOLLARS

Although the mint records state that 19,570 dollars were coined in 1804, in no place does it mention that they were dated 1804. It was the practice in those days to use old dies as long as they were serviceable with no regard in the annual reports for the dating of the coins. It is probable that the 1804 total for dollars actually covered coins that were dated 1803.

CLASS 1

Note position of words STATES OF with relation to clouds

1804 Class 1, Original (Appleton specimen sold for $150,000 in 1974.)

CLASS 2

Compare with Class 1 above

1804 Class 2, Restrike (Idler specimen offered for $225,000 in 1974.)

BIBLIOGRAPHY

Bolender, M. H. *The United States Early Silver Dollars from 1794 to 1803.* Freeport, Ill., 1950.
Newman, Eric P. and Bressett, Kenneth E. *The Fantastic 1804 Dollar.* Racine, Wis., 1962.
Haseltine, J. W. *Type Table of United States Dollars, Half Dollars and Quarter Dollars.* Philadelphia, 1881 (reprinted 1927, 1968).

GOBRECHT DOLLARS

Christian Gobrecht was born December 23, 1785. He went to Philadelphia in 1811 and became an engraver of bank notes, seals, calico printers' rolls, bookbinders' dies, etc. He was appointed assistant to Mint Engraver William Kneass in 1836. According to Edgar H. Adams, he prepared a series of dies

SILVER DOLLARS

for dollars, after designs by Sully, exquisite in design and character. The first pattern shows the familiar seated figure of Liberty on the obverse. The name C. Gobrecht F. (F. = Fecit = made it) was placed just under the figure of Liberty and over the date. In the field on the reverse was a large eagle in full flight surrounded by twenty-six stars and the legend UNITED STATES OF AMERICA ONE DOLLAR.

In response to criticism Gobrecht removed his name from the die after a few specimens had been struck, some in silver and some in copper.

Director Patterson ordered the name replaced, this time on the base. Patterns were also made in 1836 with the stars omitted from the reverse.

In 1838 the engraver's name was omitted altogether from the design and thirteen stars were placed around the seated figure of Liberty on the obverse. Stars were omitted from the reverse on one pattern and retained on another. Similar pieces were struck in 1839.

		Proof
1836 C. GOBRECHT F. in field between base and date. Rev. Eagle flying left amid stars. Plain edge (Rare.) (18)........................		——
1836 Obv. as above. Rev. Eagle flying in plain field. Plain edge (Ex. rare.) (5)...		——

	VG-20	EF-40	Proof
1836 C. GOBRECHT on base. Rev. Eagle flying left in field containing stars. Plain edge. Although scarce, this is the most common variety. (1,000)...............................	$1,300	$1,900	$4,350
1836 As above, reeded edge (Ex. rare.) (3)			——

SILVER DOLLARS

Proof

1838 As above, reeded edge. Generally considered to be very rare.
25 Struck. Also unknown quantity of restrikes...................... $6,000
1838 Obv. as above. Rev. Eagle in plain field. Plain edge.
(Ex. rare.) (3)... ——
1838 Seated Liberty. Obv. Name of designer is left off and stars added
around obverse border. Rev. Eagle flying left surrounded by
stars. Plain edge. (Ex. rare.) (3) .... ——
1839 Obv. same as 1838. Rev. Eagle in plain field. Plain edge.
(Ex. rare.) (3)... ——
1839 Obv. as above. Rev. Eagle amid stars. Plain edge.
(Ex. rare.) (3)... ——
1839 Obv. as above. Rev. Eagle in plain field. Reeded edge.
Most common 1839 variety. (Rare) (300)......................... 5,000

Quantities shown for the above pieces are probably inaccurate as restrikes of many are known to have been made.

LIBERTY SEATED TYPE — REGULAR ISSUES 1840-1873

When in 1840 silver dollars were again issued for general circulation, the seated figure of Liberty device was adopted for the obverse. For some mysterious reason the flying eagle design was rejected, and the more familiar form with olive branch and arrows was used.

Designer Christian Gobrecht; weight 26.73 grams; composition: .900 silver, .100 copper; diameter 38.1 mm; reeded edge; mints: Philadelphia, New Orleans, Carson City, San Francisco. Net weight: .77344 oz. pure silver.

Mint mark location is on the reverse below eagle.

VG-8 VERY GOOD—*Any 3 letters of LIBERTY at least two-thirds complete.*
F-12 FINE—*All 7 letters of LIBERTY visible though weak.*
VF-20 VERY FINE—*LIBERTY is strong but its ribbon shows slight wear.*
EF-40 EXTREMELY FINE—*Horizontal lines of shield complete. Eagle's eye plain.*
MS-60 UNCIRCULATED—*No trace of wear. Light marks or blemishes.*

[152]

SILVER DOLLARS

	Quan. Minted	VG-8	F-12	VF-20	EF-40	MS-60	Proof
1840	61,005	$90.00	$100.00	$135.00	$240.00	$1,000	$2,850
1841	173,000	75.00	85.00	100.00	150.00	800.00	2,750
1842	184,618	75.00	85.00	100.00	150.00	800.00	2,750
1843	165,100	75.00	85.00	100.00	150.00	800.00	2,750
1844	20,000	125.00	150.00	175.00	300.00	1,100	3,000
1845	24,500	125.00	150.00	175.00	300.00	1,000	3,000
1846	110,600	75.00	85.00	100.00	150.00	800.00	2,750
1846O	59,000	125.00	150.00	200.00	300.00	1,250	
1847	140,750	75.00	85.00	100.00	150.00	900.00	2,750
1848	15,000	110.00	135.00	175.00	275.00	1,100	2,950
1849	62,600	85.00	100.00	120.00	200.00	900.00	2,750
1850	7,500	125.00	150.00	200.00	350.00	1,400	3,400
1850O	40,000	90.00	100.00	150.00	325.00	1,350	
1851 Original, high date	1,300	875.00	1,075	1,600	2,700	6,500	5,100
1851 Restrike, date centered							4,600
1852 Original	1,100					4,800	
1852 Restrike							4,250
1853	46,110	90.00	110.00	135.00	200.00	1,000	4,000
1854	33,140	100.00	140.00	180.00	325.00	1,150	3,700
1855	26,000	120.00	150.00	200.00	400.00	1,400	5,300
1856	63,500	95.00	125.00	150.00	275.00	950.00	4,000
1857	94,000	90.00	115.00	140.00	250.00	900.00	2,800
1858 . . . . . Estimated (80)							3,500
1859	256,500	75.00	90.00	110.00	150.00	650.00	1,450
1859O	360,000	75.00	90.00	110.00	135.00	800.00	
1859S	20,000	100.00	125.00	160.00	300.00	1,100	
1860 . . (1,330)	218,930	75.00	85.00	100.00	150.00	650.00	1,350
1860O	515,000	75.00	85.00	100.00	130.00	650.00	
1861 . . (1,000)	78,500	85.00	100.00	125.00	180.00	800.00	1,300
1862 . . . . (550)	12,090	115.00	135.00	165.00	300.00	850.00	1,200
1863 . . . . (460)	27,660	95.00	110.00	135.00	275.00	900.00	1,350
1864 . . . . (470)	31,170	85.00	100.00	125.00	275.00	800.00	1,350
1865 . . . . (500)	47,000	85.00	100.00	125.00	250.00	800.00	1,350
1866 Transitional piece (2 known — see quarter on page 119)							——

Motto "In God We Trust" Added to Reverse

1866 . . . . (725)	49,625	85.00	100.00	125.00	225.00	825.00	1,350
1867 . . . . (625)	47,525	85.00	100.00	125.00	225.00	825.00	1,350
1868 . . . . (600)	162,700	75.00	90.00	110.00	175.00	725.00	1,350

SILVER DOLLARS

	Quan. Minted	VG-8	F-12	VF-20	EF-40	MS-60	Proof
1869 .... (600)	424,300	$75.00	$90.00	$110.00	$140.00	$725.00	$1,350
1870 .. (1,000)	416,000	75.00	90.00	110.00	140.00	725.00	1,350
1870CC	12,462	110.00	135.00	180.00	350.00	1,450	
1870S		Gilhousen Sale 1973				E.F.	$62,500
1871 .... (960)	1,074,760	75.00	90.00	100.00	140.00	750.00	1,350
1871CC	1,376	550.00	700.00	1,000	1,400	6,000	
1872 .... (950)	1,106,450	75.00	90.00	100.00	140.00	750.00	1,350
1872CC	3,150	225.00	350.00	500.00	675.00	3,400	
1872S	9,000	120.00	150.00	225.00	400.00	1,200	
1873 .... (600)	293,600	75.00	90.00	100.00	140.00	725.00	1,350
1873CC	2,300	575.00	825.00	1,200	1,800	9,000	
1873S	700	....			Unknown in any collection.		

LIBERTY HEAD OR MORGAN TYPE 1878-1921

The mint law of 1873 made no provision for the standard silver dollar. During the lapse in coinage of this piece the gold dollar became the unit coin and the trade dollar was used for our commercial transactions with the Orient.

The legal tender character was restored to the silver dollar by the Act of February 28, 1878 known as the Bland-Allison Act. The weight, 412½ grains and fineness .900 were to conform with the act of January 18, 1837.

George T. Morgan, formerly a pupil of Wyon in the Royal Mint in London, designed the new dollar. His initial M is found at the truncation of the neck, at the last tress. It also appears on the reverse on the left-hand loop of the ribbon.

Coinage of the silver dollar was suspended after 1904 when the bullion supply became exhausted. Under provisions of the Pittman Act of 1918, 270,232,722 silver dollars were melted and later, in 1921, coinage of the silver dollar was resumed. The Morgan design, with some slight refinements, was employed until the new Peace design was adopted later in that year.

Varieties listed are those most significant to collectors, but numerous other variations may be found. Values of variations not listed in this guide depend on collector interest and demand.

VF-20 VERY FINE—*Two-thirds of hairlines from top of forehead to ear must show. Ear well defined. Feathers on eagle's breast worn.*

EF-40 EXTREMELY FINE—*All hairlines strong and ear bold. Eagle's feathers all plain but slight wear on breast and wing tips.*

AU-50 ABOUT UNCIRCULATED—*Slight trace of wear. Most of mint luster is present although marred by bag marks.*

MS-60 UNCIRCULATED—*No trace of wear. Has full mint luster but may be noticeably marred by skuff marks or bag abrasions.*

First Reverse

8 Tail Feathers, 1878 Philadelphia Only

Mint mark location on reverse below the wreath.

SILVER DOLLARS

Most uncirculated silver dollars have scratches or nicks because of handling of mint bags. Choice coins with few blemishes are worth considerably more than listed values.

Sharply struck, or "proof-like" coins are very scarce and command substantial premiums.

Second Reverse

Parallel top arrow feather, concave breast.

Third Reverse

Slanted top arrow feather, convex breast.

Designer George T. Morgan. Standards same as previous issue. Additional mint: Denver. Net weight: .77344 oz. pure silver.

	Quan. Minted	VF-20	EF-40	AU-50	MS-60	Proof
1878, 8 tail feathers. (700)	750,000	$9.00	$11.00	$15.00	$32.00	$800.00
1878, 7 tail feathers. (300)	9,759,550					
1878, 7 feathers, 2nd reverse		8.00	9.00	12.50	25.00	2,000
1878, 7 feathers, 3rd reverse........		8.00	9.00	12.50	30.00	——
1878, 7 over 8 feathers.............		14.00	18.00	20.00	50.00	
1878CC	2,212,000	12.00	16.00	17.50	38.00	
1878S.....................	9,774,000	7.00	8.50	10.00	15.00	
1879 .... (1,100)	14,807,100	7.00	8.50	10.00	16.00	625.00
1879CC††	756,000	47.50	125.00	300.00	900.00	
1879O....................	2,887,000	7.00	8.75	11.00	27.50	
1879S second reverse ...	9,110,000	9.00	12.00	15.00	37.50	
1879S third reverse		7.00	8.50	10.00	14.00	
1880, 8 over 7*	12,601,355	110.00	200.00	250.00	——	
1880 .... (1,355)		7.00	8.50	10.00	16.00	625.00

1880CC, 80 over 79†

1880CC, 8 over high 7*

1880CC, 8 over low 7

	Quan. Minted	VF-20	EF-40	AU-50	MS-60	Proof
1880CC, 80 over 79, 2nd rev.†..........		70.00	80.00	90.00	160.00	
1880CC, 8 over 7, 2nd rev...........		35.00	50.00	65.00	110.00	
1880CC, 8 over high 7, 3rd rev.*	591,000	35.00	50.00	65.00	120.00	
1880CC, 8 over low 7, 3rd. rev............					150.00	
1880CC third reverse		35.00	50.00	60.00	95.00	
1880O, 8 over 7*	5,305,000	25.00	40.00	55.00	100.00	
1880O....................		7.00	8.75	11.00	40.00	
1880S, 8 over 7*	8,900,000				50.00	
1880S, 0 over 9		7.00	8.50	11.00	30.00	
1880S....................		7.00	8.50	10.00	12.50	
1881 .... (975)	9,163,975	7.00	8.50	10.00	16.00	625.00
1881CC	296,000	60.00	70.00	80.00	95.00	
1881O.	5,708,000	7.00	8.50	10.00	13.00	

*Several die varieties. Values shown are for the most common.
†7 and 9 show within the 80, no tip below second 8.
††One variety shows mint mark broken or irregular at top.

SILVER DOLLARS

	Quan. Minted	VF-20	EF-40	AU-50	MS-60	Proof
1881S	12,760,000	$7.00	$8.00	$9.00	$12.50	
1882	(1,100) 11,101,100	7.00	8.00	9.00	15.00	$625.00
1882CC	1,133,000	16.00	19.00	22.00	32.00	
1882O	} 6,090,000	7.00	8.00	9.00	13.50	
1882O, O over S*		9.00	13.00	18.00	27.50	
1882S	9,250,000	7.00	8.00	9.00	13.50	
1883	(1,039) 12,291,039	7.00	8.00	9.00	14.00	625.00
1883CC	1,204,000	16.00	19.00	22.00	32.00	
1883O	8,725,000	7.00	8.00	9.00	12.00	
1883S	6,250,000	10.00	22.00	80.00	400.00	
1884	(875) 14,070,875	7.00	8.00	9.00	15.00	625.00
1884CC	1,136,000	17.00	20.00	24.00	32.00	
1884O	9,730,000	7.00	8.00	9.00	12.00	
1884S	3,200,000	12.00	24.00	100.00	1,250	
1885	(930) 17,787,767	7.00	8.00	9.00	12.50	625.00
1885CC	228,000	55.00	65.00	75.00	95.00	
1885O	9,185,000	7.00	8.00	9.00	12.00	
1885S	1,497,000	11.00	17.50	23.00	85.00	
1886	(886) 19,963,886	7.00	8.00	9.00	12.00	625.00
1886O	10,710,000	9.00	15.00	25.00	250.00	
1886S	750.000	20.00	29.00	40.00	175.00	
1887, 7 over 6	} (710) 20,290,710	50.00	75.00	100.00	200.00	
1887		7.00	8.00	9.00	12.00	625.00
1887O, 7 over 6	} 11,550,000	50.00	75.00	100.00	200.00	
1887O		7.00	8.00	10.00	30.00	
1887S	1,771,000	12.00	15.00	20.00	60.00	
1888	(832) 19,183,333	7.00	8.00	9.00	15.00	625.00
1888O	12,150,000	7.00	8.00	9.00	16.00	
1888S	657,000	25.00	30.00	40.00	150.00	
1889	(811) 21,726,811	7.00	8.00	9.00	15.00	625.00
1889CC	350,000	165.00	390.00	900.00	3,500	
1889O	11,875,000	7.50	10.00	15.00	100.00	
1889S	700,000	22.50	27.50	35.00	120.00	
1890	(590) 16,802,590	7.00	8.00	9.00	17.00	650.00
1890CC	2,309,041	15.00	25.00	35.00	110.00	
1890O	10,701,000	7.00	8.50	15.00	55.00	
1890S	8,230,373	7.50	9.00	12.00	42.50	
1891	(650) 8,694,206	8.00	10.00	15.00	60.00	650.00
1891CC	1,618,000	16.00	26.00	35.00	70.00	
1891O	7,954,529	8.00	10.00	15.00	90.00	
1891S	5,296,000	8.00	10.00	15.00	50.00	
1892	(1,245) 1,037,245	10.00	17.00	25.00	125.00	650.00
1892CC	1,352,000	38.00	65.00	100.00	250.00	
1892O	2,744,000	8.50	14.00	20.00	200.00	
1892S	1,200,000	24.00	120.00	1,000	10,000	
1893	(792) 389,792	28.00	40.00	65.00	230.00	725.00
1893CC	677,000	65.00	175.00	300.00	850.00	
1893O	300,000	42.50	90.00	175.00	900.00	
1893S	100,000	650.00	1,200	5,000	20,000	
1894	(972) 110,972	125.00	170.00	275.00	750.00	1,250
1894O	1,723,000	12.00	30.00	80.00	600.00	
1894S	1,260,000	23.00	60.00	100.00	285.00	

*Several die varieties.

SILVER DOLLARS

	Quan. Minted	VF-20	EF-40	AU-50	MS-60	Proof
1895† .... (880)	12,880					$9,000
1895O.....................	450,000	$50.00	$135.00	$400.00	$2,300	
1895S.....................	400,000	100.00	250.00	600.00	1,800	
1896 .... (762)	9,976,762	7.00	8.00	9.00	14.00	625.00
1896O..................	4,900,000	8.00	17.00	60.00	500.00	
1896S.....................	5,000,000	25.00	85.00	175.00	600.00	
1897 .... (731)	2,822,731	7.00	8.00	10.00	18.00	625.00
1897O..................	4,004,000	8.00	16.00	35.00	375.00	
1897S.....................	5,825,000	8.00	10.00	15.00	65.00	
1898 .... (735)	5,884,735	7.00	8.00	10.00	15.00	625.00
1898O..................	4,440,000	7.00	8.00	9.00	13.00	
1898S.....................	4,102,000	11.00	16.00	35.00	160.00	
1899 .... (846)	330,846	25.00	30.00	35.00	55.00	625.00
1899O..................	12,290,000	7.00	8.00	9.00	13.00	
1899S.....................	2,562,000	12.00	28.00	55.00	240.00	
1900 .... (912)	8,830,912	7.00	8.00	9.00	13.00	625.00
1900O...................	12,590,000	7.00	8.00	9.00	13.00	
1900O, O over CC*.......		14.00	20.00	30.00	70.00	
1900S.....................	3,540,000	11.00	22.00	40.00	150.00	
1901 .... (813)	6,962,813	20.00	42.50	80.00	1,250	950.00
1901O..................	13,320,000	7.00	8.00	10.00	14.00	
1901S.....................	2,284,000	12.00	27.50	45.00	175.00	
1902 .... (777)	7,994,777	7.50	9.50	15.00	50.00	625.00
1902O..................	8,636,000	7.00	8.00	9.00	13.00	
1902S.....................	1,530,000	42.00	60.00	100.00	300.00	
1903 .... (755)	4,652,755	8.50	11.00	12.50	30.00	625.00
1903O..................	4,450,000	45.00	50.00	60.00	70.00	
1903S.....................	1,241,000	27.50	90.00	500.00	1,650	
1904 .... (650)	2,788,650	9.00	13.00	20.00	85.00	650.00
1904O..................	3,720,000	7.00	8.00	9.00	12.50	
1904S.....................	2,304,000	18.00	47.50	175.00	625.00	
1921	44,690,000	6.00	7.00	8.00	10.00	
1921D.................	20,345,000	6.00	7.00	10.00	32.00	
1921S.................	21,695,000	6.00	7.00	10.00	32.00	

†Beware of removed mint mark.
*Several die varieties.

BIBLIOGRAPHY

Van Allen, Leroy C. and Mallis, A. George. *Comprehensive Catalogue and Encyclopedia of U.S. Morgan and Peace Silver Dollars.* New York. 1976.

Most uncirculated silver dollars have scratches or nicks because of handling of mint bags. Choice coins with few blemishes are worth considerably more than listed values.

PEACE TYPE 1921-1935

The dollar issued from 1921 to 1935 was a commemorative peace coin, which might easily have been a half dollar. The Peace Dollar, in fact, was issued without congressional sanction, under the terms of the Pittman Act, which referred to the bullion and in no way affected the design.

Anthony De Francisci, a medalist, designed this dollar. His monogram is located in the field of the coin under the neck of Liberty.

The new Peace Dollar was placed in circulation January 3, 1922. 1,006,473 pieces were struck in December, 1921.

SILVER DOLLARS

The high relief of the 1921 design was found impractical for coinage and was slightly modified in 1922. The four known matte proof specimens of 1922 are of the high relief style of 1921.

Legislation dated August 3, 1964 authorized the coinage of 45 million silver dollars, and 316,076 dollars of the Peace design dated 1964 were struck at the Denver mint. Plans for completing this coinage were subsequently abandoned and all of these coins were melted. None were preserved or released for circulation.

VF-20 VERY FINE—*Hair over eye well worn. Some strands over ear well defined. Some eagle feathers on top and outside edge of right wing will show.*

EF-40 EXTREMELY FINE—*Hairlines over brow and ear are strong though slightly worn. Outside wing feathers at right and those at top are visible but faint.*

AU-50 ABOUT UNCIRCULATED—*Slight trace of wear. Most of mint luster is present although marred by bag marks.*

MS-60 UNCIRCULATED—*No trace of wear. Has full mint luster but may be noticeably marred by skuff marks or bag abrasions.*

Designer Anthony De Francisci. Standards same as previous issue. Mints: Philadelphia, Denver, San Francisco.

	Quan. Minted	VF-20	EF-40	AU-50	MS-60	Matte Proof
1921	1,006,473	$23.00	$36.00	$45.00	$200.00	——
1922	51,737,000	6.00	7.00	8.00	10.00	——
1922D	15,063,000	6.50	7.75	8.50	35.00	
1922S	17,475,000	6.50	7.75	8.50	35.00	
1923	30,800,000	6.00	7.00	8.00	10.00	
1923D	6,811,000	6.50	7.75	8.50	35.00	
1923S	19,020,000	6.50	7.75	8.50	35.00	
1924	11,811,000	6.00	7.00	8.00	13.00	
1924S	1,728,000	10.00	17.00	35.00	180.00	
1925	10,198,000	6.00	7.00	8.00	13.00	
1925S	1,610,000	9.50	15.00	25.00	130.00	
1926	1,939,000	9.00	12.00	17.50	30.00	
1926D	2,348,700	7.50	9.50	13.00	42.50	
1926S	6,980,000	7.00	8.50	12.50	40.00	
1927	848,000	20.00	25.00	32.50	70.00	
1927D	1,268,900	11.00	20.00	30.00	160.00	
1927S	866,000	13.00	22.50	50.00	180.00	
1928	360,649	100.00	120.00	135.00	225.00	
1928S	1,632,000	9.00	17.50	25.00	150.00	
1934	954,057	16.00	22.50	32.50	70.00	
1934D*	1,569,500	9.00	16.00	30.00	125.00	
1934S	1,011,000	25.00	90.00	275.00	1,300	
1935	1,576,000	10.00	15.00	22.50	65.00	
1935S, 3 rays below ONE...	} 1,964,000	11.00	20.00	30.00	175.00	
1935S, 4 rays below ONE...		11.00	20.00	30.00	175.00	

*Large and small mint mark varieties, see page 59.

EISENHOWER DOLLARS 1971-1978

Honoring both President Dwight D. Eisenhower and the first landing of man on the moon, this design is the work of Chief Engraver Frank Gasparro, whose initials are on the truncation and below the eagle. The reverse is an adaptation of the official Apollo 11 insignia. Collectors' coins were struck in 40% silver composition and the circulation issue is copper-nickel.

Designer Frank Gasparro. Silver issue: weight 24.59 grams; composition: outer layers of .800 silver, .200 copper bonded to inner core of .210 silver, .790 copper. Copper-nickel issue: weight 22.68 grams; composition: outer layers of .750 copper, .250 nickel bonded to inner core of pure copper. Diameter 38.1 mm; reeded edge. Net weight of silver issues: .31625 oz. pure silver.

Mint mark location is above the date.

	Proof	Quan. Minted Regular	MS-65	Proof
1971 Copper-nickel clad		47,799,000	$2.00	
1971D Copper-nickel clad		68,587,424	2.25	
1971S Silver clad	(4,265,234)	6,868,530	3.00	$6.00
1972 Copper-nickel clad		75,890,000	2.00	
1972D Copper-nickel clad		92,548,511	2.00	
1972S Silver clad	(1,811,631)	2,193,056	4.25	8.00
1973 Copper-nickel clad		*2,000,056	10.00	
1973D Copper-nickel clad		*2,000,000	10.00	
1973S Copper-nickel clad	(2,760,339)			5.00
1973S Silver clad	(1,013,646)	1,883,140	6.00	35.00
1974 Copper-nickel clad		27,366,000	1.75	
1974D Copper-nickel clad		45,517,000	1.75	
1974S Copper-nickel clad	(2,612,568)			5.00
1974S Silver clad	(1,314,608)	1,900,000	5.00	10.00
1977 Copper-nickel clad		12,596,000	2.00	
1977D Copper-nickel clad		32,983,006	2.00	
1977S Copper-nickel clad	(3,251,152)			4.50
1978 Copper-nickel clad			1.75	
1978D Copper-nickel clad			1.75	
1978S Copper-nickel clad				5.00

Since 1971, the dies for the Eisenhower dollar have been modified several times by changing the relief, strengthening the design and making the world above the eagle round and more clearly defined.

Low relief dies were used for all copper-nickel issues of 1971, all uncirculated silver of 1971, and most copper-nickel coins of 1972.

High relief dies were used for all proofs of 1971, all silver issues of 1972, and the reverse of some exceptional Philadelphia copper-nickel coins of 1972 (identified by round world and weakly defined continents).

Modified high relief reverse dies were used for late 1972 Philadelphia copper-nickel coins and for all subsequent issues. Modified high relief obverse dies were also used on all issues beginning in 1973.

A few 1974D and 1977D dollars in silver clad composition were made in error.

*1,769,258 of each sold in sets. Unissued coins destroyed at mint.

BICENTENNIAL DOLLARS
BICENTENNIAL COINAGE DATED 1776-1976

The national significance of the Bicentennial of the United States was high-lighted with the adoption of new reverse designs for the quarter, half dollar and dollar. Nearly a thousand entries were submitted after the Treasury announced in October of 1973 that an open contest was to be held for the selection of the new designs. After the field was narrowed down to twelve semifinalists, the judges chose the rendition of the Liberty Bell superimposed on the moon to appear on the dollar coins. This design is the work of Dennis R. Williams. The obverse remained unchanged except for the dual date 1776-1976, which appeared on all dollars made during 1975 and 1976. These dual-dated coins were included in the various offerings of proof and uncirculated coins made by the Mint. They were also struck for general circulation.

The design was modified early in 1975 to produce a more attractive design.

Designers Frank Gasparro and Dennis R. Williams. Silver issue: weight 24.59 grams; composition: outer layers of .800 silver, .200 copper bonded to inner core of .210 silver, .790 copper. Copper-nickel issue: weight 22.68 grams; composition: outer layers of .750 copper, .250 nickel bonded to inner core of pure copper. Diameter 38.1 mm; reeded edge. Net weight of silver issues: .31625 oz. pure silver.

Obverse and Reverse Variety II   Reverse Var. I

Variety I: Design in low relief, bold lettering on reverse.
Variety II: Sharp design, delicate lettering on reverse.

	Quan. Minted	MS-65	Proof
1976 Copper-nickel clad, variety I	4,019,000	$2.50	
1976 Copper-nickel clad, variety II	113,318,000	1.80	
1976D Copper-nickel clad, variety I	21,048,710	1.80	
1976D Copper-nickel clad, variety II	82,179,564	1.80	
1976S Copper-nickel clad, variety I	(2,845,450)		$9.00
1976S Copper-nickel clad, variety II	(4,149,730)		3.00
1976S Silver clad, variety I	4,239,722	4.50	
1976S Silver clad, variety I	(3,295,714)		9.00

TRADE DOLLARS 1873-1885

This coin was issued for circulation in the Orient to compete with dollar-size coins of other countries. It weighed 420 grains compared to 412½ grains, the weight of the regular silver dollar.

When first coined they were legal tender in the United States to the extent of $5.00 but with the decline in price of silver bullion Congress repealed the legal tender provision in 1876 and authorized the Treasury to limit coinage to export demand. In 1887 a law was passed authorizing the Treasury to redeem all Trade dollars which were not mutilated.

TRADE DOLLARS 1873 - 1885

The trade dollars of 1884 and 1885 were unknown to collectors generally until 1908. None is listed in the Director's report and numismatists believe that they are not a part of the regular mint issue. After 1878, strikings were specimen proofs only.

The law authorizing Trade Dollars was repealed in February, 1887.

VG-8 VERY GOOD—*About half of mottoes IN GOD WE TRUST and E PLURIBUS UNUM will show. Rim on both sides well defined.*

F-12 FINE—*Mottoes and LIBERTY readable but worn.*

EF-40 EXTREMELY FINE—*Mottoes and LIBERTY are sharp. Only slight wear on rims.*

MS-60 UNCIRCULATED—*No trace of wear. Light blemishes.*

Designer William Barber; weight 27.22 grams; composition: .900 silver, .100 copper; diameter 38.1 mm; reeded edge; mints: Philadelphia, Carson City, San Francisco.

1875S
S over CC

Mint mark location on reverse below eagle.

	Quan. Minted	VG-8	F-12	EF-40	MS-60	Proof
1873 . . . . (865)	397,500	$45.00	$55.00	$90.00	$575.00	$1,400
1873CC	124,500	52.50	65.00	130.00	775.00	
1873S	703,000	50.00	60.00	90.00	700.00	
1874 . . . . (700)	987,800	50.00	60.00	85.00	475.00	1,400
1874CC	1,373,200	55.00	65.00	100.00	650.00	
1874S	2,549,000	50.00	60.00	85.00	475.00	
1875 . . . . (700)	218,900	60.00	75.00	150.00	800.00	1,400
1875CC	1,573,700	55.00	65.00	110.00	650.00	
1875S . . . . }	4,487,000	50.00	60.00	85.00	475.00	
1875S, S over CC . . . . . }		100.00	225.00	475.00	1,600	
1876 . . . . (1,150)	456,150	50.00	60.00	85.00	500.00	1,400
1876CC	509,000	55.00	65.00	110.00	650.00	
1876S	5,227,000	50.00	60.00	85.00	475.00	
1877 . . . . (510)	3,039,710	50.00	60.00	85.00	500.00	1,400
1877CC	534,000	55.00	70.00	140.00	900.00	
1877S	9,519,000	50.00	60.00	85.00	475.00	
1878 . . . . (900)	900.					1,450
1878CC	*97,000	145.00	200.00	475.00	2,800	
1878S	4,162,000	50.00	60.00	85.00	475.00	
1879 . . . . (1,541)	1,541.					1,400
1880 . . . . (1,987)	1,987.					1,400
1881 . . . . (960)	960.					1,400
1882 . . . . (1,097)	1,097.					1,400
1883 . . . . (979)	979.					1,500
1884 . . . . (10)	10.		1974 Herstal Sale		30,000
1885 . . . . (5)	5.					——

*44,148 Trade dollars were melted on July 19, 1878. Many of these may have been 1878CC.

BIBLIOGRAPHY

Willem, John M. *The United States Trade Dollar.* Second edition Racine, Wis., 1965.

GOLD

Gold has served as money or established the monetary value of currencies longer than any other material. The use of gold coins was widespread in Europe by the fourth century B.C.

The earliest coins circulated in the United States were foreign coins, mostly gold, brought from Europe. The Coinage Act in 1792 established an independent monetary system with the dollar as the basic United States monetary unit containing 24¾ grains of fine gold, based on the world price of $19.39 a troy ounce (480 grains). Congress changed the gold specification in 1834 and again in 1837, when it set the dollar-price of gold at $20.67 an ounce.

In 1934 residents of the United States were prohibited from holding gold in this country for monetary purposes — a prohibition that was extended in 1961 to include U.S. citizens holding gold abroad. For all practical purposes, gold ceased to exist as a monetary unit in the United States in 1934, when the gold content of the dollar was reduced to 13 5/7 grains and the dollar-price of gold was increased to $35 an ounce. Use of gold in international trade was further restricted when the world price of gold again rose, and in 1972 it was officially revalued by the United States government at $38.00 per ounce, and in 1973 again raised to $42.22. All regulations were removed in 1975.

> Above average, Choice Uncirculated gold coins
> may be worth up to 50% more than values indicated.

GOLD DOLLARS 1849-1889

Coinage of the gold dollar was authorized by the Act of March 3, 1849. The weight was 25.8 grains, fineness .900. The first type, struck until 1854, is known as the Liberty Head or Small-sized type.

In 1854 the piece was made larger in diameter and thinner. The design was changed to a feather headdress on a female, generally referred to as the Indian Head or Large-sized type. In 1856 the type was changed slightly by enlarging the size of the head.

LIBERTY HEAD TYPE 1849-1854

F-12 FINE—*Full LIBERTY but knobs over coronet partially worn.*

VF-20 VERY FINE—*LIBERTY on headband complete and readable. Knobs on coronet are defined.*

EF-40 EXTREMELY FINE—*Slight wear on Liberty's hair. Knobs on coronet sharp.*

MS-60 UNCIRCULATED—*No trace of wear. Light blemishes.*

Designer James B. Longacre; weight 1.672 grams; composition: .900 gold, .100 copper; diameter 13 mm; reeded edge. Net weight: .04837 oz. pure gold.

Type 1

With open or closed wreath.

Mint mark is below wreath.

	Quan. Minted	F-12	VF-20	EF-40	MS-60
1849 Open wreath - All kinds	688,567	$120.00	$145.00	$175.00	$400.00
1849 Closed wreath					
(wreath ends closer to numeral)		120.00	145.00	175.00	400.00
1849C Closed wreath	⎫ 11,634	185.00	325.00	575.00	1,600
1849C Open wreath *(4 known)*	⎭	—	—		
1849D Open wreath	21,588	180.00	310.00	500.00	1,400
1849O Open wreath	215,000	120.00	150.00	200.00	450.00
1850	481,953	120.00	145.00	175.00	400.00
1850C	6,966	225.00	350.00	625.00	1,650
1850D	8,382	200.00	325.00	550.00	1,475
1850O	14,000	135.00	185.00	250.00	550.00
1851	3,317,671	120.00	145.00	175.00	400.00
1851C	41,267	160.00	300.00	475.00	1,100
1851D	9,882	190.00	325.00	575.00	1,600

GOLD DOLLARS

	Quan. Minted	F-12	VF-20	EF-40	MS-60	Proof
1851O	290,000	$120.00	$145.00	$175.00	$450.00	
1852	2,045,351	120.00	145.00	175.00	400.00	
1852C	9,434	180.00	325.00	550.00	1,750	
1852D	6,360	175.00	300.00	550.00	1,600	
1852O	140,000	120.00	145.00	185.00	525.00	
1853	4,076,051	120.00	145.00	175.00	400.00	
1853C	11,515	180.00	300.00	500.00	1,500	
1853D	6,583	200.00	325.00	500.00	1,700	
1853O	290,000	120.00	145.00	175.00	450.00	
1854	736,709	120.00	145.00	175.00	400.00	
1854D	2,935	325.00	550.00	950.00	3,500	
1854S	14,632	150.00	275.00	475.00	1,500	

INDIAN HEAD TYPE, Small Head 1854-1856

Type 2

F-12 FINE—*Feather curl tips partially worn away.*
VF-20 VERY FINE—*Feather curl tips outlined but details worn.*
EF-40 EXTREMELY FINE—*Slight wear on tips of feather curls on headdress.*
MS-60 UNCIRCULATED—*No trace of wear. Light blemishes.*

Standards same as previous issue. Diameter changed to 15 mm.

1854	902,736	200.00	300.00	500.00	1,900	
1855	758,269	200.00	300.00	500.00	1,900	
1855C	9,803	375.00	625.00	1,450	5,500	
1855D	1,811	1,500	2,500	4,000	12,500	
1855O	55,000	375.00	550.00	1,000	4,200	
1856S	24,600	275.00	390.00	750.00	3,750	

INDIAN HEAD TYPE, Large Head 1856-1889

Type 3

F-12 FINE—*Full LIBERTY on headband but beads partially worn. Curled feathers flat—no detail.*
VF-20 VERY FINE—*Curled feathers have slight detail. Details worn smooth at eyebrow, hair below headdress and behind ear and bottom curl.*
EF-40 EXTREMELY FINE—*Slight wear above and to right of eye and on top of curled feathers.*
MS-60 UNCIRCULATED—*No trace of wear. Light blemishes.*

1856 Upright 5	33,660	110.00	135.00	200.00	450.00	
1856 Slant 5	1,729,276	110.00	135.00	165.00	400.00	$2,500
1856D	1,460	1,750	3,000	4,250	12,000	
1857	774,789	110.00	135.00	165.00	350.00	2,500
1857C	13,280	250.00	350.00	550.00	1,500	
1857D	3,533	425.00	650.00	1,000	2,500	
1857S	10,000	150.00	225.00	375.00	1,300	
1858	117,995	110.00	135.00	165.00	350.00	3,000
1858D	3,477	500.00	750.00	1,150	3,000	
1858S	10,000	135.00	200.00	400.00	1,100	
1859	168,244	110.00	135.00	165.00	350.00	2,500
1859C	5,235	250.00	400.00	600.00	1,500	
1859D	4,952	300.00	450.00	900.00	2,000	
1859S	15,000	130.00	225.00	400.00	1,050	
1860 (154)	36,668	110.00	135.00	165.00	375.00	2,000
1860D	1,566	1,800	3,500	5,000	10,000	
1860S	13,000	130.00	215.00	375.00	975.00	
1861 (349)	527,499	110.00	135.00	165.00	350.00	2,000

GOLD DOLLARS

	Quan. Minted	F-12	VF-20	EF-40	MS-60	Proof
1861D.............................		$3,500	$5,000	$9,000	$17,000	
1862 .... (35)	1,361,390	110.00	135.00	165.00	350.00	$2,500
1862 Doubled die obverse				—	—	
1863 .... (50)	6,250	225.00	375.00	700.00	1,950	3,250
1864 .... (50)	5,950	200.00	325.00	500.00	1,300	3,100
1865 .... (25)	3,725	225.00	350.00	525.00	1,800	3,250
1866 .... (30)	7,130	165.00	265.00	400.00	1,200	2,750
1867 .... (50)	5,250	175.00	275.00	400.00	1,200	2,750
1868 .... (25)	10,525	150.00	230.00	375.00	1,000	2,750
1869 .... (25)	5,925	160.00	260.00	400.00	1,100	2,750
1870 .... (35)	6,335	150.00	250.00	375.00	975.00	2,750
1870S........................	3,000	325.00	600.00	1,000	3,000	
1871 .... (30)	3,930	150.00	275.00	385.00	950.00	2,500
1872 .... (30)	3,530	150.00	275.00	385.00	1,100	2,500
1873 Closed 3........... (25)	125,125	150.00	250.00	400.00	1,000	2,750
1873 Open 3.................		115.00	140.00	170.00	375.00	
1874 .... (20)	198,820	110.00	135.00	165.00	350.00	2,500
1875 .... (20)	420	1,500	2,600	3,750	8,000	12,500
1876 .... (45)	3,245	125.00	240.00	350.00	900.00	2,300
1877 .... (20)	3,920	150.00	250.00	375.00	1,000	2,500
1878 .... (20)	3,020	150.00	250.00	375.00	1,000	2,500
1879 .... (30)	3,030	150.00	250.00	375.00	900.00	2,100
1880 .... (36)	1,636	150.00	225.00	350.00	775.00	1,900
1881 .... (87)	7,707	125.00	175.00	250.00	575.00	1,600
1882 .... (125)	5,125	125.00	175.00	250.00	575.00	1,600
1883 .... (207)	11,007	120.00	160.00	225.00	600.00	1,500
1884 .... (1,006)	6,236	120.00	160.00	225.00	575.00	1,300
1885 .... (1,105)	12,261	120.00	160.00	225.00	575.00	1,300
1886 .... (1,016)	6,016	120.00	160.00	225.00	575.00	1,300
1887 .... (1,043)	8,543	120.00	160.00	225.00	575.00	1,300
1888 .... (1,079)	16,580	120.00	160.00	225.00	575.00	1,300
1889 .... (1,779)	30,729	115.00	150.00	200.00	500.00	1,300

BIBLIOGRAPHY

Akers, David W., *Gold Dollars.* Englewood, Ohio, 1975.
Breen, Walter, *Major Varieties of U.S. Gold Dollars.* Chicago. 1964.

QUARTER EAGLES—1796-1929

($2.50 GOLD PIECES)

Authorized by the Act of April 2, 1792, they weighed 67.5 grains, 916 2/3 fine until the weight was changed to 64.5 grains, fineness 899.225, by the Act of June 28, 1834. The Act of January 18, 1837 established fineness at .900. Most dates before 1834 are rare. The first issue was struck in 1796, most of which had no stars on the obverse.

Proofs of some dates prior to 1855 are known to exist, and all are rare.

CAPPED BUST TO RIGHT 1796-1807

Variety 1 —
No Stars on Obverse 1796 Only

F-12 FINE—*Hair worn smooth on high spots. E PLURIBUS UNUM weak but readable.*

VF-20 VERY FINE—*Some wear on high spots.*

EF-40 EXTREMELY FINE—*Only slight wear on hair and cheek.*

MS-60 UNCIRCULATED—*No trace of wear. Light blemishes.*

Designer Robert Scot; weight 4.37 grams; composition: .9167 gold, .0833 copper; approx. diameter 20 mm; reeded edge.

QUARTER EAGLES

Variety 2 —
Stars on Obverse 1796-1807

	Quan. Minted	F-12	VF-20	EF-40	MS-60
1796 No stars on obverse	963	$5,000	$8,250	$14,000	$27,500
1796 Stars on obverse	432	4,250	7,500	11,000	25,000
1797	427	2,750	4,500	6,750	12,500
1798	1,094	2,000	3,500	5,500	11,000
1802, 2 over 1	3,035	1,000	2,250	3,500	7,500
1804, 13-Star reverse	} 3,327	1,800	3,200	5,000	11,000
1804, 14-Star reverse		1,250	2,000	3,000	7,500
1805	1,781	1,000	2,000	3,000	7,000
1806, 6 over 4	} 1,616	1,250	2,250	3,500	7,750
1806, 6 over 5		1,500	3,000	4,750	10,000
1807	6,812	1,000	1,750	3,000	6,000

CAPPED BUST TO LEFT, Large Size 1808

F-12 FINE—*E PLURIBUS UNUM and LIBERTY on headband readable but weak.*

VF-20 VERY FINE—*Motto and LIBERTY clear.*

EF-40 EXTREMELY FINE—*All details of hair are plain.*

MS-60 UNCIRCULATED—*No trace of wear. Light blemishes.*

Designer John Reich. Standards same as previous issue.

1808	2,710	4,500	7,500	13,500	26,000

CAPPED HEAD TO LEFT 1821-1834

Those dated 1829 through 1834 are smaller in diameter than the 1821-1827 pieces. They also have smaller letters, dates and stars.

Standards same as previous issue. Diameter changed to approximately 18.5 mm.

1821	6,448	1,200	2,200	4,000	8,500
1824, 4 over 1	2,600	1,200	2,200	4,000	8,500
1825	4,434	1,200	2,200	4,000	8,500
1826, 6 over 5	760	1,750	3,400	5,500	14,500
1827	2,800	1,200	2,200	4,000	8,000
1829	3,403	1,000	1,800	3,100	7,000
1830	4,540	1,000	1,700	2,800	6,500
1831	4,520	1,000	1,700	2,800	6,500
1832	4,400	1,000	1,700	2,800	6,500
1833	4,160	1,000	1,700	2,800	6,500
1834 (Motto)	4,000	2,500	3,750	7,000	15,000

QUARTER EAGLES

CLASSIC HEAD TYPE, No Motto on Reverse 1834-1839

In 1834 the quarter eagle was redesigned. A ribbon binding the hair, bearing the word LIBERTY, replaces the Liberty cap. The motto was omitted from the reverse. In 1840 a coronet and smaller head were designed to conform in appearance with that of the larger gold coins.

F-12 FINE—*LIBERTY readable and complete. Curl under ear outlined but no detail.*

VF-20 VERY FINE—*LIBERTY plain. Hair curl has detail.*

EF-40 EXTREMELY FINE—*Small amount of wear on top of hair and below L in LIBERTY. Wear evident on wing.*

MS-60 UNCIRCULATED—*No trace of wear. Light blemishes.*

Mint mark location.

Designer William Kneass; weight 4.18 grams; composition: .8992 gold, .1008 copper; diameter 18.2 mm; reeded edge.

	Quan. Minted	F-12	VF-20	EF-40	MS-60
1834 No motto	112,234	$125.00	$175.00	$300.00	$2,000
1835	131,402	125.00	175.00	300.00	2,000
1836	547,986	125.00	175.00	300.00	2,000
1837	45,080	150.00	200.00	325.00	2,000
1838	47,030	150.00	200.00	325.00	2,000
1838C	7,880	250.00	425.00	800.00	3,500
1839	27,021	150.00	200.00	325.00	1,850
1839C	18,140	225.00	350.00	650.00	3,000
1839D	13,674	250.00	375.00	750.00	3,000
1839O	17,781	150.00	225.00	350.00	2,000

1839, 9 over 8 varieties exist for P, C and D mints.

CORONET TYPE 1840-1907

Mint mark location.

Designer Christian Gobrecht; weight 4.18 grams; composition: .900 gold, .100 copper; diameter 18 mm; reeded edge. Net weight: .12094 oz. pure gold.

1840	18,859	100.00	140.00	225.00	600.00
1840C	12,822	200.00	300.00	500.00	1,600
1840D	3,532	250.00	400.00	750.00	2,200
1840O	33,580	100.00	135.00	215.00	700.00
1841 Proof only		—	20,000	50,000	
1841C	10,281	225.00	325.00	475.00	1,250
1841D	4,164	250.00	375.00	600.00	1,750
1842	2,823	215.00	350.00	575.00	1,750
1842C	6,729	200.00	300.00	525.00	1,500
1842D	4,643	225.00	350.00	550.00	1,700
1842O	19,800	100.00	150.00	250.00	750.00
1843	100,546	90.00	120.00	150.00	400.00
1843C Small date, crosslet 4	} 26,064	500.00	900.00	1,750	3,500
1843C Large date, plain 4		175.00	275.00	400.00	1,150
1843D Small date, crosslet 4	36,209	175.00	275.00	400.00	1,150
1843O Small date, crosslet 4	} 368,002	110.00	150.00	200.00	475.00
1843O Large date, plain 4		100.00	135.00	200.00	600.00

QUARTER EAGLES

	Quan. Minted	F-12	VF-20	EF-40	MS-60
1844	6,784	$140.00	$250.00	$400.00	$1,000
1844C	11,622	200.00	275.00	450.00	1,250
1844D	17,332	175.00	250.00	475.00	1,250
1845	91,051	90.00	120.00	165.00	450.00
1845D	19,460	165.00	250.00	475.00	1,250
1845O	4,000	200.00	400.00	800.00	——
1846	21,598	90.00	120.00	175.00	500.00
1846C	4,808	250.00	400.00	650.00	1,750
1846D	19,303	175.00	300.00	500.00	1,250
1846O	62,000	90.00	120.00	175.00	500.00
1847	29,814	90.00	120.00	175.00	450.00
1847C	23,226	175.00	275.00	400.00	1,150
1847D	15,784	175.00	275.00	400.00	1,250
1847O	124,000	90.00	120.00	185.00	475.00
1848	7,497	375.00	575.00	900.00	1,650

CAL. Above Eagle on Reverse

California Gold Quarter Eagle

In 1848 about two hundred and thirty ounces of gold were sent to Secretary of War Marcy by Col. R. B. Mason, Military Governor of California. The gold was turned over to the mint and made into quarter eagles. The distinguishing mark "CAL." was punched above the eagle on the reverse side, while the coins were in the die. Two specimens with proof surface are known.

	Quan. Minted	F-12	VF-20	EF-40	MS-60
1848 CAL. above eagle	1,389	3,000	5,000	8,000	17,500
1848C	16,788	175.00	275.00	425.00	1,300
1848D	13,771	175.00	300.00	475.00	1,400
1849	23,294	100.00	115.00	150.00	400.00
1849C	10,220	175.00	300.00	475.00	1,300
1849D	10,945	175.00	300.00	475.00	1,300
1850	252,923	90.00	120.00	150.00	350.00
1850C	9,148	175.00	275.00	450.00	1,250
1850D	12,148	175.00	275.00	450.00	1,250
1850O	84,000	90.00	120.00	170.00	475.00
1851	1,372,748	90.00	120.00	150.00	350.00
1851C	14,923	175.00	275.00	450.00	1,250
1851D	11,264	175.00	275.00	450.00	1,250
1851O	148,000	90.00	120.00	200.00	450.00
1852	1,159,681	90.00	120.00	150.00	350.00
1852C	9,772	175.00	300.00	475.00	1,400
1852D	4,078	275.00	400.00	600.00	1,750
1852O	140,000	90.00	120.00	150.00	425.00
1853	1,404,668	90.00	120.00	150.00	350.00
1853D	3,178	375.00	550.00	850.00	2,750
1854	596,258	90.00	120.00	150.00	350.00
1854C	7,295	175.00	300.00	450.00	1,300
1854D	1,760	1,250	2,000	3,100	6,200
1854O	15,300	100.00	130.00	175.00	500.00
1854S	246		15,000	32,500	——

QUARTER EAGLES

	Quan. Minted	F-12	VF-20	EF-40	MS-60	Proof
1855	235,480	$90.00	$120.00	$150.00	$350.00	——
1855C	3,677	450.00	775.00	1,400	3,500	
1855D	1,123	900.00	1,500	2,500	7,300	
1856	384,240	90.00	120.00	150.00	350.00	——
1856C	7,913	200.00	300.00	500.00	1,750	
1856D	874	1,500	3,000	5,500	13,500	
1856O	21,100	100.00	140.00	200.00	800.00	
1856S	72,120	100.00	150.00	225.00	800.00	
1857	214,130	90.00	120.00	150.00	350.00	——
1857D	2,364	375.00	550.00	900.00	2,500	
1857O	34,000	100.00	125.00	200.00	600.00	
1857S	69,200	100.00	130.00	210.00	900.00	
1858	47,377	90.00	120.00	170.00	375.00	——
1858C	9,056	220.00	300.00	475.00	1,400	
1859	39,444	90.00	120.00	150.00	425.00	$5,500
1859D	2,244	325.00	550.00	950.00	2,500	
1859S	15,200	100.00	135.00	225.00	850.00	
1860	(112) 22,675	90.00	120.00	150.00	475.00	3,750
1860C	7,469	220.00	325.00	500.00	1,500	
1860S	35,600	90.00	120.00	200.00	700.00	
1861	(90) 1,283,878	90.00	120.00	150.00	350.00	3,750
1861S	24,000	95.00	130.00	200.00	650.00	

1862 Quarter Eagle
Overdate 2 over 1

	Quan. Minted	F-12	VF-20	EF-40	MS-60	Proof
1862, 2 over 1	} 98,543		1,200	2,000		
1862	(35)	90.00	120.00	150.00	400.00	4,000
1862S	8,000	110.00	200.00	325.00	1,100	
1863 Proofs only	(30) 30					——
1863S	10,800	100.00	150.00	225.00	1,250	
1864	(50) 2,874	350.00	525.00	1,100	2,500	6,500
1865	(25) 1,545	375.00	575.00	1,200	2,750	6,500
1865S	23,376	100.00	130.00	190.00	700.00	
1866	(30) 3,110	175.00	300.00	425.00	1,200	4,500
1866S	38,960	90.00	120.00	175.00	600.00	
1867	(50) 3,250	175.00	300.00	425.00	1,100	4,000
1867S	28,000	100.00	125.00	175.00	600.00	
1868	(25) 3,625	175.00	250.00	375.00	900.00	4,250
1868S	34,000	100.00	125.00	150.00	525.00	
1869	(25) 4,345	125.00	170.00	250.00	700.00	4,250
1869S	29,500	100.00	125.00	170.00	550.00	
1870	(35) 4,555	115.00	175.00	300.00	700.00	4,250
1870S	16,000	100.00	130.00	175.00	700.00	
1871	(30) 5,350	130.00	185.00	300.00	725.00	4,250
1871S	22,000	100.00	125.00	160.00	550.00	
1872	(30) 3,030	170.00	250.00	400.00	1,000	4,250
1872S	18,000	100.00	130.00	160.00	425.00	
1873 Closed 3	(25) } 178,025	90.00	120.00	150.00	350.00	4,250
1873 Open 3		90.00	120.00	150.00	350.00	
1873S	27,000	90.00	125.00	160.00	400.00	
1874	(20) 3,940	150.00	200.00	325.00	775.00	5,250

QUARTER EAGLES

	Quan. Minted		F-12	VF-20	EF-40	MS-60	Proof
1875	(20)	420	$1,300	$2,800	$4,500	$8,000	——
1875S		11,600	100.00	150.00	200.00	550.00	
1876	(45)	4,221	125.00	200.00	325.00	750.00	$3,750
1876S		5,000	100.00	160.00	225.00	750.00	
1877	(20)	1,652	325.00	450.00	600.00	1,600	5,000
1877S		35,400	90.00	120.00	150.00	350.00	
1878	(20)	286,260	90.00	115.00	140.00	225.00	4,000
1878S		178,000	90.00	115.00	140.00	225.00	
1879	(30)	88,990	90.00	115.00	140.00	225.00	3,500
1879S		43,500	90.00	115.00	140.00	225.00	
1880	(36)	2,996	140.00	200.00	275.00	725.00	3,750
1881	(51)	691	400.00	600.00	1,200	2,750	4,500
1882	(67)	4,067	140.00	200.00	275.00	700.00	3,000
1883	(82)	2,002	175.00	250.00	325.00	850.00	3,000
1884	(73)	2,023	175.00	250.00	325.00	850.00	3,000
1885	(87)	887	325.00	625.00	1,000	2,500	4,500
1886	(88)	4,088	140.00	200.00	300.00	625.00	2,750
1887	(122)	6,282	120.00	175.00	225.00	425.00	2,250
1888	(97)	16,098	100.00	125.00	135.00	250.00	2,250
1889	(48)	17,648	100.00	125.00	135.00	250.00	2,300
1890	(93)	8,813	100.00	130.00	175.00	350.00	2,300
1891	(80)	11,040	90.00	120.00	150.00	300.00	2,300
1892	(105)	2,545	125.00	200.00	250.00	600.00	2,200
1893	(106)	30,106	90.00	115.00	135.00	250.00	2,200
1894	(122)	4,122	100.00	150.00	225.00	500.00	2,000
1895	(119)	6,119	100.00	150.00	200.00	350.00	2,000
1896	(132)	19,202	90.00	115.00	140.00	225.00	2,000
1897	(136)	29,904	90.00	115.00	140.00	225.00	2,000
1898	(165)	24,165	90.00	115.00	140.00	225.00	1,800
1899	(150)	27,350	90.00	115.00	140.00	225.00	1,800
1900	(205)	67,205	90.00	115.00	140.00	225.00	1,800
1901	(223)	91,323	90.00	115.00	130.00	200.00	1,800
1902	(193)	133,733	90.00	115.00	130.00	200.00	1,800
1903	(197)	201,257	90.00	115.00	130.00	200.00	1,800
1904	(170)	160,960	90.00	115.00	130.00	200.00	1,800
1905*	(144)	217,944	90.00	115.00	130.00	200.00	1,800
1906	(160)	176,490	90.00	115.00	130.00	200.00	1,800
1907	(154)	336,448	90.00	115.00	130.00	200.00	1,800

*Pieces dated 1905S are counterfeit.

INDIAN HEAD TYPE 1908-1929

The new type represents a departure from all preceding coin types in the United States series. Bela Lyon Pratt was the designer of this and the half eagle piece. The coin has no raised milling and the main devices and legends are incuse.

Designer Bela Lyon Pratt; weight 4.18 grams; composition: .900 gold, .100 copper; diameter 18 mm; reeded edge. Net weight: .12094 oz. pure gold.

F-12 FINE—*Knot in hair cord must show, small feathers on top of head will be faint.*

VF-20 VERY FINE—*Hair cord knot distinct. Feathers at top of head clear. Cheekbone worn.*

EF-40 EXTREMELY FINE—*Cheekbone, war bonnet and headband feathers slightly worn.*

MS-60 UNCIRCULATED—*No trace of wear. Light blemishes.*

Mint mark location is on reverse left of fasces.

QUARTER EAGLES

	Quan. Minted	F-12	VF-20	EF-40	MS-60	Matte Proof
1908	(236) 565,057	$80.00	$95.00	$110.00	$235.00	$1,800
1909	(139) 441,899	80.00	95.00	110.00	185.00	1,800
1910	(682) 492,682	80.00	95.00	110.00	185.00	1,800
1911	(191) 704,191	80.00	95.00	110.00	185.00	1,800
1911D	55,680	285.00	450.00	650.00	1,500	
1912	(197) 616,197	80.00	95.00	110.00	185.00	1,800
1913	(165) 722,165	80.00	95.00	110.00	185.00	1,800
1914	(117) 240,117	80.00	95.00	110.00	185.00	1,800
1914D	448,000	80.00	95.00	110.00	185.00	
1915	(100) 606,100	80.00	95.00	110.00	185.00	1,800
1925D	578,000	80.00	95.00	110.00	185.00	
1926	446,000	80.00	95.00	110.00	185.00	
1927	388,000	80.00	95.00	110.00	185.00	
1928	416,000	80.00	95.00	110.00	185.00	
1929	532,000	80.00	95.00	110.00	185.00	

THREE-DOLLAR GOLD PIECES — 1854-1889

The three-dollar gold piece was authorized by Act of February 21, 1853. The coin was first struck in 1854. It was never popular and saw very little circulation.

The coin weighs 77.4 grains, .900 fine. The head on the obverse represents an Indian princess with hair tightly curling over the neck, head crowned with a circle of feathers, the band of which is inscribed LIBERTY. A wreath of tobacco, wheat, corn and cotton occupies the field of the reverse, with the denomination and date within it.

Restrikes of some years were made at the Mint; particularly 1873 and 1876.

In the year 1854 only, the word DOLLARS is in much smaller letters than in years 1855 through 1889. A variety of the 1856 proof has DOLLARS in large letters cut over the same word in small letters.

Designer James B. Longacre; weight 5.015 grams; composition: .900 gold, .100 copper; diameter 20.5 mm; reeded edge. Net weight: .14512 oz. pure gold.

F-12 FINE—*Top of headdress worn flat. Full LIBERTY. Beads above band partially worn.*

VF-20 VERY FINE—*Eyebrow, hair about forehead and ear and bottom curl are worn smooth. Curled feather-ends have faint details showing.*

EF-40 EXTREMELY FINE—*Only trace of wear above and to right of eye. Slight wear on top of curled feathers.*

MS-60 UNCIRCULATED—*No trace of wear. Light blemishes.*

Mint mark location is on reverse below wreath.

	Quan. Minted	F-12	VF-20	EF-40	MS-60	Proof
1854	138,618	275.00	375.00	500.00	1,750	——
1854D	1,120	1,800	2,800	4,250	11,500	
1854O	24,000	325.00	425.00	600.00	2,850	
1855	50,555	300.00	400.00	550.00	2,100	35,000
1855S	6,600	350.00	450.00	800.00	4,200	
1856	26,010	300.00	400.00	575.00	2,000	21,000
1856S*	34,500	300.00	425.00	650.00	3,250	
1857	20,891	300.00	400.00	575.00	2,000	17,000
1857S	14,000	300.00	425.00	650.00	3,500	
1858	2,133	425.00	625.00	900.00	3,000	12,500
1859	15,638	325.00	425.00	575.00	2,250	10,000

*Small, medium and large S varieties exist.

THREE-DOLLAR GOLD PIECES

	Quan. Minted	F-12	VF-20	EF-40	MS-60	Proof
1860 .... (119)	7,155	$350.00	$450.00	$650.00	$2,250	$6,000
1860S .... (2,592 melted at Mint)	7,000	350.00	475.00	775.00	3,200	
1861 .... (113)	6,072	350.00	450.00	625.00	2,200	6,000
1862 .... (35)	5,785	350.00	450.00	625.00	2,200	7,500
1863 .... (39)	5,039	350.00	475.00	675.00	2,600	8,000
1864 .... (50)	2,680	375.00	525.00	775.00	2,900	7,500
1865 .... (25)	1,165	400.00	600.00	925.00	4,250	9,000
1866 .... (30)	4,030	350.00	475.00	725.00	2,800	7,500
1867 .... (50)	2,650	375.00	500.00	750.00	2,900	7,000
1868 .... (25)	4,875	350.00	475.00	725.00	2,500	8,000
1869 .... (25)	2,525	375.00	500.00	750.00	2,800	8,000
1870 .... (35)	3,535	325.00	425.00	700.00	2,500	8,000
1870S (One known) 2		——				
1871 .... (30)	1,330	400.00	550.00	750.00	2,950	8,000
1872 .... (30)	2,030	375.00	450.00	650.00	2,800	8,000
1873 Open 3 .... (25)	25					22,500
1873 Closed 3					8,500	12,500
1874 .... (20)	41,820	275.00	375.00	500.00	1,500	9,500
1875 Proofs only .... (20)	20	Garrett Sale 1976				91,000
1876 Proofs only .... (45)	45					20,000
1877 .... (20)	1,488	500.00	825.00	1,600	4,100	11,000
1878 .... (20)	82,324	275.00	375.00	500.00	1,500	9,500
1879 .... (30)	3,030	350.00	450.00	575.00	2,300	6,000
1880 .... (36)	1,036	400.00	600.00	800.00	2,500	6,000
1881 .... (54)	554	600.00	800.00	1,250	4,100	7,000
1882 .... (76)	1,576	400.00	550.00	750.00	2,500	6,000
1883 .... (89)	989	450.00	650.00	900.00	2,800	6,000
1884 .... (106)	1,106	450.00	650.00	850.00	2,800	5,500
1885 .... (109)	910	475.00	700.00	1,100	3,000	5,500
1886 .... (142)	1,142	425.00	625.00	850.00	2,500	5,500
1887 .... (160)	6,160	375.00	525.00	700.00	2,250	5,000
1888 .... (290)	5,291	375.00	500.00	675.00	2,000	5,000
1889 .... (129)	2,429	375.00	500.00	675.00	2,000	5,000

FOUR-DOLLAR GOLD OR "STELLA"

These pattern coins were first suggested by the Hon. John A. Kasson, then U.S. Minister to Austria; and it was through the efforts of Dr. W. W. Hubbell, who patented the goloid metal used in making the goloid metric dollars, that we have these beautiful and interesting pieces.

There are two distinct types in both years of issue. Barber designed the flowing hair type, and Morgan the coiled hair. They were struck in gold, aluminum, copper and white metal. Only those struck in gold are listed.

	Proof		Proof
1879 Flowing hair (415)	$20,000	1880 Flowing hair (15)	$40,000
1879 Coiled hair (10)	90,000	1880 Coiled Hair (10)	90,000

HALF EAGLES — 1795-1929
($5.00 GOLD PIECES)

The half eagle was the first gold coin actually struck for the United States. The $5.00 piece was authorized to be coined by the Act of April 2, 1792 and the first type weighed 135 grains, 916 2/3 fine. The weight was changed by Act of June 28, 1834 to 129 grains, 899.225 fine. Fineness became .900 by Act of January 18, 1837.

There are many varieties among the early dates caused by changes in the number of stars, style of eagle, overdates, and differences in the size of figures in the dates. Those dated prior to 1807 do not bear any mark of value. The 1822 half eagle is considered the most valuable regular issue coin of the entire United States series. Proofs of some dates prior to 1855 are known to exist, and all are rare. The half eagle was the only U.S. denomination struck in each of the seven mints.

CAPPED BUST TO RIGHT, SMALL EAGLE 1795-1798

This type was struck from mid-1795 to early 1798, when the small eagle reverse was changed to the large or "heraldic" eagle. Note that the 1795 and 1797 dates exist for both types, but the heraldic reverses of these dates were probably struck under emergency conditions in late 1798.

F-12 FINE—*Hair worn smooth but with distinct outline. For heraldic type, E PLURIBUS UNUM is faint but readable.*

VF-20 VERY FINE—*Slight to noticeable wear on high spots such as hair, turban, eagle's head and wings.*

EF-40 EXTREMELY FINE—*Slight wear on hair and highest part of cheek.*

MS-60 UNCIRCULATED—*No trace of wear. Light blemishes.*

Designer Robert Scot; weight 8.75 grams; composition: .9167 gold, .0833 copper; approx. diameter 25 mm; reeded edge.

	Quan. Minted	F-12	VF-20	EF-40	MS-60
1795 Small eagle*	8,707	$2,500	$3,750	$5,000	$12,000

*One variety has final S in STATES over D.

1796, 6 over 5	1797, 15 Stars		1797, 16 Stars

1796, 6 over 5	6,196	2,500	4,200	5,250	13,000
1797, 15 stars	} 3,609	3,250	4,750	9,000	15,500
1797, 16 stars		3,250	4,750	9,000	15,500
1798 Small eagle (6 known)		—	—	—	—

HALF EAGLES
CAPPED BUST TO RIGHT, HERALDIC EAGLE 1795-1807

	Quan. Minted	F-12	VF-20	EF-40	MS-60
1795 Heraldic eagle*		$3,500	$5,750	$9,000	$15,000
1797, 7 over 5*		3,000	4,250	6,200	12,000
1797, 16 star obverse*		—	—	—	
1798 Small 8		700.00	875.00	1,600	4,250
1798 Large 8, 13 star reverse	24,867	750.00	1,200	1,900	4,250
1798 Large 8, 14 star reverse		850.00	1,500	2,400	5,500
1799	7,451	750.00	1,000	1,600	3,750

*These three pieces are thought to have been struck in 1798 and included in the mintage figure for that year.

1802 over 1   1803 over 2   Small 8 over Large 8

1800	37,628	750.00	1,000	1,700	3,750
1802, 2 over 1	53,176	725.00	900.00	1,400	3,500
1803, 3 over 2	33,506	725.00	900.00	1,400	3,500
1804 Small 8	30,475	725.00	900.00	1,400	3,500
1804 Small 8 over large 8		725.00	900.00	1,400	3,500
1805	33,183	725.00	900.00	1,400	3,500

Pointed 6, 8 and 5 Stars   Round Top 6, 7 and 6 Stars

1806 Pointed top 6	64,093	700.00	875.00	1,500	3,750
1806 Round top 6		700.00	875.00	1,300	3,400
1807	32,488	700.00	875.00	1,300	3,400

HALF EAGLES
CAPPED DRAPED BUST TO LEFT 1807-1812

Designer John Reich. Standards same as previous issue.

F-12 FINE—*LIBERTY readable but partly weak.*

VF-20 VERY FINE—*Headband edges slightly worn. LIBERTY is bold.*

EF-40 EXTREMELY FINE—*Slight wear on highest portions of hair. 80% of major curls are plain.*

MS-60 UNCIRCULATED—*No trace of wear. Light blemishes.*

	Quan. Minted	F-12	VF-20	EF-40	MS-60
1807	51,605	$750.00	$850.00	$1,200	$3,000

1808, 8 over 7   Normal Date

	Quan. Minted	F-12	VF-20	EF-40	MS-60
1808, 8 over 7	} 55,578	625.00	800.00	1,050	2,750
1808		625.00	800.00	1,050	2,600
1809, 9 over 8	33,875	625.00	800.00	1,050	2,700

Small Date   Large Date   Small 5   Tall 5

	Quan. Minted	F-12	VF-20	EF-40	MS-60
1810 Small date, small 5	} 100,287	1,000	1,450	2,600	——
1810 Small date, tall 5		650.00	800.00	1,000	2,500
1810 Large date, small 5		650.00	825.00	1,100	2,800
1810 Large date, tall 5		625.00	750.00	1,000	2,500
1811 Small 5	} 99,581	625.00	800.00	1,100	2,500
1811 Large 5		625.00	800.00	1,100	2,500
1812	58,087	625.00	800.00	1,100	2,850

CAPPED HEAD TO LEFT 1813-1834

	Quan. Minted	F-12	VF-20	EF-40	MS-60
1813	95,428	650.00	900.00	1,300	3,400
1814, 4 over 3	15,454	900.00	1,300	1,650	4,900
1815	635	A.N.A. Sale 1976 . . . . $75,000			
1818 Normal dies	} 48,588	875.00	1,275	1,550	4,400
1818 STATESOF one word		875.00	1,275	1,550	4,750
1818, 5D over 50		875.00	1,275	1,550	4,750
1819	} 51,723		15,000	25,000	——
1819, 5D over 50					——

[174]

HALF EAGLES

Curved Base 2

Square Base 2

Small Letters

Large Letters

	Quan. Minted	F-12	VF-20	EF-40	MS-60
1820 Curved-base 2, small letters...... ⎫		$750.00	$1,250	$1,700	$5,000
1820 Curved-base 2, large letters...... ⎬ 263,806		850.00	1,350	1,900	5,500
1820 Square-base 2.................. ⎭		850.00	1,350	1,900	5,500
1821 34,641		1,800	3,750	5,900	16,000

1822

1825, 5 over 1

1825, 5 over 4

		F-12	VF-20	EF-40	MS-60
1822 (3 known)	17,796	——	——	——	——
1823	14,485	1,250	2,000	2,900	10,000
1824	17,340	3,750	6,000	10,000	22,500
1825, 5 over 1 .... ⎫		2,000	3,500	5,100	12,500
1825, 5 over 4 .... ⎬ 29,060		——	——	——	——
1826	18,069	2,250	4,000	6,000	14,000
1827	24,913	4,000	7,500	10,000	——

1828, 8 over 7

Large Date

Small Date

		F-12	VF-20	EF-40	MS-60
1828, 8 over 7 .... ⎫		3,000	4,250	9,500	——
1828 .... ⎬ 28,029		3,750	6,500	12,500	——
1829 Large date .... ⎫		——	——	——	——
1829 Small date .... ⎬ 57,442		1974 MANA Sale $100,000			

The half eagles dated 1829 (small date) through 1834 are smaller in diameter
than the earlier pieces. They also have smaller letters, dates and stars.

HALF EAGLES

| | Large 5D | Small 5D | 13 Stars, Square Base 2 |

	Quan. Minted	F-12	VF-20	EF-40	MS-60
1830 Small 5 D	} 126,351	$1,500	$2,000	$3,750	$9,200
1830 Large 5 D		1,500	2,000	3,750	9,200
1831	140,594	1,500	2,000	3,750	9,200
1832 Curved-base 2, 12 stars	} 157,487	—	—		
1832 Square-base 2, 13 stars		3,000	5,000	7,000	13,000
1833	193,630	1,600	2,400	3,800	8,500

4
Plain 4

4
Crosslet 4

		F-12	VF-20	EF-40	MS-60
1834 Plain 4	} 50,141	1,750	3,000	4,200	10,500
1834 Crosslet 4		1,750	3,000	4,200	10,500

CLASSIC HEAD TYPE 1834-1838

As on the quarter dollar of 1831, the motto E PLURIBUS UNUM was omitted from the new, reduced size half eagle in 1834, presumably for lack of space.

Designer William Kneass; weight 8.36 grams; composition: .8992 gold, .1008 copper; diameter 22.5 mm; reeded edge.

1834 Plain 4	} 657,460	125.00	200.00	350.00	1,400
1834 Crosslet 4		225.00	300.00	550.00	2,000
1835	371,534	125.00	200.00	350.00	1,400
1836	553,147	125.00	200.00	350.00	1,400
1837	207,121	125.00	200.00	350.00	1,400
1838	286,588	125.00	200.00	350.00	1,400
1838C	17,179	500.00	725.00	1,250	4,250
1838D	20,583	500.00	725.00	1,250	4,250

CORONET TYPE, No Motto Above Eagle 1839-1866

Designer Christian Gobrecht; weight 8.359 grams; composition: .900 gold, .100 copper; diameter (1839-40) 22.5 mm, (1840-1929) 21.6 mm; reeded edge. Net weight: .24187 oz. pure gold.

F-12 FINE—*LIBERTY readable, but partly weak. Neck hair worn, but outlines clear.*

VF-20 VERY FINE—*LIBERTY bold. Major lines show in neck hair.*

EF-40 EXTREMELY FINE—*Neck hair details clear. Slight wear on top and lower part of coronet, and hair.*

MS-60 UNCIRCULATED—*No trace of wear. Light blemishes.*

Mint mark above date 1839 only.
Mint mark below eagle 1840-1908.

HALF EAGLES

	Quan. Minted	F-12	VF-20	EF-40	MS-60
1839, 9 over 8, well curved date....... }	118,143			—	
1839 Normal date.................... }		$115.00	$165.00	$275.00	$850.00
1839C..................................	17,205	285.00	450.00	750.00	2,000
1839D..................................	18,939	285.00	450.00	750.00	2,000
1840*.................................	137,382	100.00	135.00	200.00	675.00
1840C*................................	18,992	250.00	400.00	675.00	2,000
1840D*................................	22,896	250.00	400.00	675.00	2,000
1840O*................................	40,120	170.00	230.00	350.00	1,500
1841.................................	15,833	135.00	225.00	325.00	1,400
1841C..................................	21,467	275.00	400.00	625.00	2,000
1841D..................................	29,392	275.00	400.00	625.00	2,000
1841O (2 known).........................	50			—	

*Scarce varieties of the 1840 coins have the large diameter and wide rims of the 1839 issues.

1842 Large Date	Small Letters			Large Letters	

	Quan. Minted	F-12	VF-20	EF-40	MS-60
1842 Small letters.................... }	27,578	110.00	150.00	250.00	850.00
1842 Large letters .... }		110.00	150.00	250.00	825.00
1842C Small date .... }	27,432	600.00	800.00	1,250	3,000
1842C Large date.................... }		225.00	325.00	500.00	1,800
1842D Small date.................... }	59,608	225.00	325.00	500.00	1,800
1842D Large date.................... }		275.00	475.00	775.00	2,000
1842O.................................	16,400	160.00	265.00	400.00	1,300
1843	611,205	95.00	130.00	165.00	800.00
1843C..................................	44,277	225.00	300.00	575.00	1,600
1843D..................................	98,452	225.00	300.00	575.00	1,600
1843O Small letters.....................	19,075	150.00	215.00	350.00	1,200
1843O Large letters.....................	82,000	150.00	215.00	325.00	1,100
1844	340,330	95.00	130.00	165.00	700.00
1844C..................................	23,631	250.00	350.00	650.00	2,000
1844D..................................	88,982	225.00	300.00	575.00	1,650
1844O.................................	364,600	150.00	215.00	325.00	950.00
1845	417,099	95.00	130.00	165.00	700.00
1845D..................................	90,629	225.00	300.00	525.00	1,400
1845O.................................	41,000	150.00	225.00	350.00	950.00
1846	395,942	95.00	130.00	165.00	650.00
1846C..................................	12,995	275.00	400.00	675.00	1,850
1846D..................................	80,294	200.00	325.00	600.00	1,400
1846O.................................	58,000	150.00	225.00	350.00	1,100
1847	915,981	95.00	130.00	165.00	650.00
1847, top of extra very low 7 at border				—	—
1847C..................................	84,151	225.00	325.00	550.00	1,500
1847D..................................	64,405	225.00	325.00	550.00	1,500
1847O.................................	12,000	225.00	325.00	550.00	1,650
1848	260,775	95.00	130.00	165.00	550.00
1848C..................................	64,472	225.00	325.00	550.00	1,500
1848D..................................	47,465	225.00	325.00	550.00	1,500
1849	133,070	95.00	130.00	165.00	650.00
1849C..................................	64,823	225.00	325.00	575.00	1,600
1849D..................................	39,036	225.00	325.00	575.00	1,600

HALF EAGLES

	Quan. Minted	F-12	VF-20	EF-40	MS-60	Proof
1850	64,491	$95.00	$130.00	$165.00	$650.00	
1850C	63,591	225.00	325.00	550.00	1,500	
1850D	43,984	225.00	325.00	550.00	1,500	
1851	377,505	95.00	130.00	165.00	650.00	
1851C	49,176	225.00	325.00	550.00	1,500	
1851D	62,710	225.00	325.00	550.00	1,500	
1851O	41,000	150.00	275.00	450.00	1,150	
1852	573,901	95.00	130.00	165.00	525.00	
1852C	72,574	225.00	325.00	550.00	1,500	
1852D	91,584	225.00	325.00	550.00	1,500	
1853	305,770	95.00	130.00	165.00	525.00	
1853C	65,571	225.00	325.00	550.00	1,500	
1853D	89,678	225.00	325.00	550.00	1,500	
1854	160,675	95.00	130.00	165.00	525.00	
1854C	39,283	225.00	325.00	550.00	1,500	
1854D	56,413	225.00	325.00	550.00	1,500	
1854O	46,000	200.00	325.00	425.00	1,000	
1854S	268			——	——	
1855	117,098	90.00	115.00	150.00	525.00	——
1855C	39,788	225.00	325.00	550.00	1,500	
1855D	22,432	225.00	325.00	550.00	1,500	
1855O	11,100	225.00	325.00	575.00	1,600	
1855S	61,000	110.00	140.00	240.00	900.00	
1856	197,990	90.00	115.00	150.00	525.00	——
1856C	28,457	225.00	325.00	550.00	1,500	
1856D	19,786	225.00	325.00	550.00	1,500	
1856O	10,000	250.00	400.00	875.00	2,000	
1856S	105,100	100.00	125.00	200.00	750.00	
1857	98,188	90.00	115.00	150.00	525.00	——
1857C	31,360	225.00	325.00	550.00	1,500	
1857D	17,046	225.00	325.00	550.00	1,500	
1857O	13,000	225.00	325.00	525.00	1,250	
1857S	87,000	100.00	125.00	200.00	750.00	
1858	15,136	165.00	250.00	350.00	850.00	——
1858C	38,856	225.00	325.00	550.00	1,500	
1858D	15,362	225.00	325.00	550.00	1,500	
1858S	18,600	165.00	275.00	375.00	1,100	
1859	16,814	140.00	225.00	325.00	850.00	7,500
1859C	31,847	225.00	325.00	550.00	1,500	
1859D	10,366	250.00	400.00	825.00	1,800	
1859S	13,220	165.00	275.00	450.00	1,100	
1860	(62) 19,825	140.00	200.00	300.00	750.00	6,750
1860C	14,813	225.00	350.00	725.00	1,650	
1860D	14,635	225.00	350.00	725.00	1,750	
1860S	21,200	140.00	250.00	375.00	975.00	
1861	(66)688,150	90.00	115.00	150.00	525.00	6,750
1861C	6,879	900.00	1,300	2,500	4,600	
1861D	1,597	2,400	3,800	6,500	12,500	
1861S	18,000	140.00	225.00	350.00	1,150	
1862	(35) 4,465	250.00	350.00	525.00	1,350	6,750
1862S	9,500	200.00	300.00	450.00	1,250	
1863	(30) 2,472	350.00	550.00	825.00	2,400	6,750
1863S	17,000	165.00	275.00	425.00	1,350	
1864	(50) 4,220	275.00	400.00	625.00	1,800	6,750
1864S	3,888	850.00	1,500	2,200	——	

HALF EAGLES

	Quan. Minted	F-12	VF-20	EF-40	MS-60	Proof
1865 .... (25)	1,295	$525.00	$800.00	$950.00	$2,400	$6,750
1865S	27,612	140.00	225.00	325.00	900.00	
1866S	9,000	175.00	275.00	525.00	1,300	

Variety 2 — Motto Above Eagle 1866-1908

Designer Christian Gobrecht; weight 8.359 grams; composition: .900 gold, .100 copper; diameter 21.6 mm; reeded edge. Net weight: .24187 oz. pure gold.

F-12 FINE—*All letters in motto IN GOD WE TRUST readable.*

VF-20 VERY FINE—*Half of hairlines above coronet missing. Hair curls under ear evident, but worn. Motto and its ribbon sharp.*

EF-40 EXTREMELY FINE—*Small amount of wear on top of hair and below L in LIBERTY. Wear evident on wing tips and neck of eagle.*

MS-60 UNCIRCULATED—*No trace of wear. Light blemishes.*

	Quan. Minted	F-12	VF-20	EF-40	MS-60	Proof
1866 .... (30)	6,730	$250.00	$375.00	$600.00	$1,300	$6,500
1866S	34,920	200.00	325.00	500.00	1,100	
1867 .... (50)	6,920	175.00	300.00	450.00	1,200	6,500
1867S	29,000	135.00	225.00	325.00	1,200	
1868 .... (25)	5,725	165.00	275.00	425.00	1,250	6,500
1868S	52,000	110.00	175.00	300.00	850.00	
1869 .... (25)	1,785	325.00	525.00	825.00	1,750	6,500
1869S	31,000	110.00	175.00	300.00	850.00	
1870 .... (35)	4,035	175.00	350.00	500.00	1,100	6,500
1870CC	7,675	1,100	1,700	3,500		
1870S	17,000	125.00	200.00	325.00	800.00	
1871 .... (30)	3,230	225.00	375.00	525.00	1,100	6,500
1871CC	20,770	300.00	475.00	725.00	1,800	
1871S	25,000	125.00	175.00	275.00	800.00	
1872 .... (30)	1,690	425.00	650.00	1,000	1,700	6,500
1872CC	16,980	425.00	650.00	1,000	1,700	
1872S	36,400	125.00	175.00	250.00	575.00	
1873 Closed 3........... (25)	112,505	90.00	110.00	135.00	250.00	6,500
1873 Open 3..............		90.00	110.00	135.00	250.00	
1873CC	7,416	400.00	700.00	1,000	2,100	
1873S	31,000	100.00	150.00	225.00	650.00	
1874 .... (20)	3,508	200.00	325.00	575.00	1,300	6,500
1874CC	21,198	200.00	325.00	575.00	1,600	
1874S	16,000	125.00	225.00	325.00	650.00	
1875 .... (20)	220	—	—	—	—	—
1875CC	11,828	300.00	525.00	1,000	1,850	
1875S	9,000	150.00	325.00	525.00	1,200	
1876 .... (45)	1,477	400.00	650.00	1,300	2,500	6,500
1876CC	6,887	325.00	500.00	950.00	1,800	
1876S	4,000	325.00	550.00	875.00	1,600	
1877 .... (20)	1,152	350.00	725.00	950.00	2,700	7,750
1877CC	8,680	325.00	500.00	950.00	1,800	
1877S	26,700	110.00	140.00	195.00	475.00	
1878 .... (20)	131,740	90.00	110.00	135.00	200.00	5,750
1878CC	9,054	850.00	1,500	2,500		
1878S	144,700	90.00	110.00	125.00	175.00	
1879 .... (30)	301,950	90.00	110.00	125.00	175.00	3,750
1879CC	17,281	195.00	300.00	600.00	950.00	
1879S	426,200	90.00	110.00	125.00	215.00	
1880 .... (36)	3,166,436	85.00	105.00	120.00	160.00	3,750

HALF EAGLES

	Quan. Minted	F-12	VF-20	EF-40	MS-60	Proof
1880CC 51,017		$125.00	$165.00	$250.00	$600.00	
1880S........................ 1,348,900		85.00	105.00	120.00	150.00	
1881, 1 over 0 .... }	5,708,802	—	—	—	—	
1881 ....(42) {		85.00	105.00	120.00	160.00	$3,000
1881CC 13,886		150.00	250.00	400.00	800.00	
1881S........................ 969,000		85.00	105.00	120.00	160.00	
1882 ....(48)	2,514,568	85.00	105.00	120.00	160.00	3,000
1882CC 82,817		125.00	165.00	275.00	500.00	
1882S........................ 969,000		85.00	105.00	120.00	150.00	
1883 ....(61)	233,461	85.00	105.00	120.00	170.00	3,000
1883CC 12,958		150.00	195.00	375.00	650.00	
1883S........................ 83,200		85.00	105.00	120.00	160.00	
1884 ....(48)	191,078	85.00	105.00	120.00	160.00	3,000
1884CC 16,402		150.00	195.00	325.00	600.00	
1884S........................ 177,000		85.00	105.00	120.00	170.00	
1885 ....(66)	601,506	85.00	105.00	120.00	160.00	3,000
1885S........................ 1,211,500		85.00	105.00	120.00	160.00	
1886 ....(72)	388,432	85.00	105.00	120.00	170.00	3,000
1886S........................ 3,268,000		85.00	105.00	120.00	150.00	
1887 Proofs only........ (87)	87..........................					14,500
1887S........................ 1,912,000		85.00	105.00	120.00	150.00	
1888 ....(95)	18,296	110.00	150.00	175.00	275.00	2,750
1888S........................ 293,900		85.00	105.00	120.00	160.00	
1889 ....(45)	7,565	225.00	350.00	400.00	850.00	2,750
1890 ....(88)	4,328	275.00	375.00	475.00	950.00	2,750
1890CC 53,800		125.00	175.00	225.00	375.00	
1891 ....(53)	61,413	85.00	105.00	135.00	275.00	2,750
1891CC 208,000		115.00	175.00	250.00	425.00	
1892 ....(92)	753,572	85.00	105.00	120.00	150.00	2,500
1892CC 82,968		110.00	150.00	225.00	400.00	
1892O........................ 10,000		425.00	775.00	1,100	2,200	
1892S........................ 298,400		85.00	105.00	120.00	150.00	
1893 ....(77)	1,528,197	85.00	105.00	120.00	150,00	2,500
1893CC 60,000		110.00	165.00	225.00	425.00	
1893O........................ 110,000		140.00	195.00	275.00	600.00	
1893S........................ 224,000		85.00	105.00	120.00	150.00	
1894 ....(75)	957,955	85.00	105.00	120.00	150.00	2,500
1894O........................ 16,600		165.00	250.00	375.00	750.00	
1894S........................ 55,900		90.00	120.00	135.00	200.00	
1895 ....(81)	1,345,936	85.00	105.00	120.00	150.00	2,250
1895S........................ 112,000		85.00	105.00	120.00	160.00	
1896 ....(103)	59,063	85.00	105.00	120.00	160.00	2,250
1896S........................ 155,400		85.00	105.00	120.00	150.00	
1897 ....(83)	867,883	85.00	105.00	120.00	150.00	2,250
1897S........................ 354,000		85.00	105.00	120.00	150.00	
1898 ....(75)	633,495	85.00	105.00	120.00	150.00	2,250
1898S........................ 1,397,400		85.00	105.00	120.00	150.00	
1899 ....(99)	1,710,729	85.00	105.00	120.00	150.00	2,250
1899S........................ 1,545,000		85.00	105.00	120.00	150.00	
1900 ....(230)	1,405,730	85.00	105.00	120.00	150.00	2,250
1900S........................ 329,000		85.00	105.00	120.00	150.00	
1901 ....(140)	616,040	85.00	105.00	120.00	150.00	2,250
1901S, 1 over 0 .... }	3,648,000	100.00	135.00	190.00	600.00	
1901S. .... {		85.00	105.00	120.00	150.00	
1902 ....(162)	172,562	85.00	105.00	120.00	160.00	2,250
1902S........................ 939,000		85.00	105.00	120.00	150.00	

HALF EAGLES

	Quan. Minted	F-12	VF-20	EF-40	MS-60	Proof
1903 . . . . (154)	227,024	$85.00	$105.00	$120.00	$150.00	$2,250
1903S	1,855,000	85.00	105.00	120.00	150.00	
1904 . . . . (136)	392,136	85.00	105.00	120.00	150.00	2,250
1904S	97,000	100.00	125.00	150.00	275.00	
1905 . . . . (108)	302,308	85.00	105.00	120.00	150.00	2,250
1905S	880,700	85.00	105.00	120.00	150.00	
1906 . . . . (85)	348,820	85.00	105.00	120.00	150.00	2,250
1906D	320,000	85.00	105.00	125.00	175.00	
1906S	598,000	85.00	105.00	120.00	150.00	
1907 . . . . (92)	626,192	85.00	105.00	120.00	150.00	2,250
1907D	888,000	85.00	105.00	120.00	150.00	
1908	421,874	85.00	105.00	120.00	150.00	

INDIAN HEAD TYPE 1908-1929

This type conforms to the quarter eagle of the same date. The incuse designs and lettering make this a unique series, along with the quarter eagle, in our United States coinage.

Designer Bela Lyon Pratt; weight 8.359 grams; composition: .900 gold, .100 copper; diameter 21.6 mm; reeded edge. Net weight: .24187 oz. pure gold.

Mint mark location.

F-12 FINE—*The knot in hair cord must show but small feathers on top of head will be faint.*
VF-20 VERY FINE—*Noticeable wear on large middle feathers and tip of eagle's wing.*
EF-40 EXTREMELY FINE—*Cheekbone, war bonnet and headband feathers slightly worn. Feathers on eagle's upper wing show considerable wear.*

The scarcer coins with mint marks well struck command higher prices.

		F-12	VF-20	EF-40	MS-60	Matte Proof
1908 . . . . (167)	578,012	90.00	120.00	140.00	275.00	3,750
1908D	148,000	90.00	120.00	140.00	275.00	
1908S	82,000	150.00	250.00	675.00	2,000	
1909 . . . . (78)	627,138	90.00	120.00	140.00	275.00	3,750
1909D	3,423,560	90.00	120.00	140.00	275.00	
1909O*	34,200	295.00	475.00	850.00	4,100	
1909S	297,200	100.00	125.00	150.00	700.00	
1910 . . . . (250)	604,250	90.00	120.00	140.00	275.00	3,750
1910D	193,600	100.00	125.00	150.00	450.00	
1910S	770,200	90.00	120.00	140.00	400.00	
1911 . . . . (139)	915,139	90.00	120.00	140.00	275.00	3,750
1911D	72,500	125.00	200.00	350.00	2,200	
1911S	1,416,000	100.00	125.00	170.00	600.00	
1912 . . . . (144)	790,144	90.00	120.00	140.00	275.00	3,750
1912S	392,000	100.00	125.00	170.00	700.00	
1913 . . . . (99)	916,000	90.00	120.00	140.00	275.00	3,750
1913S	408,000	100.00	135.00	200.00	900.00	
1914 . . . . (125)	247,125	90.00	120.00	140.00	275.00	3,750
1914D	247,000	100.00	125.00	145.00	350.00	
1914S	263,000	100.00	130.00	165.00	500.00	

*Beware spurious "O" mint mark.

HALF EAGLES

	Quan. Minted	F-12	VF-20	EF-40	MS-60	Matte Proof
1915* .... (75)	588,075	$90.00	$120.00	$140.00	$275.00	$4,250
1915S........................	164,000	110.00	135.00	240.00	1,000	
1916S........................	240,000	115.00	145.00	240.00	900.00	
1929	662,000	1,600	1,900	2,300	3,900	

*Pieces dated 1915D are counterfeit.

EAGLES ($10.00 Gold Pieces) — 1795-1933

Coinage authority including specified weights and fineness of the eagle conforms to that of the half eagle. The small eagle reverse was used until 1797 when the large, heraldic eagle replaced it. The early dates have variations in the number of stars, the rarest date being 1798. Many of these early pieces show file scratches from the mint's practice of adjusting weight. No eagles were struck dated 1805 to 1837. Proofs of some dates prior to 1855 are known to exist, and all are rare.

CAPPED BUST TO RIGHT, SMALL EAGLE 1795-1797

Designer Robert Scot; weight 17.50 grams; composition: .9167 gold, .0833 copper; approx. diameter 33 mm; reeded edge.

F-12 FINE—Details on turban and head obliterated.

VF-20 VERY FINE—Neck hairlines and details under turban and over forehead are worn but distinguishable.

EF-40 EXTREMELY FINE—Definite wear on hair to left of eye and strand of hair across and around turban, also on eagle's wing tips.

MS-60 UNCIRCULATED—No trace of wear. Light blemishes.

	Quan. Minted	F-12	VF-20	EF-40	MS-60
1795 9 leaves below eagle	} 5,583	$2,800	$4,250	$7,750	$21,000
1795 12 leaves below eagle		2,500	4,000	6,000	17,500
1796	4,146	2,500	4,000	6,000	17,500
1797 Small eagle........................	3,615	2,750	4,500	7,000	18,500

CAPPED BUST TO RIGHT, HERALDIC EAGLE 1797-1804

		F-12	VF-20	EF-40	MS-60
1797 Large eagle	10,940	1,200	2,200	3,200	8,000
1798, 8 over 7, 9 stars left, 4 right	900	3,000	6,000	9,000	16,000
1798, 8 over 7, 7 stars left, 6 right	842	6,500	15,000	—	—
1799	37,449	1,150	1,500	2,200	5,500
1800	5,999	1,300	1,850	2,900	7,250

EAGLES

	Quan. Minted	F-12	VF-20	EF-40	MS-60
1801	44,344	$1,150	$1,500	$2,200	$6,000
1803	15,017	1,250	1,850	2,600	6,750
1804	3,757	1,700	2,750	4,500	11,000

CORONET TYPE, No Motto Above Eagle 1838-1866

In 1838 the weight and diameter of the eagle were reduced and the obverse and reverse were redesigned. Liberty now faces left and the word LIBERTY is placed on the coronet. A more natural appearing eagle is used on the reverse. The value, TEN D., is shown for the first time on this denomination.

Designer Christian Gobrecht; weight 16.718 grams; composition: .900 gold, .100 copper, diameter 27 mm; reeded edge. Net weight: .48375 oz. pure gold.

F-12 FINE—*LIBERTY readable but may be slightly worn.*

VF-20 VERY FINE—*Hairlines above coronet partly worn. Curls under ear worn but defined.*

EF-40 EXTREMELY FINE—*Small amount of wear on top of hair and below L in LIBERTY. Wear evident on wing tips and neck of eagle.*

MS-60 UNCIRCULATED—*No trace of wear. Light blemishes.*

Mint mark location on reverse below eagle.

1838	7,200	575.00	800.00	1,500	6,500
1839 Large letters	25,801	500.00	700.00	1,250	5,000

The Liberty head style of 1838 and 1839 (large letters) differs from that used for subsequent issues.

1839 Small letters	12,447	450.00	650.00	1,200	5,000
1840	47,338	140.00	175.00	250.00	1,200
1841	63,131	140.00	175.00	250.00	1,200
1841O	2,500	400.00	550.00	950.00	5,000
1842 Small date	} 81,507	135.00	165.00	225.00	1,100
1842 Large date		135.00	165.00	225.00	1,100
1842O	27,400	145.00	185.00	250.00	1,750
1843	75,462	135.00	165.00	225.00	1,200

EAGLES

	Quan. Minted	F-12	VF-20	EF-40	MS-60	Proof
1843O	175,162	$135.00	$165.00	$250.00	$1,700	
1844	6,361	225.00	400.00	800.00	2,500	
1844O	118,700	135.00	165.00	250.00	1,200	
1845	26,153	135.00	165.00	250.00	1,750	
1845O	47,500	135.00	165.00	250.00	1,750	
1846	20,095	135.00	165.00	250.00	1,600	
1846O	81,780	135.00	165.00	250.00	1,600	
1847	862,258	135.00	165.00	225.00	1,250	
1847O	571,500	135.00	165.00	225.00	1,250	
1848	145,484	135.00	165.00	225.00	1,250	
1848O	35,850	135.00	165.00	250.00	1,750	
1849	653,618	135.00	165.00	225.00	1,000	
1849O	23,900	145.00	200.00	300.00	1,750	
1850	291,451	135.00	165.00	225.00	1,000	
1850O	57,500	135.00	165.00	250.00	1,100	
1851	176,328	135.00	165.00	225.00	1,000	
1851O	263,000	135.00	165.00	250.00	1,100	
1852	263,106	135.00	165.00	225.00	1,050	
1852O	18,000	150.00	225.00	375.00	1,800	
1853	201,253	135.00	165.00	225.00	1,000	
1853, 3 over 2		250.00	400.00	750.00		
1853O	51,000	135.00	165.00	250.00	1,200	
1854	54,250	135.00	165.00	250.00	1,200	
1854O Large or small date	52,500	145.00	200.00	300.00	1,300	
1854S	123,826	150.00	210.00	325.00	1,750	
1855	121,701	135.00	165.00	225.00	1,000	——
1855O	18,000	160.00	225.00	400.00	2,350	
1855S	9,000	250.00	400.00	700.00	2,750	——
1856	60,490	135.00	165.00	250.00	1,100	
1856O	14,500	150.00	220.00	375.00	1,900	
1856S	68,000	145.00	175.00	300.00	1,500	
1857	16,606	160.00	250.00	350.00	1,800	
1857O	5,500	400.00	850.00	1,200	3,250	
1857S	26,000	150.00	225.00	325.00	2,000	
1858*	2,521	3,500	4,500	7,000	25,000	——
1858O	20,000	150.00	250.00	375.00	2,100	
1858S	11,800	165.00	250.00	375.00	1,500	
1859	16,093	150.00	225.00	325.00	1,200	$8,000
1859O	2,300	600.00	1,200	2,000	4,000	
1859S	7,000	350.00	600.00	1,000	2,750	
1860 (50)	15,105	150.00	200.00	300.00	1,250	7,000
1860O	11,100	175.00	300.00	425.00	2,000	
1860S	5,000	350.00	550.00	1,000	3,250	
1861 (69)	113,233	135.00	165.00	250.00	1,100	7,000
1861S	15,500	150.00	225.00	350.00	1,200	
1862 (35)	10,995	175.00	275.00	400.00	2,000	7,000
1862S	12,500	175.00	275.00	400.00	1,750	
1863 (30)	1,248	1,750	2,750	4,250	7,500	16,000
1863S	10,000	250.00	450.00	725.00	2,750	
1864 (50)	3,580	450.00	750.00	1,200	3,000	13,000
1864S	2,500	1,100	2,000	3,200		
1865 (25)	4,005	450.00	800.00	1,000	3,250	8,500
1865 All kinds	} 16,700	375.00	750.00	1,250	3,250	
1865S, 865 over inverted 186		400.00	900.00	1,400		
1866S	8,500	500.00	1,000	1,500	3,500	

*Beware removed mint mark.

[184]

EAGLES
Variety 2 — Motto Above Eagle 1866-1907

Mint mark location is on the reverse below the eagle.

F-12 FINE—*All letters in LIBERTY are complete.*

VF-20 VERY FINE—*Half of hairlines over coronet visible. Curls under ear worn but defined. IN GOD WE TRUST and its ribbon are sharp.*

EF-40 EXTREMELY FINE—*Small amount of wear on top of hair and below L in LIBERTY. Wear evident on wing tips and neck of eagle.*

MS-60 UNCIRCULATED—*No trace of wear. Light blemishes.*

	Quan. Minted	F-12	VF-20	EF-40	MS-60	Proof
1866 . . . . (30)	3,780	$300.00	$475.00	$700.00	$1,900	$12,000
1866S	11,500	250.00	325.00	500.00	1,650	
1867 . . . . (50)	3,140	250.00	475.00	650.00	1,800	9,000
1867S	9,000	225.00	300.00	500.00	1,300	
1868 . . . . (25)	10,655	175.00	250.00	325.00	900.00	9,000
1868S	13,500	175.00	250.00	325.00	900.00	
1869 . . . . (25)	1,855	600.00	1,000	1,500	2,000	9,000
1869S	6,430	225.00	375.00	500.00	1,400	
1870 . . . . (35)	4,025	300.00	500.00	650.00	1,650	9,000
1870CC	5,908	800.00	1,800	3,000		
1870S	8,000	210.00	350.00	500.00	1,300	
1871 . . . . (30)	1,820	500.00	750.00	1,200	3,500	9,000
1871CC	8,085	500.00	750.00	1,500		
1871S	16,500	175.00	300.00	425.00	1,100	
1872 . . . . (30)	1,650	600.00	900.00	1,500	2,750	9,000
1872CC	4,600	450.00	750.00	1,100	2,300	
1872S	17,300	150.00	225.00	350.00	1,000	
1873 . . . . (25)	825	1,250	2,100	3,750	7,000	15,000
1873CC	4,543	700.00	1,400	2,500	4,500	
1873S	12,000	150.00	225.00	350.00	1,000	
1874 . . . . (20)	53,160	135.00	160.00	200.00	350.00	9,000
1874CC	16,767	215.00	375.00	500.00	1,500	
1874S	10,000	200.00	350.00	450.00	1,000	
1875 . . . . (20)	120	—	—	—		—
1875CC	7,715	400.00	650.00	950.00	2,000	
1876 . . . . (45)	732	950.00	1,800	3,250	6,500	9,500
1876CC	4,696	525.00	850.00	1,150	2,450	
1876S	5,000	300.00	450.00	800.00	1,750	
1877 . . . . (20)	817	1,200	2,250	3,500	7,500	15,000
1877CC	3,332	600.00	900.00	1,300	2,750	
1877S	17,000	150.00	175.00	275.00	500.00	
1878 . . . . (20)	73,800	110.00	125.00	150.00	200.00	9,000
1878CC	3,244	600.00	950.00	1,750	3,250	
1878S	26,100	125.00	150.00	200.00	225.00	
1879 . . . . (30)	384,770	110.00	125.00	145.00	200.00	6,000
1879CC	1,762	1,500	3,500	5,000	9,500	
1879O	1,500	800.00	1,500	2,750	6,000	
1879S	224,000	110.00	125.00	145.00	200.00	

EAGLES

	Quan. Minted	F-12	VF-20	EF-40	MS-60	Proof
1880 .... (36)	1,644,876	$125.00	$145.00	$160.00	$225.00	$6,000
1880CC	11,190	150.00	250.00	350.00	725.00	
1880O........................	9,200	165.00	275.00	400.00	800.00	
1880S........................	506,250	125.00	145.00	160.00	220.00	
1881 .... (40)	3,877,260	125.00	145.00	160.00	210.00	6,000
1881CC	24,015	165.00	275.00	375.00	650.00	
1881O........................	8,350	165.00	275.00	400.00	850.00	
1881S........................	970,000	125.00	145.00	160.00	210.00	
1882 .... (40)	2,324,480	125.00	145.00	160.00	210.00	6,000
1882CC	6,764	200.00	310.00	500.00	1,000	
1882O........................	10,820	175.00	225.00	300.00	600.00	
1882S........................	132,000	125.00	145.00	160.00	210.00	
1883 .... (40)	208,740	125.00	145.00	160.00	210.00	6,000
1883CC	12,000	175.00	225.00	375.00	700.00	
1883O........................	800	1,500	2,500	4,250	8,000	
1883S........................	38,000	135.00	175.00	225.00	325.00	
1884 .... (15)	76,905	125.00	145.00	160.00	210.00	15,000
1884CC	9,925	175.00	275.00	400.00	850.00	
1884S........................	124,250	125.00	145.00	170.00	225.00	
1885 .... (65)	253,527	125.00	145.00	160.00	210.00	4,500
1885S........................	228,000	125.00	145.00	160.00	210.00	
1886 .... (60)	236,160	125.00	145.00	160.00	210.00	4,500
1886S........................	826,000	125.00	145.00	160.00	210.00	
1887 .... (80)	53,680	125.00	145.00	160.00	210.00	4,500
1887S........................	817,000	125.00	145.00	160.00	210.00	
1888 .... (75)	132,996	125.00	145.00	160.00	210.00	4,500
1888O........................	21,335	150.00	175.00	250.00	400.00	
1888S........................	648,700	125.00	145.00	160.00	210.00	
1889 .... (45)	4,485	250.00	375.00	600.00	925.00	5,500
1889S........................	425,400	125.00	145.00	160.00	210.00	
1890 .... (63)	58,043	130.00	150.00	170.00	225.00	4,500
1890CC	17,500	175.00	225.00	300.00	550.00	
1891 .... (48)	91,868	125.00	145.00	160.00	210.00	5,000
1891CC	103,732	160.00	200.00	275.00	500.00	
1892 .... (72)	797,552	125.00	145.00	160.00	210.00	4,500
1892CC	40,000	200.00	300.00	375.00	500.00	
1892O........................	28,688	130.00	150.00	175.00	300.00	
1892S........................	115,500	125.00	145.00	160.00	210.00	
1893 .... (55)	1,840,895	125.00	145.00	160.00	210.00	4,500
1893CC	14,000	160.00	200.00	275.00	550.00	
1893O........................	17,000	160.00	200.00	275.00	550.00	
1893S........................	141,350	125.00	145.00	160.00	210.00	
1894 .... (43)	2,470,778	125.00	145.00	160.00	210.00	4,500
1894O........................	107,500	125.00	145.00	160.00	250.00	
1894S........................	25,000	125.00	145.00	160.00	250.00	
1895 .... (56)	567,826	125.00	145.00	160.00	210.00	4,500
1895O........................	98,000	125.00	145.00	160.00	225.00	
1895S........................	49,000	125.00	145.00	160.00	210.00	
1896 .... (78)	76,348	125.00	145.00	160.00	210.00	4,500
1896S........................	123,750	125.00	145.00	160.00	210.00	
1897 .... (69)	1,000,159	125.00	145.00	160.00	210.00	4,500
1897O........................	42,500	125.00	145.00	160.00	250.00	
1897S........................	234,750	125.00	145.00	160.00	210.00	
1898 .... (67)	812,197	125.00	145.00	160.00	210.00	4,000
1898S........................	473,600	125.00	145.00	160.00	210.00	

EAGLES

	Quan. Minted	F-12	VF-20	EF-40	MS-60	Proof
1899 . . . . (86)	1,262,305	$125.00	$145.00	$160.00	$210.00	$4,000
1899O 37,047		125.00	145.00	160.00	250.00	
1899S 841,000		125.00	145.00	160.00	210.00	
1900 . . . . (120)	293,960	125.00	145.00	160.00	210.00	4,000
1900S 81,000		125.00	145.00	160.00	225.00	
1901 . . . . (85)	1,718,825	125.00	145.00	160.00	210.00	4,000
1901O 72,041		125.00	145.00	160.00	250.00	
1901S 2,812,750		125.00	145.00	160.00	210.00	
1902 . . . . (113)	82,513	125.00	145.00	160.00	225.00	4,000
1902S 469,500		125.00	145.00	160.00	210.00	
1903 . . . . (96)	125,926	125.00	145.00	160.00	210.00	4,000
1903O 112,771		125.00	145.00	160.00	225.00	
1903S 538,000		125.00	145.00	160.00	210.00	
1904 . . . . (108)	162,038	125.00	145.00	160.00	210.00	4,000
1904O 108,950		125.00	145.00	160.00	250.00	
1905 . . . . (86)	201,078	125.00	145.00	160.00	210.00	4,000
1905S 369,250		125.00	145.00	160.00	210.00	
1906 . . . . (77)	165,497	125.00	145.00	160.00	210.00	4,000
1906D 981,000		125.00	145.00	160.00	210.00	
1906O 86,895		125.00	145.00	160.00	270.00	
1906S 457,000		125.00	145.00	160.00	210.00	
1907 . . . . (74)	1,203,973	125.00	145.00	160.00	210.00	4,000
1907D 1,030,000		125.00	145.00	160.00	210.00	
1907S 210,500		125.00	145.00	160.00	210.00	

INDIAN HEAD TYPE 1907-1933

Variety 1 — No Motto on Reverse 1907-1908

Augustus Saint-Gaudens, considered by many the greatest of modern sculptors introduced a new high standard of art in United States coins evidenced by his eagle and double eagle types of 1907. The obverse of the eagle shows the head of Liberty crowned with an Indian war bonnet while an impressively majestic eagle dominates the reverse side. A departure from older standards is found on the edge of the piece, where 46 raised stars are arranged signifying the states of the Union, instead of a lettered or reeded edge. (48 stars 1912 and later.)

The first eagles struck had no motto IN GOD WE TRUST as did the later issues starting in 1908. President Theodore Roosevelt personally objected to the use of the Deity's name on coins. The motto was restored to the coins by Act of Congress in 1908.

F-12 FINE—*Feathers on bonnet show definite wear. Full LIBERTY.*

VF-20 VERY FINE—*Bonnet feathers worn near band. Hair high points show wear.*

EF-40 EXTREMELY FINE—*Slight wear on cheekbone and headdress feathers. Eagle's eye and left wing will show slight wear.*

MS-60 UNCIRCULATED—*No trace of wear. Light blemishes.*

Designer Augustus Saint-Gaudens. Standards same as previous issue. Edge 1907-1911: 46 raised stars; 1912-1933: 48 raised stars.

EAGLES

No Motto

With Motto
IN GOD WE TRUST

Mint mark location is on the reverse at left of fasces.

Choice uncirculated (MS-65) coins are worth substantial premiums.

	Quan. Minted	F-12	VF-20	EF-40	MS-60	Proof
1907 "Wire edge" (rim), periods before and after •E•PLURIBUS•UNUM•.......... 500				$3,250	$6,750	$10,000
1907 Same, no stars on edge.......... (Unique).......................						——
1907 Rounded edge, periods .... 42...............................						30,000
1907 No periods 239,406	$175.00	$225.00	300.00	700.00	
1908 No motto.................. 33,500	200.00	250.00	450.00	1,600	
1908D No motto 210,000	175.00	225.00	300.00	900.00	

Variety 2 — Motto on Reverse 1908-1933

						Matte Proof
1908 .... (116)	341,486	175.00	200.00	240.00	325.00	5,500
1908D........................	836,500	175.00	200.00	240.00	350.00	
1908S........................	59,850	200.00	250.00	475.00	2,500	
1909 .... (74)	184,863	175.00	200.00	240.00	325.00	5,500
1909D........................	121,540	175.00	200.00	240.00	350.00	
1909S........................	292,350	185.00	225.00	250.00	500.00	
1910 .... (204)	318,704	175.00	200.00	240.00	300.00	5,500
1910D........................	2,356,640	175.00	200.00	240.00	300.00	
1910S........................	811,000	175.00	200.00	250.00	600.00	
1911 .... (95)	505,595	175.00	200.00	240.00	300.00	5,500
1911D........................	30,100	225.00	300.00	525.00	2,750	
1911S........................	51,000	200.00	250.00	400.00	1,250	
1912 .... (83)	405,083	175.00	200.00	240.00	300.00	5,500
1912S........................	300,000	175.00	200.00	250.00	600.00	
1913 .... (71)	442,071	175.00	200.00	240.00	300.00	5,500
1913S........................	66,000	200.00	250.00	450.00	1,500	
1914 .... (50)	151,050	175.00	200.00	240.00	325.00	6,750
1914D........................	343,500	175.00	200.00	240.00	350.00	
1914S........................	208,000	175.00	200.00	250.00	600.00	
1915 .... (75)	351,075	175.00	200.00	240.00	300.00	5,500
1915S........................	59,000	200.00	275.00	400.00	1,250	
1916S........................	138,500	200.00	275.00	375.00	1,200	
1920S........................	126,500	4,500	5,500	8,500	20,000	
1926	1,014,000	175.00	200.00	240.00	300.00	
1930S........................	96,000	2,750	3,500	4,250	8,000	
1932	4,463,000	175.00	200.00	240.00	300.00	
1933	312,500				40,000	

DOUBLE EAGLES ($20.00 Gold Pieces) — 1849-1933

This largest denomination of all regular United States issues was authorized to be coined by the Act of March 3, 1849. Its weight was 516 grains, .900 fine. The 1849 double eagle is a unique pattern and reposes in the Mint collection. The rarest date obtainable is 1883. The 1861S reverse design by Anthony C. Paquet was withdrawn soon after striking. Very few specimens are known.

F-12 FINE—*LIBERTY worn but readable. All hairlines show considerable wear.*

VF-20 VERY FINE—*LIBERTY is bold. Jewels on crown defined. Lower half worn flat. Hair worn about ear.*

EF-40 EXTREMELY FINE—*Trace of wear on rounded prongs of crown and down hair curls. Minor bag marks.*

MS-60 UNCIRCULATED—*No trace of wear. Light blemishes.*

Designer James B. Longacre; weight 33.436 grams; composition: .900 gold, .100 copper; diameter 34 mm; reeded edge. Net weight: .96750 oz. pure gold.

Mint mark location is below the eagle.   1861S Paquet Reverse

Without Motto on Reverse 1849-1866

	Quan. Minted	F-12	VF-20	EF-40	MS-60	Proof
1849	1		U.S. Mint Collection			——
1850	1,170,261	$350.00	$450.00	$650.00	$2,600	
1850O	141,000	475.00	600.00	950.00	3,250	
1851	2,087,155	325.00	400.00	450.00	1,800	
1851O	315,000	425.00	575.00	750.00	2,750	
1852	2,053,026	300.00	350.00	400.00	1,800	
1852O	190,000	425.00	575.00	750.00	2,750	
1853	1,261,326	300.00	350.00	400.00	1,800	
1853O	71,000	475.00	600.00	900.00	3,250	
1854	757,899	300.00	350.00	400.00	1,800	
1854O (Scott Sale 1975)	3,250			30,000		
1854S	141,468	350.00	450.00	650.00	3,750	
1855	364,666	300.00	350.00	400.00	1,800	
1855O	8,000	900.00	1,800	3,000	5,000	
1855S	879,675	300.00	350.00	400.00	1,800	
1856	329,878	300.00	350.00	400.00	1,800	
1856O	2,250	15,000	20,000	30,000		
1856S	1,189,750	300.00	350.00	400.00	1,800	
1857	439,375	300.00	350.00	400.00	1,800	
1857O	30,000	550.00	775.00	1,150	3,000	
1857S	970,500	300.00	350.00	400.00	1,800	
1858	211,714	300.00	350.00	400.00	1,800	——
1858O	35,250	450.00	700.00	1,300	4,000	
1858S	846,710	300.00	350.00	400.00	1,800	
1859	43,597	350.00	450.00	550.00	2,000	——
1859O	9,100	950.00	2,000	2,800	7,000	
1859S	636,445	300.00	350.00	400.00	1,800	
1860 (59)	577,670	300.00	350.00	400.00	1,800	——
1860O	6,600	1,500	2,500	3,500	8,000	
1860S	544,950	300.00	350.00	400.00	1,800	
1861 (66)	2,976,453	300.00	350.00	400.00	1,800	——

DOUBLE EAGLES

	Quan. Minted	F-12	VF-20	EF-40	MS-60	Proof
1861O	17,741	$950.00	$1,500	$2,200	$5,500	
1861S	768,000	300.00	350.00	400.00	1,800	
1861 — A.C. Paquet rev. (Ex. Rare)					——	
1861S — A.C. Paquet rev. (Tall letters)			4,000	5,500	10,000	
1862 (35)	92,133	350.00	450.00	650.00	3,000	$17,500
1862S	854,173	300.00	350.00	400.00	1,800	
1863 (30)	142,790	300.00	350.00	500.00	2,100	16,000
1863S	966,570	300.00	350.00	400.00	1,800	
1864 (50)	204,285	300.00	350.00	500.00	2,000	16,000
1864S	793,660	300.00	350.00	400.00	1,800	
1865 (25)	351,200	300.00	350.00	400.00	1,800	18,500
1865S	1,042,500	300.00	350.00	400.00	1,800	
1866S		400.00	600.00	1,100	3,250	

Motto Above Eagle, Value TWENTY D. 1866-1876

	Quan. Minted	F-12	VF-20	EF-40	MS-60	Proof
1866 (30)	698,775	275.00	325.00	375.00	1,800	15,000
1866S	842,250	275.00	325.00	375.00	1,500	
1867 (50)	251,065	275.00	325.00	375.00	850.00	15,000
1867S	920,750	275.00	325.00	375.00	1,200	
1868 (25)	98,600	325.00	425.00	500.00	1,400	15,000
1868S	837,500	275.00	325.00	375.00	1,200	
1869 (25)	175,155	275.00	325.00	375.00	1,300	15,000
1869S	686,750	275.00	325.00	375.00	1,200	
1870 (35)	155,185	275.00	325.00	375.00	1,300	15,000
1870CC	3,789	10,000	20,000	25,000		
1870S	982,000	275.00	325.00	375.00	900.00	
1871 (30)	80,150	275.00	325.00	450.00	1,500	15,000
1871CC	17,387	900.00	1,500	2,250		
1871S	928,000	275.00	325.00	375.00	800.00	
1872 (30)	251,880	275.00	325.00	375.00	950.00	15,000
1872CC	26,900	550.00	750.00	1,000	2,400	
1872S	780,000	275.00	325.00	375.00	700.00	
1873 Closed 3 (25)	1,709,825	500.00	650.00	1,000	1,750	15,000
1873 Open 3		275.00	325.00	375.00	650.00	
1873CC Closed 3	22,410	550.00	800.00	1,150	2,600	
1873S	1,040,600	275.00	325.00	375.00	650.00	
1874 (20)	366,800	275.00	325.00	375.00	650.00	15,000
1874CC	115,085	350.00	425.00	500.00	1,000	
1874S	1,214,000	275.00	325.00	375.00	650.00	
1875 (20)	295,740	275.00	325.00	375.00	650.00	——

DOUBLE EAGLES

	Quan. Minted	F-12	VF-20	EF-40	MS-60	Proof
1875CC	111,151	$350.00	$425.00	$475.00	$900.00	
1875S	1,230,000	275.00	325.00	375.00	650.00	
1876 .... (45)	583,905	275.00	325.00	375.00	650.00	$15,000
1876CC	138,441	350.00	425.00	475.00	900.00	
1876S	1,597,000	275.00	325.00	375.00	650.00	

TWENTY DOLLARS 1877-1907

	Quan. Minted	F-12	VF-20	EF-40	MS-60	Proof
1877 .... (20)	397,670	225.00	250.00	275.00	350.00	12,000
1877CC	42,565	350.00	425.00	475.00	1,500	
1877S	1,735,000	225.00	250.00	275.00	350.00	
1878 .... (20)	543,645	225.00	250.00	275.00	350.00	12,000
1878CC	13,180	450.00	600.00	850.00	2,500	
1878S	1,739,000	225.00	250.00	275.00	350.00	
1879 .... (30)	207,630	225.00	250.00	275.00	350.00	12,000
1879CC	10,708	600.00	825.00	1,250	3,000	
1879O	2,325	2,000	3,250	4,500	8,000	
1879S	1,223,800	225.00	250.00	275.00	350.00	
1880 .... (36)	51,456	300.00	350.00	400.00	600.00	12,000
1880S	836,000	225.00	250.00	275.00	350.00	
1881 .... (61)	2,260	1,750	3,500	5,500	9,000	20,000
1881S	727,000	225.00	250.00	275.00	350.00	
1882 .... (59)	630	2,000	6,000	9,500	17,500	——
1882CC	39,140	400.00	475.00	575.00	1,000	
1882S	1,125,000	225.00	250.00	275.00	350.00	
1883 Proofs only .... (92)	92					——
1883CC	59,962	350.00	425.00	500.00	1,000	
1883S	1,189,000	225.00	250.00	275.00	350.00	
1884 Proofs only .... (71)	71					——
1884CC	81,139	350.00	425.00	500.00	950.00	
1884S	916,000	225.00	250.00	275.00	350.00	
1885 .... (77)	828	2,000	5,000	8,000	15,000	——
1885CC	9,450	550.00	750.00	1,150	2,450	
1885S	683,500	225.00	250.00	275.00	350.00	
1886 .... (106)	1,106	2,000	5,000	11,000	17,500	27,500
1887 Proofs only ...... (121)	121					30,000
1887S	283,000	225.00	250.00	275.00	400.00	
1888 .... (105)	226,266	225.00	250.00	275.00	350.00	12,000
1888S	859,600	225.00	250.00	275.00	350.00	
1889 .... (41)	44,111	250.00	275.00	300.00	500.00	12,000
1889CC	30,945	375.00	425.00	525.00	1,200	
1889S	774,700	225.00	250.00	275.00	350.00	
1890 .... (55)	75,995	225.00	250.00	275.00	400.00	12,000

DOUBLE EAGLES

	Quan. Minted	F-12	VF-20	EF-40	MS-60	Proof
1890CC	91,209	$350.00	$400.00	$450.00	$850.00	
1890S	802,750	225.00	250.00	275.00	325.00	
1891 (52)	1,442	1,150	2,150	3,500	7,500	$12,000
1891CC	5,000	900.00	1,400	2,250	4,600	
1891S	1,288,125	225.00	250.00	275.00	325.00	
1892 (93)	4,523	750.00	1,350	1,850	4,750	12,000
1892CC	27,265	400.00	500.00	600.00	1,250	
1892S	930,150	225.00	250.00	275.00	325.00	
1893 (59)	344,339	225.00	250.00	275.00	325.00	8,000
1893CC	18,402	450.00	550.00	650.00	1,600	
1893S	996,175	225.00	250.00	275.00	325.00	
1894 (50)	1,368,990	225.00	250.00	275.00	325.00	8,000
1894S	1,048,550	225.00	250.00	275.00	325.00	
1895 (51)	1,114,656	225.00	250.00	275.00	325.00	8,000
1895S	1,143,500	225.00	250.00	275.00	325.00	
1896 (128)	792,663	225.00	250.00	275.00	325.00	8,000
1896S	1,403,925	225.00	250.00	275.00	325.00	
1897 (86)	1,383,261	225.00	250.00	275.00	325.00	8,000
1897S	1,470,250	225.00	250.00	275.00	325.00	
1898 (75)	170,470	225.00	250.00	275.00	350.00	8,000
1898S	2,575,175	225.00	250.00	275.00	325.00	
1899 (84)	1,669,384	225.00	250.00	275.00	325.00	8,000
1899S	2,010,300	225.00	250.00	275.00	325.00	
1900 (124)	1,874,584	225.00	250.00	275.00	325.00	8,000
1900S	2,459,500	225.00	250.00	275.00	325.00	
1901 (96)	111,526	225.00	250.00	275.00	350.00	8,000
1901S	1,596,000	225.00	250.00	275.00	325.00	
1902 (114)	31,254	275.00	300.00	340.00	525.00	8,000
1902S	1,753,625	225.00	250.00	275.00	325.00	
1903 (158)	287,428	225.00	250.00	275.00	325.00	8,000
1903S	954,000	225.00	250.00	275.00	325.00	
1904 (98)	6,256,797	225.00	250.00	275.00	325.00	8,000
1904S	5,134,175	225.00	250.00	275.00	325.00	
1905 (92)	59,011	275.00	300.00	325.00	500.00	8,000
1905S	1,813,000	225.00	250.00	275.00	325.00	
1906 (94)	69,690	275.00	300.00	325.00	500.00	8,000
1906D	620,250	225.00	250.00	275.00	325.00	
1906S	2,065,750	225.00	250.00	275.00	325.00	
1907 (78)	1,451,864	225.00	250.00	275.00	325.00	8,000
1907D	842,250	225.00	250.00	275.00	325.00	
1907S	2,165,800	225.00	250.00	275.00	350.00	

SAINT-GAUDENS TYPE 1907-1933

A few experimental pieces were struck having an extremely high relief. They are easily distinguished from the ones issued later for general circulation.

The field of the rare experimental pieces is excessively concave and connects directly with the edge without any border, giving it a sharp knifelike appearance; Liberty's skirt shows two folds on the side of her right leg; the Capitol building in the background at left is very small; the sun, on the reverse side, has 14 rays, as opposed to the regular high relief coins that have only 13 rays extending from the sun.

11,250 high relief pieces were struck for general circulation. The relief is somewhat lower but both have the date 1907 in Roman numerals. High relief proofs are trial or experimental pieces. Flat-relief double eagles were issued later in 1907 with Arabic numerals.

DOUBLE EAGLES

				Proof
1907 Ex. high relief, plain edge (Unique)				——
1907 Ex. high relief, lettered edge				——

VF-20 VERY FINE—*Minor wear on legs and toes. Eagle's left wing and breast feathers worn.*

EF-40 EXTREMELY FINE—*Drapery lines on chest visible. Wear on left breast, knee and below. Eagle's feathers on breast and right wing are bold.*

MS-60 UNCIRCULATED—*No trace of wear. Light marks or blemishes.*

Designer Augustus Saint-Gaudens. Standards same as previous issue. Edge: E. PLURIBUS UNUM with words divided by stars. One high relief variety with plain edge is known.

	Quan. Minted	VF-20	EF-40	MS-60	Proof
1907 High relief, Roman numerals (MCMVII), wire rim	} 11,250	$1,500	$2,500	$4,500	——
1907 Same, flat rim		1,500	2,500	4,500	——

Arabic Numerals

No Motto

	Quan. Minted	VF-20	EF-40	MS-60	Proof
1907 Large letters on edge (Proof only. Unique)					——
1907 Small letters on edge	361,667	300.00	335.00	400.00	
1908	4,271,551	280.00	300.00	350.00	
1908D	663,750	280.00	300.00	350.00	

With Motto IN GOD WE TRUST, 1908-1933

Mint mark location is on obverse above date.

					Matte Proof
1908	(101) 156,359	280.00	300.00	350.00	$8,000

DOUBLE EAGLES

	Quan. Minted	VF-20	EF-40	MS-60	Matte Proof
1908D	349,500	$280.00	$300.00	$350.00	
1908S	22,000	450.00	900.00	3,500	

These coins have a border of 46 stars on the obverse from 1907 to 1911, and 48 stars from 1912 to 1933.

1909, 9 over 8

	Quan. Minted	VF-20	EF-40	MS-60	Matte Proof
1909, 9 over 8	} 161,282	$350.00	$425.00	$750.00	
1909 (67)		280.00	300.00	350.00	$8,000
1909D	52,500	400.00	625.00	2,500	
1909S	2,774,925	280.00	300.00	350.00	
1910 (167)	482,167	280.00	300.00	350.00	8,000
1910D	429,000	280.00	300.00	350.00	
1910S	2,128,250	280.00	300.00	350.00	
1911 (100)	197,350	280.00	300.00	350.00	8,000
1911D	846,500	280.00	300.00	350.00	
1911S	775,750	280.00	300.00	350.00	
1912 (74)	149,824	300.00	350.00	425.00	8,000
1913 (58)	168,838	280.00	300.00	350.00	8,000
1913D	393,500	280.00	300.00	350.00	
1913S	34,000	325.00	450.00	750.00	
1914 (70)	95,320	280.00	300.00	350.00	8,000
1914D	453,000	280.00	300.00	350.00	
1914S	1,498,000	280.00	300.00	350.00	
1915 (50)	152,050	300.00	325.00	400.00	9,000
1915S	567,500	280.00	300.00	350.00	
1916S	796,000	300.00	325.00	400.00	
1920	228,250	280.00	300.00	350.00	
1920S	558,000	4,000	5,500	11,000	
1921	528,500	5,000	7,000	14,000	
1922	1,375,500	280.00	300.00	350.00	
1922S	2,658,000	375.00	450.00	750.00	
1923	566,000	280.00	300.00	350.00	
1923D	1,702,250	280.00	300.00	350.00	
1924	4,323,500	280.00	300.00	350.00	
1924D	3,049,500	425.00	525.00	1,000	
1924S	2,927,500	425.00	550.00	1,000	
1925	2,831,750	280.00	300.00	350.00	
1925D	2,938,500	500.00	750.00	2,100	
1925S	3,776,500	375.00	475.00	1,125	
1926	816,750	280.00	300.00	350.00	
1926D	481,000	600.00	900.00	2,500	
1926S	2,041,500	375.00	500.00	1,200	
1927	2,946,750	280.00	300.00	350.00	
1927D	180,000			150,000	
1927S	3,107,000		2,500	5,750	
1928	8,816,000	280.00	300.00	350.00	
1929	1,779,750		3,250	6,250	
1930S	74,000		7,500	15,000	
1931	2,938,250		5,000	10,000	
1931D	106,500		7,000	14,000	
1932	1,101,750		5,500	13,000	

1933 None placed in circulation.

COMMEMORATIVE COINS

Commemorative coins have been popular since the days of the Greeks and Romans. In the beginning they served to record and honor important events and in the absence of newspapers they proved highly useful in passing along news of the day.

Many modern nations have issued commemorative coins and such pieces are highly esteemed by collectors. Yet no nation has surpassed our own country when it comes to commemorative coins and in this we have reason to be proud.

The unique position occupied by commemoratives in United States coinage is largely due to the fact that with few exceptions they are the only coins that have a real historical significance. The progress and advance of people in the New World are presented in an interesting and instructive manner on the commemorative issues. Such a record of facts artistically presented on our gold and silver memorial issues appeals strongly to the collector who favors the historical side of numismatics. It is the historical features of the commemoratives, in fact, which create interest among many people who would otherwise have little interest in coins.

Commemorative issues are considered for coinage by two committees of Congress — The Committee on Banking, Housing and Urban Affairs, and the Committee on Banking and Currency of the House. Congress is guided to a great extent by the reports of these committees when passing upon bills authorizing commemorative coins.

These special coins are usually issued either to commemorate events or to help pay for monuments or celebrations that commemorate historical persons, places or things. The commemorative coins are offered in most instances by a commission in charge of the event to be commemorated, and sold at a price in advance of the face value of the piece. All are of the standard weight and fineness of circulating coins of this period.

During a half century over fifty different types of commemorative coins have been issued in the United States. A complete type set of commemorative half dollars consists of forty-eight pieces. The addition of mint mark varieties makes a total of 142 coins in the series.

No commemorative coins were struck from 1940 to 1945, and none since 1954.

Unless otherwise stated, the coinage figures given represent the total outstanding coinage. In many cases, larger quantities were minted but were not all sold. The unsold coins were usually returned to the mint and melted, although some were placed in circulation at face value.

Note: The Commemorative section following is arranged alphabetically.

Perfect brilliant uncirculated commemoratives are worth more than the listed values.

A limited number of proof strikings were made for many issues. These are all very rare and valuable.

COMMEMORATIVE SILVER — Isabella, Lafayette
ISABELLA QUARTER DOLLAR

In 1893 the Board of Lady Managers of the Columbian Exposition petitioned for a souvenir quarter-dollar. Authority was granted March 3, 1893. The coin known as the Isabella quarter was designed by C. E. Barber. These souvenir quarters were sold for $1.00. The obverse has

the crowned bust of Queen Isabella of Spain. The kneeling female on the reverse with distaff and spindle is emblematic of women's industry.

		Quan. Issued	AU-50	MS-65
1893	Columbian Exposition, Chicago	24,214	$110.00	$275.00

LAFAYETTE DOLLAR

The heads of Washington and Lafayette appear on this commemorative issue, which was the first commemorative coin of one dollar denomination, and the first authorized United States coin to bear a portrait of one of our presidents. The dies were prepared by C. E. Barber. The statue on the reverse is similar to the monument of General Lafayette which was erected in Paris as a gift of the American people. The coins were sold by the Lafayette Memorial Commission for $2.00 each.

1900	Lafayette Dollar	36,026	250.00	900.00

ALABAMA CENTENNIAL

The Alabama half dollars were authorized in 1920 for the centennial which was celebrated in 1919, but they were not struck until 1921. The coins designed by Laura Gardin Fraser, were offered first during President Harding's visit to Birmingham, October 26, 1921. The St. Andrews cross, an emblem on the state flag, appears on a part of the issue between the figures 22 indicating the twenty-second state of the Union. The obverse has busts of W. W. Bibb, first governor of Alabama, and T. E. Kilby, governor at the time of the centennial. This is the first instance of the use of a living person's portrait on a United States coin.

COMMEMORATIVE SILVER — Alabama, Albany, Antietam

2x2 in Field

		Quan. Issued	AU-50	MS-65
1921	Alabama Centennial, with 2 x 2 in field of obverse	6,006	$80.00	$250.00
1921	Alabama Centennial, no 2 x 2	59,038	50.00	230.00

ALBANY, NEW YORK CHARTER

The two hundred and fiftieth anniversary of the granting of a charter to the city of Albany was the occasion for a commemorative half dollar. The reverse design shows Governor Dongan, Peter Schuyler and Robert Livingston. The obverse has a beaver which is gnawing on a maple branch. Gertrude K. Lathrop of Albany was the designer.

1936	Albany, New York	17,671	110.00	140.00

BATTLE OF ANTIETAM

A souvenir half dollar was designed by William Marks Simpson and struck in 1937 to commemorate the seventy-fifth anniversary of the famous Civil War battle to thwart Lee's invasion of Maryland. The opposing generals McClellan and Lee are featured on the obverse while the Burnside Bridge, an important tactical objective, is shown on the reverse. The Battle of Antietam on September 17, 1862, was one of the bloodiest single-day battles of the war with total losses of about 25,000 men.

1937	Battle of Antietam 1862-1937	18,028	120.00	165.00

ARKANSAS CENTENNIAL

This souvenir issue marked the one hundredth anniversary of the admission of Arkansas into the Union. Edward Everett Burr designed the piece and models were prepared by Emily Bates of Arkansas. Although 1936 was the centennial year the first of several issues was brought out in 1935 from all three mints. During 1936 a new design was authorized by Congress. The late Senator Joseph T. Robinson consented to have his portrait placed on the obverse side of the coins which were struck in January 1937 at the Philadelphia Mint. The 1937 and 1938 issues were the same as those of 1935 except for the dates. They were sold by the distributors at $8.75 per set of three coins. The obverse shows accolated heads of an Indian chief of 1836 and an American girl of 1936.

		Quan. Issued		MS-65
1935	Arkansas Centennial	13,012		
1935D	Same type D mint	5,505	Set	$140.00
1935S	Same type S mint	5,506		
1936	Arkansas Centennial, same as 1935—			
	date 1936 on rev	9,660		
1936D	Same type D mint	9,660	Set	105.00
1936S	Same type S mint	9,662		
1937	Arkansas Centennial (same as 1935)	5,505		
1937D	Same type D mint	5,505	Set	135.00
1937S	Same type S mint	5,506		
1938	Arkansas Centennial (same as 1935)	3,156		
1938D	Same type D mint	3,155	Set	215.00
1938S	Same type S mint	3,156		
1939	Arkansas Centennial (same as 1935)	2,104		
1939D	Same type D mint	2,104	Set	450.00
1939S	Same type S mint	2,105		
	Single, type coin			35.00

BAY BRIDGE SAN FRANCISCO-OAKLAND

The opening of the San Francisco Bay Bridge was the occasion for a special souvenir fifty-cent piece. The designs were the work of Jacques Schnier, a San Francisco artist. A California grizzly bear dominates the obverse. The famous bridge is shown on the reverse. The coins were struck at the San Francisco Mint in November 1936. The bear depicted was Monarch II.

	Quan. Issued	AU-50	MS-65
1936 San Francisco-Oakland Bay Bridge S mint	71,424	$33.50	$48.00

DANIEL BOONE BICENTENNIAL

This coin, issues for which covered several dates, was struck to commemorate the two hundredth anniversary of the famous frontiersman's birth. The commemorative date, 1934, was removed after the first issue. The change of date to 1935 for the next year's coinage brought about the addition of 1934 above the words PIONEER YEAR. Coinage covered several years similar to the schedule for the Texas issues. The models for this coin were prepared by Augustus Lukeman. The obverse bears a portrait of Daniel Boone. The reverse shows Boone with Chief Black Fish.

		Quan. Issued	MS-65
1934	Daniel Boone Bicentennial...................... 10,007		$65.00
1935	Same type.................................... 10,010	⎫	
1935D	Same type D mint 5,005	⎬ Set	140.00
1935S	Same type S mint............................. 5,005	⎭	

Date added in field.

1935	Daniel Boone Bicentennial same as 1934 but small 1934 added on reverse 10,008	⎫	
1935D	Same type D mint 2,003	⎬ Set	500.00
1935S	Same type S mint................................. 2,004	⎭	
1936	Daniel Boone Bicentennial (same as 1934) 12,012	⎫	
1936D	Same type D mint 5,005	⎬ Set	125.00
1936S	Same type S mint................................. 5,006	⎭	
1937	Daniel Boone Bicentennial (same as 1934) 9,810	⎫	
1937D	Same type D mint 2,506	⎬ Set	300.00
1937S	Same type S mint................................. 2,506	⎭	
1938	Daniel Boone Bicentennial (same as 1934) 2,100	⎫	
1938D	Same type D mint 2,100	⎬ Set	450.00
1938S	Same type S mint................................. 2,100	⎭	
	Single, type coin .... Abt. Unc.	$30.00	37.50

BRIDGEPORT, CONNECTICUT CENTENNIAL

In commemoration of the one hundredth anniversary of the incorporation of the city of Bridgeport a special fifty-cent piece was authorized May 15, 1936. Henry Kreiss designed this coin which somewhat resembles the Connecticut Tercentenary issue. The head of P. T. Barnum, who was Bridgeport's best known citizen, occupies the obverse. An ultra-modernistic eagle dominates the reverse.

		Quan. Issued	AU-50	MS-65
1936	Bridgeport, Conn., Centennial	25,015	$48.00	$70.00

CALIFORNIA DIAMOND JUBILEE

The California half dollar was designed by Jo Mora, a noted California sculptor. The obverse bears a kneeling figure of a forty-niner. The reverse shows a walking grizzly bear, the state emblem. The celebration for which these coins were struck marked the seventy-fifth anniversary of the admission of California into the Union. The jubilee was held in 1925.

1925S	California Diamond Jubilee	86,594	35.00	62.50

CINCINNATI MUSIC CENTER

Although the head of Stephen Foster, "America's Troubadour," dominates the obverse of this special issue the anniversary celebrated bears no relation to him. The coins, designed by Constance Ortmayer of Washington, D. C., were struck to commemorate the fiftieth anniversary in 1936 of Cincinnati as a center of music. The coins were struck at the three mints and were sold only in sets at $7.75, the highest initial cost of a new type.

1936	Cincinnati Musical Center	5,005		
1936D	Same type D	5,005	Set	475.00
1936S	Same type S	5,006		
	Single, type coin			150.00

COMM. SILVER — Cleveland, Columbia, South Carolina, Columbian

CLEVELAND GREAT LAKES EXPOSITION

A special coinage of fifty-cent pieces was authorized in commemoration of the centennial celebration of Cleveland, Ohio on the occasion of the Great Lakes Exposition held there in 1936. The designs were prepared by Brenda Putnam. Although half the coinage was struck in 1937 all were dated 1936. The obverse has a bust of Moses Cleaveland and the reverse displays a map of the Great Lakes region with a compass pointed at Cleveland. Nine Great Lakes cities are marked by stars.

		Quan. Issued	AU-50	MS-65
1936	Cleveland, Great Lakes Exposition	50,030	$22.00	$32.00

COLUMBIA, SOUTH CAROLINA SESQUICENTENNIAL

Souvenir half dollars were authorized to help finance the extensive celebrations marking the sesquicentennial of the founding of Columbia in 1786. A. Wolfe Davidson designed the coin which was struck at all three mints and sold only in sets. The obverse bears the figure of Justice with sword and scales. At the left is the Capitol of 1786 and at the right the Capital of 1936. A palmetto tree, the state emblem, is the reverse device.

1936	Columbia, S. C., Sesquicentennial	9,007	Set	275.00
1936D	Same type D mint	8,009		
1936S	Same type S mint	8,007		
	Single, type coin		70.00	90.00

COLUMBIAN EXPOSITION HALF DOLLAR

The first United States commemorative coin was the Columbian half dollar. C. E. Barber designed the obverse showing the bust of Columbus; and G. T. Morgan designed the reverse having a representation of Columbus' flagship the Santa Maria above two hemispheres. The coins were sold for $1.00 each at the World's Columbian Exposition in Chicago during 1893. A great many remained unsold and a substantial quantity was later released for circulation at face value. Approximately 100 brilliant proofs were struck for each date.

1892	Columbian Exposition, Chicago	950,000	5.00	21.00
1893	Same type	1,550,405	5.00	20.00

COMMEMORATIVE SILVER — Connecticut, Delaware, Elgin

CONNECTICUT TERCENTENARY

In commemoration of the three hundredth anniversary of the founding of the Colony of Connecticut a souvenir half dollar was struck. Henry Kreiss designed the coin. The famous "Charter Oak" is the main device on the obverse. According to tradition the Royal Charter was secreted in the tree during the reign of James II who wished to revoke it. The Charter was produced after the king's overthrow in 1688 and the Colony continued under its protection.

		Quan. Issued	AU-50	MS-65
1935	Connecticut Tercentenary	25,018	$90.00	$125.00

DELAWARE TERCENTENARY

The three hundredth anniversary of the landing of the Swedes in Delaware was the occasion for a souvenir issue of half dollars. The colonists landed on a spot which is now Wilmington and established a church which is the oldest Protestant church still used for worship. Their ship "Kalmar Nyckel" is shown on the obverse of the coin and the Old Swedes Church is on the reverse. Designs were chosen from a competition which was won by Carl L. Schmitz. This coin was authorized in 1936, struck in 1937 and dated 1938 on the obverse and 1936 on the reverse. The anniversary was celebrated in 1938 both in Sweden and America. A two kronor coin was issued in Sweden to commemorate the same event.

1936	Delaware Tercentenary	20,993	95.00	115.00

ELGIN, ILLINOIS CENTENNIAL

The one hundredth anniversary of the founding of Elgin was marked by a special issue of half dollars in 1936. The proceeds were devoted to financing a Pioneer Memorial statue, which is depicted on the reverse of the coin. The year 1673 bears no relation to the event but refers to the year in which Joliet and Marquette entered Illinois Territory. The designs were prepared by Trygve Rovelstad who also designed the Memorial.

1936	Elgin, Illinois, Centennial	20,015	67.50	95.00

COMMEMORATIVE SILVER — Gettysburg, Grant, Hawaiian

BATTLE OF GETTYSBURG

On June 16, 1936 Congress authorized a coinage of fifty-cent pieces in commemoration of the Battle of Gettysburg. The models were prepared by Frank Vittor, a Philadelphia sculptor. Portraits of a Union and a Confederate veteran are shown on the obverse. Two shields representing the Union and Confederate armies separated by a double-bladed fasces are on the reverse.

		Quan. Issued	AU-50	MS-65
1936	Battle of Gettysburg 1863-1938	26,928	$70.00	$100.00

GRANT MEMORIAL

This coin was struck during 1922 as a centenary souvenir of Ulysses S. Grant's birth. A star which appeared on the first issues was later removed, creating a second variety. The star has no particular significance. Laura Gardin Fraser designed both the Grant half dollar and gold dollar. The reverse shows a log cabin in Point Pleasant, Ohio, where Grant lived as a boy.

(Fake stars have flattened spot on reverse.)

1922	Grant Memorial. Star in obverse field	4,256	210.00	500.00
1922	Same, no star	67,405	30.00	62.00

HAWAIIAN SESQUICENTENNIAL

This small issue was struck to commemorate the 150th anniversary of the rediscovery of the Hawaiian Islands by Captain James Cook in 1778. The design was sketched by Juliette May Fraser of Honolulu and exe-

cuted by Chester Beach. Captain Cook is shown on the obverse and a native chief on the reverse. The coins were distributed in 1928 and sold for $2.00 each, the highest initial sale price up to that time.

1928	Hawaiian Sesquicentennial	9,958	500.00	875.00
1928	Hawaiian Sesquicentennial — sandblast proof presentation piece	50		—

COMMEMORATIVE SILVER — Hudson, Huguenot, Iowa

HUDSON, NEW YORK SESQUICENTENNIAL

This souvenir half dollar marked the one hundred and fiftieth anniversary of the founding of Hudson, New York, which was named after the explorer Hendrik Hudson. The designs by Chester Beach show Hudson's flagship the "Half Moon" on the obverse and the seal of the City of Hudson on the reverse. Details of the seal include representations of Neptune with trident on a spouting whale and a mermaid blowing a conch shell.

		Quan. Issued	AU-50	MS-65
1935	Hudson, N.Y. Sesquicentennial.........	10,008	$375.00	$450.00

HUGUENOT-WALLOON TERCENTENARY

Settling of the Huguenots and Walloons in the New World was the occasion commemorated by this issue. New Netherlands, now New York, was founded in 1624 by a group of Dutch colonists. The persons represented on the obverse were not directly concerned with the occasion, however. They are Admiral Coligny and William the Silent. The reverse shows the vessel "Nieu Nederland." G. T. Morgan prepared the models for this coin.

1924	Huguenot-Walloon Tercentenary	142,080	35.00	60.00

IOWA CENTENNIAL

This half dollar, commemorating the one hundredth anniversary of Iowa's statehood, was designed by Adam Pietz of Philadelphia. The obverse shows the Iowa state seal and the reverse has the first stone capitol building at Iowa City. This issue was sold first to the residents of Iowa and only a small remainder to others. The entire issue was disposed of in a few weeks.

1946	Iowa Centennial	100,057	27.00	37.50

LEXINGTON-CONCORD SESQUICENTENNIAL

The two famous battles fought in 1775 are commemorated on this coin. A statue of the familiar Minute Man is depicted on the obverse, and the old Belfry at Lexington is the reverse device. Chester Beach designed the coin. The famous statue by Daniel Chester French located in Concord was used for the design.

	Quan. Issued	AU-50	MS-65
1925 Lexington-Concord Sesquicentennial	162,013	$28.50	$50.00

LINCOLN-ILLINOIS CENTENNIAL

The obverse was designed by G. T. Morgan and the reverse by J. R. Sinnock. The obverse shows the head of Lincoln taken from the statue by Andrew O'Connor in Springfield, Illinois. The reverse is based on the Illinois State Seal. This coin was authorized to commemorate the one hundredth anniversary of the admission of Illinois into the Union, the first souvenir piece for such an event.

1918 Illinois Centennial	100,058	30.00	57.50

LONG ISLAND TERCENTENARY

This souvenir issue was authorized to commemorate the three hundredth anniversary of the first white settlement on Long Island which was at Jamaica Bay by Dutch colonists. The design was prepared by Howard Kenneth Weinman, son of the sculptor, A. A. Weinman, who designed the regular Liberty walking type half dollar. Accolated heads depicting a Dutch settler and an Indian are shown on the obverse, while a Dutch sailing vessel is the reverse device. This was the first issue for which a date was specified (1936) irrespective of the year minted or issued.

1936 Long Island Tercentenary	81,826	25.00	36.00

COMMEMORATIVE SILVER — Lynchburg, Maine, Maryland

LYNCHBURG, VIRGINIA SESQUICENTENNIAL

The issuance of a charter to the city of Lynchburg in 1786 was commemorated in 1936 by a special coinage of half dollars. The models for the coin were prepared by Charles Keck. The obverse bears a portrait of Senator Carter Glass, a native of Lynchburg and former Secretary of the Treasury, who objected to the idea of using portraits of living men on coins. Despite his protests his likeness was incorporated on the coin. The reverse shows Liberty standing, with the old Lynchburg courthouse in the background.

		Quan. Issued	AU-50	MS-65
1936	Lynchburg, Va., Sesquicentennial ...	20,013	$65.00	$95.00

MAINE CENTENNIAL

Congress authorized the Maine Centennial half dollar May 10, 1920, to be sold at the Centennial celebration at Portland. They were received too late for this event and were sold by the state Treasurer until all were sold. Anthony de Francisci modeled this coin according to specifications furnished him. The latin word DIRIGO means: I direct. The obverse device is the arms of the state of Maine.

1920	Maine Centennial	50,028	37.50	75.00

MARYLAND TERCENTENARY

The three hundredth anniversary of the founding of the Maryland Colony by Cecil Calvert (known as Lord Baltimore) was the occasion for this special coin. The profits from the sale of this issue were used to finance the celebration in Baltimore during 1934. Hans Schuler designed the coin which shows the facing head of Lord Baltimore on the obverse and the arms of Maryland on the reverse, reminiscent of the Maryland colonial pieces.

1934	Maryland Tercentenary	25,015	65.00	85.00

COMM. SILVER — Missouri, Monroe, New Rochelle
MISSOURI CENTENNIAL

The one hundredth anniversary of the admission of Missouri to the Union was celebrated at Sedalia during August, 1921. To mark the occasion Congress authorized the coinage of a fifty-cent piece. Robert Aitken designed the piece which shows the bust of a frontiersman on the obverse, and another frontiersman and Indian on the reverse. The first coins struck show 2★4 incused, indicating that Missouri was the twenty-fourth star in the flag. The type without the star was struck later, but was the first to be sold.

2★4 in field

		Quan. Issued	AU-50	MS-65
1921	Missouri Centennial 2★4 in field of obverse	5,000	$180.00	$550.00
1921	Missouri Centennial, no 2★4	15,428	165.00	550.00

MONROE DOCTRINE CENTENNIAL

The motion picture industry promoted this issue in conjunction with a motion picture exposition in June 1923. The obverse shows the heads of James Monroe and John Quincy Adams who were identified with the Monroe Doctrine. The Western Hemisphere is portrayed on the reverse by two female figures. Chester Beach prepared the models for this coin.

1923S	Monroe Doctrine Centennial	274,077	15.00	55.00

NEW ROCHELLE, NEW YORK

To observe the founding of New Rochelle in 1688 by French Huguenots, a special half dollar was issued in 1938. The title to the land which the Huguenots purchased from John Pell provided that a fattened calf be given away every year on June 20th. This will explain the appearance of the calf and figure representing John Pell on the obverse of the coin. The fleur-de-

COMMEMORATIVE SILVER — Norfolk, Oregon

lis which is shown on the reverse is adopted from the Seal of the city. Both sides of the coin were designed by Gertrude K. Lathrop.

		Quan. Issued	AU-50	MS-65
1938	New Rochelle, N. Y. 1688-1938	15,266	$120.00	$165.00

NORFOLK, VIRGINIA BICENTENNIAL

To provide funds for the celebration of Norfolk's anniversary of its growth from a township in 1682 to a royal borough in 1736, Congress first passed a law for the striking of medals. The proponents, however, being dissatisfied finally succeeded in winning authority for half dollars commemorating the 300th anniversary of the original Norfolk land grant and the 200th anniversary of the establishment of the borough. William Marks Simpson and his wife Marjorie Emory Simpson designed the piece. The obverse shows the Seal of the City of Norfolk with a three-masted ship as the central device. The reverse features the Royal Mace of Norfolk presented by Lieutenant Governor Dinwiddie in 1753.

1936	Norfolk, Va., Bicentennial	16,936	120.00	165.00

OREGON TRAIL MEMORIAL

This memorial coin was struck in commemoration of the Oregon trail and in memory of the pioneers, many of whom lie buried along the famous 2,000 mile highway of history. James Earle Fraser and his wife, Laura Gardin Fraser, prepared the designs. The original issue was struck at Philadelphia and San Francisco in 1926. The coin was reissued in 1928 (released in 1933), 1933, 1934, 1936, and 1938. The 1933 half dollar was the first commemorative coin struck at the Denver Mint.

1926	Oregon Trail Memorial	47,955	35.00	42.00
1926S	Same type S mint	83,055	35.00	42.00
1928	Oregon Trail Memorial (same as 1926)	6,028		100.00
1933D	Oregon Trail Memorial, same type, D mint	5,008		110.00
1934D	Oregon Trail Memorial, same type, D mint	7,006		80.00
1936	Oregon Trail Memorial (same as 1926)	10,006		70.00
1936S	Same type S mint	5,006		110.00
1937D	Oregon Trail Memorial D mint (same as 1926)	12,008		55.00
1938	Oregon Trail Memorial (same as 1926)	6,006		
1938D	Same type D mint	6,005	Set	185.00
1938S	Same type S mint	6,006		
1939	Oregon Trail (same as 1926)	3,004		
1939D	Same type D mint	3,004	Set	290.00
1939S	Same type S mint	3,005		
	Single, type coin			42.00

[208]

PANAMA-PACIFIC EXPOSITION

This half dollar was designed by C. E. Barber. The exposition held in San Francisco in 1915 celebrated the opening of the Panama Canal. The coins were struck at the San Francisco Mint and were sold at $1.00 each during the exposition. The Panama-Pacific coins have the distinction of being the first commemorative coins to carry the motto. IN GOD WE TRUST appears above the eagle. A representation of Columbia with the golden gate in the background is the principal feature of the obverse.

	Quan. Issued	AU-50	MS-65
1915S Panama-Pacific Exposition	27,134	$110.00	$425.00

PILGRIM TERCENTENARY

To commemorate the landing of the Pilgrims at Plymouth, Massachusetts in 1620, Congress authorized a special half dollar May 12, 1920. Cyrus E. Dallin, a Boston sculptor, executed the designs furnished him by the Commission. The obverse has a portrait of Governor Bradford. The reverse shows the "Mayflower." The first issue had no date on the obverse. The coins struck in 1921 show that date in addition to 1620-1920. There was a large coinage of both issues and not all were sold. A total of 128,000 were returned to the mint and melted.

1920 Pilgrim Tercentenary	152,112	21.50	40.00

With 1921 date
added in field
on obverse

1921 Same type	20,053	42.50	75.00

RHODE ISLAND, TERCENTENARY PROVIDENCE

The three hundredth anniversary of Roger Williams' founding of Providence was the occasion for this special half dollar in 1935. The designs were the work of Arthur Graham Carey and John Howard Benson. The obverse shows Roger Williams in a canoe being welcomed by an Indian. The reverse has the anchor of Hope with a shield and mantling in the background. Although the founding of Providence was being celebrated, no mention of the city is to be found on the coin.

		Quan. Issued	AU-50	MS-65
1936	Rhode Island Tercentenary	20,013 ⎫		
1936D	Same type D mint	15,010 ⎬ Set		$130.00
1936S	Same type S mint	15,011 ⎭		
	Single, type coin		$30.00	45.00

ROANOKE ISLAND, NORTH CAROLINA

A celebration was held in Old Fort Raleigh in 1937 to commemorate the three hundred and fiftieth anniversary of Sir Walter Raleigh's "Lost Colony" and the birth of Virginia Dare, the first white child born on the American continent. A special half dollar was minted for the occasion which was designed by William Marks Simpson of Baltimore. The obverse bears a portrait of Sir Walter Raleigh and the reverse has a figure representing Eleanor Dare holding the child Virginia Dare.

1937	Roanoke Island, N.C., 1587-1937	29,030	50.00	75.00

ROBINSON-ARKANSAS CENTENNIAL

A new obverse design for the Arkansas Centennial coin was authorized by the Act of June 26, 1936. Senator Joseph T. Robinson is the subject for the new issue designed by Henry Kreiss. The reverse, designed by Everett Burr, was unchanged. The law specified a change in the reverse, because of the fact that the obverse side is that which bears the date. From a numismatic viewpoint, however, the side which has the portrait is usually considered the obverse. Thus in this instance, the side with the eagle device is considered the reverse.

1936	Arkansas Centennial (Robinson)	25,265	50.00	85.00

COMM. SILVER — San Diego, Sesquicentennial, Old Spanish Trail

SAN DIEGO-CALIFORNIA-PACIFIC EXPOSITION

Congress approved the coinage of souvenir half dollars for the exposition May 3, 1935. Robert Aitken designed the coin which was struck at the San Francisco Mint. The same type with date 1936 was struck at the Denver Mint, under authority of the special Recoinage Act of May 6, 1936, which specified that 180,000 pieces could be recoined with the date 1936 irrespective of the year of issue. The obverse displays a seated female with spear and a bear in the left background. The reverse shows the observation tower and the State of California building at the Exposition.

		Quan. Issued	AU-50	MS-65
1935S	San Diego, California-Pacific Exp. S mint	70,132	$25.00	$40.00
1936D	San Diego, California-Pacific Exposition D mint (same as 1935)	30,092	32.00	50.00

SESQUICENTENNIAL OF AMERICAN INDEPENDENCE

The one hundred and fiftieth anniversary of the signing of the Declaration of Independence was the occasion for an International Fair held in Philadelphia in 1926. To help raise funds for financing the fair special issues of half dollars and quarter-eagles were authorized by Congress. For the first time a portrait of a president appeared on a coin struck during his lifetime. President Coolidge and Washington are depicted on the obverse of the half-dollar. The reverse bears an accurate model of the Liberty Bell. John R. Sinnock, Chief Engraver of the United States mint, designed the sesquicentennial coins. The dies were in very low relief causing much loss of detail in the coin.

1926	Sesquicentennial of American Independence	141,120	20.00	42.00

OLD SPANISH TRAIL

This coin commemorated the four hundredth anniversary of the overland trek of the Cabeza de Vaca Expedition through the gulf states in 1535. L. W. Hoffecker designed the coin models which were prepared by Edmund J. Senn.

COMMEMORATIVE SILVER — Stone Mountain, Texas

The explorer's name literally translated means "head of a cow," therefore this device was chosen for the obverse. The reverse bears a yucca tree and a map showing the Old Spanish Trail.

		Quan. Issued	AU-50	MS-65
1935	Old Spanish Trail 1535-1935	10,008	$375.00	$475.00

STONE MOUNTAIN MEMORIAL

The models for this coin were prepared by Gutzon Borglum. The first coins were struck at Philadelphia January 21, 1925, General Thomas "Stonewall" Jackson's birthday. General Robert E. Lee and Jackson, mounted, are shown on the obverse. The reverse has an eagle and the words MEMORIAL TO THE VALOR OF THE SOLDIER OF THE SOUTH. The funds received from the sale of this large issue of half dollars were devoted to the expense of carving figures of Confederate leaders and soldiers on Stone Mountain in Georgia. The carving was completed and dedicated in 1970.

1925	Stone Mountain Memorial....................	1,314,709	12.00	21.00

TEXAS CENTENNIAL

This issue commemorated the independence of Texas. The first of several dates was offered in 1934. The later dates were struck at all three mints. The models were prepared by Pompeo Coppini. The reverse shows the kneeling figure of winged Victory, and on each side, medallions with portraits of General Sam Houston and Stephen Austin, founders of the Republic and State of Texas. The large five-pointed star behind the eagle on the obverse carries out the "Lone star" tradition.

1934	Texas Centennial	61,463		42.00
1935	Texas Centennial (same as 1934)..................	9,996		
1935D	Same type D mint	10,007	Set	135.00
1935S	Same type S mint................................	10,008		
1936	Texas Centennial (same as 1934)..................	8,911		
1936D	Same type D mint	9,039	Set	140.00
1936S	Same type S mint................................	9,055		
1937	Texas Centennial (same as 1934)..................	6,571		
1937D	Same type D mint	6,605	Set	165.00
1937S	Same type S mint................................	6,637		
1938	Texas Centennial (same as 1934)..................	3,780		
1938D	Same type D mint	3,775	Set	350.00
1938S	Same type S mint................................	3,814		
	Single, type coin		32.00	45.00

COMM. SILVER — Vancouver, Vermont, B. T. Washington

FORT VANCOUVER CENTENNIAL

Dr. John McLaughlin, shown on the obverse of this coin, built Fort Vancouver on the Columbia River in 1825. The sale of the coins at $1.00 each helped to finance the pageant staged for the celebration. Laura Gardin Fraser prepared the models for this coin which was minted in San Francisco. The S Mint mark was omitted. The reverse has a pioneer settler in buckskin suit with a musket in his hands. Fort Vancouver is in the background.

		Quan. Issued	AU-50	MS-65
1925	Fort Vancouver Centennial	14,994	$125.00	$245.00

VERMONT SESQUICENTENNIAL

This souvenir issue commemorates the 150th Anniversary of the Battle of Bennington and the Independence of Vermont. Authorized in 1925 it was not coined until 1927. The models were prepared by Charles Keck. The obverse shows the head of Ira Allen, founder of Vermont. The reverse bears a catamount on a pedestal.

1927	Vermont Sesquicentennial (Bennington)	28,142	65.00	95.00

BOOKER T. WASHINGTON MEMORIAL

This commemorative coin was issued to perpetuate the ideals and teachings of Booker T. Washington and to construct memorials to his memory. Issued from all mints, it received wide distribution from the start. The reverse has the legend FROM SLAVE CABIN TO HALL OF FAME. His log cabin birthplace is shown beneath. Designed by Isaac Scott Hathaway, as was the Washington-Carver half dollar issued under the same authority.

		Quan. Issued		MS-65
1946	Booker T. Washington	*1,000,546		
1946D	Same type D mint	200,113	Set	$19.00
1946S	Same type S mint	500,279		
1947	Same type as 1946	100,017		
1947D	Same type D mint	100,017	Set	32.00
1947S	Same type S mint	100,017		
1948	Same type as 1946	8,005		
1948D	Same type D mint	8,005	Set	65.00
1948S	Same type S mint	8,005		
1949	Same type as 1946	6,004		
1949D	Same type D mint	6,004	Set	90.00
1949S	Same type S mint	6,004		
1950	Same type as 1946	6,004		
1950D	Same type D mint	6,004	Set	95.00
1950S	Same type S mint	512,091		
1951	Same type as 1946	510,082		
1951D	Same type D mint	7,004	Set	65.00
1951S	Same type S mint	7,004		
	Single, type coin			6.00

*Minted; quantity melted unknown.

WASHINGTON-CARVER

Designed by Isaac Scott Hathaway, this coin shows the conjoined busts of two prominent black Americans. Booker T. Washington was a lecturer, educator, and principal of Tuskegee Institute. He urged training to advance independence and efficiency for his race. George Washington Carver was an agricultural chemist who worked to improve the economy of the south. He spent his life teaching crop improvement and new uses for soybeans, peanuts, sweet potatoes and cotton waste.

Money obtained from the sale of these commemoratives was to be used "to oppose the spread of communism among Negroes in the interest of national defense."

1951	Washington-Carver	110,018		
1951D	Same type D mint	10,004	Set	50.00
1951S	Same type S mint	10,004		
1952	Same type as 1951	2,006,292		
1952D	Same type D mint	8,006	Set	55.00
1952S	Same type S mint	8,006		
1953	Same type as 1951	8,003		
1953D	Same type D mint	8,003	Set	90.00
1953S	Same type S mint	108,020		
1954	Same type as 1951	12,006		
1954D	Same type D mint	12,006	Set	42.00
1954S	Same type S mint	122,024		
	Single, type coin			5.50

WISCONSIN TERRITORIAL CENTENNIAL

The one hundredth anniversary of the Wisconsin Territorial government was the occasion for a special half dollar issue. The original design was made by David Parsons, a University of Wisconsin student. Benjamin Hawkins, a New York artist, made changes to conform with technical requirements. The reverse has the Territorial Seal, which includes a forearm holding a pickaxe over a mound of lead ore, and the inscription 4th DAY OF JULY ANNO DOMINI 1836. The obverse shows a badger on a log typifying the early fur trade, and the state emblem.

		Quan. Issued	AU-50	MS-65
1936	Wisconsin Centennial	25,015	$65.00	$90.00

YORK COUNTY, MAINE TERCENTENARY

A souvenir half dollar was authorized by Congress upon the three hundredth anniversary of the founding of York County, Maine. Brown's Garrison on the Saco River was the site of a town which was settled in 1636. The designs were made by Walter H. Rich of Portland. The reverse design shows a stockade and the obverse has an adaptation of the York County seal. The oversize border inscriptions have been the basis for much adverse criticism.

1936	York County, Maine Centennial	25,015	65.00	85.00

COMMEMORATIVE GOLD —
Grant, Lewis & Clark, Louisiana Purchase

GRANT MEMORIAL GOLD DOLLARS

Like the half-dollar commemorative coins the gold dollars were issued first with a star which was removed for the later issues. The designs by Laura Gardin Fraser are the same as for the half-dollar coinage.

		Quan. Issued	VF-20	AU-50	MS-65
1922	Grant Memorial Dollar with star........	5,016	$220.00	$350.00	$850.00
1922	Grand Memorial Dollar w/out star......	5,000	220.00	350.00	850.00

LEWIS AND CLARK EXPOSITION

The Lewis and Clark Centennial Exposition was held in Portland, Oregon in 1905. A souvenir issue of gold dollars was struck to mark the event with the dates 1904 and 1905. The two famous explorers are represented on each side of the coin which was designed by C. E. Barber. A bronze memorial of the Indian guide, Sacagawea, who assisted in the famous expedition, was erected in Portland, Oregon and financed by the sale of these coins.

1904	Lewis and Clark Exposition Dollar	10,025	225.00	375.00	1,075
1905	Lewis and Clark Exposition Dollar	10,041	225.00	375.00	1,075

LOUISIANA PURCHASE EXPOSITION

The first souvenir gold coins were authorized for the Louisiana Purchase Exposition held in St. Louis in 1904. There are two varieties of gold dollars — one with the head of Jefferson who was president when the Louisiana Territory was purchased from France; and the other President William McKinley who sanctioned the Exposition. The reverse is the same for each variety. The designs were by C. E. Barber.

*1903	Louisiana Purchase Jefferson				
	Dollar.............................	17,500	125.00	175.00	400.00
*1903	Louisiana Purchase McKinley				
	Dollar.............................	17,500	125.00	175.00	400.00

*Proofs exist of each type.

COMMEMORATIVE GOLD — McKinley, Panama-Pacific

McKINLEY MEMORIAL GOLD DOLLARS

The sale of the McKinley dollars aided in paying for a memorial building at Niles, Ohio, the martyred president's birthplace. The obverse showing a profile of McKinley was designed by C. E. Barber and the reverse with the memorial building designed by G. T. Morgan.

		Quan. Issued	VF-20	AU-50	MS-65
1916	McKinley Memorial Dollar	9,977	$110.00	$140.00	$350.00
1917	McKinley Memorial Dollar	10,000	130.00	175.00	400.00

PANAMA-PACIFIC EXPOSITION

Charles Keck designed the gold dollar, the obverse of which has the head of a man representing a Panama Canal laborer. Two dolphins encircle ONE DOLLAR on the reverse.

1915S	Panama-Pacific Exposition Dollar	15,000	110.00	135.00	290.00

The quarter-eagle was the work of Charles E. Barber and George T. Morgan. It was the first commemorative coin of this denomination. The obverse shows Columbia with a caduceus in her left hand seated on a hippocampus typifying the use of the Panama Canal. An American eagle with raised wings is shown on the reverse.

1915S	Panama-Pacific Exposition $2.50	6,749	450.00	550.00	1,300

The fifty-dollar gold piece was designed by Robert Aitken and was issued in round and octagonal form. The obverse bears the helmeted head of Minerva; the owl, symbol of wisdom, is on the reverse. The octagonal issue has eight dolphins in the angles on both sides. The devices are smaller on the octagonal variety.

COMMEMORATIVE GOLD — Philadelphia
Sesquicentennial

		Quan. Issued	*AU-50*	*MS-65*
1915S	Panama-Pacific $50 Round.......................... 483		$9,000	$15,000
1915S	Panama-Pacific $50 Octagonal...................... 645		7,000	13,000

PHILADELPHIA SESQUICENTENNIAL—QUARTER EAGLES

The obverse of this special gold issue has a standing female figure symbolic of Liberty, holding in one hand a scroll representing the Declaration of Independence and in the other the Torch of Freedom. The reverse bears a representation of Independence Hall in Philadelphia. The coin was designed by J. R. Sinnock.

1926	Philadelphia Sesquicentennial $2.50 46,019	110.00	225.00

BIBLIOGRAPHY

Bullowa, David M. *The Commemorative Coinage of the United States 1892-1938.* New York, 1938.
Mosher, Stuart. *United States Commemorative Coins 1892-1939.* New York, 1940.
Slabaugh, Arlie. *United States Commemorative Coinage.* Racine, 1975.
Taxay, Don. *An Illustrated History of U.S. Commemorative Coinage.* New York, 1967.

PRIVATE OR TERRITORIAL GOLD COINS

The words "Private Gold," used with reference to coins struck outside of the United States Mint, are a general term. In the sense that no state or territory had authority to coin money, private gold simply refers to those interesting necessity pieces of various shapes, denominations and degrees of intrinsic worth which were circulated in isolated areas of our country by individuals, assayers, bankers, etc. Some will use the words "Territorial" and "State" to cover certain issues because they were coined and circulated in a Territory or State. While the state of California properly sanctioned the ingots stamped by F. D. Kohler as state assayer, in no instance were any of the gold pieces struck by authority of any of the territorial governments.

The stamped ingots put out by Augustus Humbert, the United States assayer of gold, were not recognized at the United States Mint as an official issue of coins, but simply as ingots, though Humbert placed the value and fineness on the pieces as an official agent of the federal government.

Private coins were circulated in most instances because of a shortage of regular coinage. In the western states particularly, money became so scarce that the very commodity which the pioneers had come so far to acquire was converted into a local medium of exchange.

Ephraim Brasher's New York doubloon of 1787 described on page 40 also falls into this class.

BIBLIOGRAPHY

Adams, Edgar H. *Private Gold Coinage of California 1849-1855.* Brooklyn, N.Y., 1913.
Adams, Edgar H. *Official Premium Lists of Private and Territorial Gold Coins.* Brooklyn, N.Y., 1909.
Griffin, Clarence. *The Bechtlers and Bechtler Coinage and Gold Mining in North Carolina 1814-1830.* Spindale, N.C., 1929.
Lee, Ed. M. *California Gold — Quarters, Halves and Dollars.* Glendale, Cal., 1932.
Lee, Kenneth W. *California Gold — Dollars, Half Dollars, Quarter Dollars.* Glendale, Cal., 1970.
Seymour, Dexter C. *The 1830 Coinage of Templeton Reid.* American Numismatic Society Museum Notes No. 22. New York, 1977.

TEMPLETON REID
Georgia 1830

The first Private Gold coinage under the Constitution was struck by Templeton Reid, a jeweler and gunsmith, in Milledgeville, Georgia in July, 1830. To be closer to the mines, he moved to Gainesville where most of his coins were made. Although weights were accurate, Reid's assays were not and his coins were slightly short of claimed value. Accordingly, he was severely attacked in the newspapers and soon lost the public's confidence. He closed his mint before the end of October, 1830 and his output amounted only to about 1,600 coins. Denominations struck were $2.50, $5.00 and $10.00.

1830 $2.50 — Beck Sale 1976 . . . . Unc. $27,000
1830 $5.00. . . . .

TEMPLETON REID — GEORGIA

1830 TEN DOLLARS — Moskowitz Sale 1977............................ V.G. $41,000
(No date) TEN DOLLARS — Waldorf Sale 1966......................... Unc. 29,000

TEMPLETON REID
San Francisco, California 1849

The enigmatic later issues of Templeton Reid were made from California gold probably in 1849. Reid, who never went to California, was then a cotton gin maker in Columbus, Georgia, where he died in 1851. The coins were in denominations of ten and twenty-five dollars. Struck copies of both exist in various metals.

1849 TEN DOLLAR GOLD (Smithsonian Collection)............................ Unique
1849 TWENTY-FIVE DOLLARS GOLD .... Unknown

The only specimen known of this piece was stolen from the Cabinet of the U.S. Mint on August 16, 1858. It was never recovered.

THE BECHTLERS
Rutherford County, N. C. 1830-1852

Two skilled German metallurgists, Christopher Bechtler and his son, August Bechtler, and later Christopher Bechtler, Junior, a nephew of Christopher the elder, operated a "private" mint at Rutherfordton, North Carolina. Rutherford county in which Rutherfordton is located was the principal source of the nation's gold supply from 1790 to 1840.

The coins minted by the Bechtlers were of only three denominations, but they cover a wide variety of weights and sizes.

THE BECHTLERS

The Bechtlers have the distinction of producing the first gold dollar in the United States. The government mint did not release the first regular series until 1849.

The inscription "Aug. 1, 1834" on one variety of the five-dollar piece has a special significance. The Secretary of the Treasury recommended to the Director of the Mint that the gold coins of the reduced weight bear the date "Aug. 1, 1834." Instead of this, however, a new U.S. gold design was used (the motto was omitted). Christopher Bechtler evidently acted on the official recommendation to avoid any difficulty with Treasury authorities.

CHRISTOPHER BECHTLER

	V. Fine	E. Fine	Unc.
ONE DOLLAR CAROLINA, 28 gr. N reversed	$325.00	$675.00	$1,000
ONE DOLLAR N. CAROLINA, 28 gr. centered, no star	700.00	1,000	1,800
ONE DOLLAR N. CAROLINA, 28 gr. high, no star	900.00	1,250	2,250

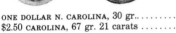

ONE DOLLAR N. CAROLINA, 30 gr.	400.00	850.00	1,400
$2.50 CAROLINA, 67 gr. 21 carats	600.00	1,000	1,800

$2.50 CAROLINA, 70 gr. 20 carats	725.00	1,200	2,100
$2.50 GEORGIA, 64 gr. 22 carats	750.00	1,300	2,200
$2.50 GEORGIA, 64 gr. 22 carats — even 22	800.00	1,400	2,250

$2.50 NORTH CAROLINA, 75 gr. 20 carats.			
RUTHERFORD in a circle. Border of lg. beads	1,350	2,100	3,700
$2.50 NORTH CAROLINA, without 75 G	1,350	2,100	3,700

THE BECHTLERS

	V. Fine	E. Fine	Unc.
\$2.50 NORTH CAROLINA, without 75 G, CAROLINA above 250 instead of GOLD			(Unique)
\$2.50 NORTH CAROLINA, 20 carats on obv. 75 gr. on rev. Border finely serrated.............	\$2,400	\$3,600	———

5 DOLLARS CAROLINA, RUTHERFORD, 140 gr. 20 carats. Date August 1, 1834.			
Plain edge.....................................	900.00	1,200	\$2,000
Reeded edge...................................	1,500	2,000	2,500
5 DOLLARS CAROLINA, 134 gr. 21 carats...............	700.00	1,100	1,850

5 DOLLARS GEORGIA, RUTHERFORD.			
128 gr. 22 carats................................	900.00	1,400	2,800
5 DOLLARS GEORGIA, RUTHERF. 128 gr. 22 carats.......	800.00	1,200	1,800
5 DOLLARS CAROLINA, RUTHERF.			
140 gr. 20 carats. Date August 1, 1834..............	800.00	1,200	1,800

Without
150 G

5 DOLLARS NORTH CAROLINA, 150 gr. 20 carats.........	1,400	2,250	3,500
5 DOLLARS. Same as last variety without 150 G........	3,250	4,500	5,750

THE BECHTLERS
AUGUST BECHTLER
1842-1852

	V. Fine	E. Fine	Unc.
1 DOLLAR CAROLINA, 27 gr. 21 carats..................	$300.00	$500.00	$900.00
5 DOLLARS CAROLINA, 134 gr. 21 carats................	800.00	1,200	1,700

5 DOLLARS CAROLINA, 128 gr. 22 carats................	1,200	2,100	3,200
5 DOLLARS CAROLINA, 141 gr. 20 carats................	1,200	2,000	3,100

(Restrikes in "proof" exist from original dies.)

NORRIS, GRIEG & NORRIS
San Francisco 1849

Edgar H. Adams considered this piece the first of the California private gold coins. A newspaper account dated May 31, 1849, described a five-dollar gold coin, struck at Benicia City, though with the imprint San Francisco. It mentioned the private stamp of Norris, Grieg and Norris. The initials N. G. and N. were not identified until 1902 when the coins of Augustus Humbert were sold.

	Fine	V. Fine	E. Fine	Unc.
1849 HALF EAGLE — Plain edge	$800.00	$1,300	$2,300	$4,500
1849 HALF EAGLE — Reeded edge	800.00	1,300	2,300	4,500
1850 HALF EAGLE with STOCKTON beneath date				(Unique)

MOFFAT & CO.
San Francisco 1849-1853

The firm of Moffat and Company was perhaps the most important of the California private coiners. The assay office they conducted was semi-official in character. The successors to this firm, Curtis, Perry and Ward, later established the United States Branch mint of San Francisco.

In June or July, 1849, Moffat & Co. began to issue small rectangular pieces of gold owing to lack of coin in the locality, in values from $9.43 to $264. The $9.43, $14.25 and $16.00 varieties are the only types known today.

$14.25 Ingot 1849

The only specimen known of the $9.43 ingot is in the National Coin Collection.

$9.43 Ingot (Unique) .... ——
$14.25 Ingot (Unique) .... ——
$16.00 Ingot (Beware of spurious specimens cast in base metal) .... E.F. $17,000

The dies for the $10 piece were cut by a Bavarian, Albert Kuner. The words MOFFAT & CO. appear on the coronet of Liberty instead of the word LIBERTY as in regular United States issues.

	Fine	V. Fine	E. Fine	Unc.
1849 FIVE DOL. (All varieties)	$450.00	$700.00	$1,000	$2,000
1850 FIVE DOL. (All varieties)	500.00	750.00	1,200	2,100
1849 TEN DOL.	900.00	1,300	2,700	5,250
1849 TEN D.............................	1,500	2,300	4,400	——

United States Assay Office
AUGUSTUS HUMBERT
U. S. Assayer 1851

Augustus Humbert, a New York watch-case maker, was appointed United States Assayer, and he placed his name and the government stamp on the ingots of gold issued by Moffat & Co. The assay office, a Provisional Government Mint, was a temporary expedient to accommodate the Californians until the establishment of a permanent branch mint.

The fifty-dollar gold piece was accepted as legal tender on a par with standard U.S. gold coins and was known variously as a slug, quintuple eagle or five-eagle piece. It was officially termed an ingot.

MOFFAT — HUMBERT

LETTERED EDGE VARIETIES

	Fine	*V. Fine*	*E. Fine*	*Unc.*
1851 50 D C 880 THOUS., no 50 on Reverse. Sunk in edge: AUGUSTUS HUMBERT UNITED STATES ASSAYER OF GOLD CALIFORNIA 1851	$3,200	$4,500	$7,000	——

Reverse, Rays from Central Star

	Fine	*V. Fine*	*E. Fine*	*Unc.*
1851 50 D C Similar to last variety, but 50 on Reverse	3,750	6,500	9,000	——
1851 Similar to last variety, but 887 THOUS	3,750	6,500	9,000	——
1851 50 D C 887 THOUS., no 50 on Reverse	——	——	——	
1851 50 D C 880 THOUS. Rev. Rays from central star (Unique)				——

REEDED EDGE VARIETIES

	Fine	V. Fine	E. Fine	Unc.
1851 FIFTY DOLLS 880 THOUS.				
"Target" Reverse	$2,750	$4,000	$6,000	——
1851 FIFTY DOLLS 887 THOUS.				
"Target" Reverse	3,250	4,750	7,000	——
1852 FIFTY DOLLS. 887 THOUS.	3,500	5,000	7,500	——

The withdrawal of the discredited private coins of $5, $10 and $20 denominations as a result of the new U.S. Assay operations caused a new turn of affairs for Californians.

The fractional currency coins of almost every nation were pressed into service by the Californians, but the supply was too small to help to any extent. Moffat & Co. proceeded in January, 1852 to issue a new ten-dollar piece bearing the stamp MOFFAT & CO.

1852 TEN D. MOFFAT & CO. (Wide date)	900.00	1,600	2,500	——
1852 TEN D. MOFFAT & CO. (Close date)	800.00	1,500	2,250	——

	Fine	V. Fine	E. Fine	Unc.
1852 TWENTY DOLS. 1852, 2 over 1	$2,750	$3,750	$6,000	——

1852 TEN DOLS. 1852, 2 over 1	825.00	1,300	1,900	——
1852 TEN DOLS	700.00	1,000	1,450	2,750

UNITED STATES ASSAY OFFICE OF GOLD

1852

The firm of Moffat & Co. dissolved and a new reorganized company known as the United States Assay Office of Gold, composed of Curtis, Perry and Ward took over the contract.

1852 FIFTY DOLLS. 887 THOUS	2,750	4,000	6,000	——
1852 FIFTY DOLLS. 900 THOUS	2,750	4,000	6,500	——

UNITED STATES ASSAY OFFICE

	Fine	V. Fine	E. Fine	Unc.
1852 TEN DOLS 884 THOUS................	$500.00	$800.00	$1,300	$2,200

| 1853 TEN D. 884 THOUS .... | — | — | — | — |
| 1853 TEN D. 900 THOUS .... | 1,100 | 1,900 | 3,300 | — |

| 1853 TWENTY D. 884 THOUS............... | 3,000 | 6,000 | 14,000 | — |

| 1853 TWENTY D. 900 THOUS............... | 650.00 | 1,200 | 2,000 | 3,000 |

U. S. ASSAY — MOFFAT

The last Moffat issue was the 1853 Twenty-dollar piece which is very similar to the U.S. Double Eagle of that period. It was struck after the retirement of Mr. Moffat from the Assay Office.

	Fine	V. Fine	E. Fine	Unc.
1853 TWENTY D.	$950.00	$1,600	$2,100	$3,750

CINCINNATI MINING & TRADING CO.

The origin and location of this company are unknown.

	Fine	Unc.
1849 FIVE DOLLARS	——	——
1849 TEN DOLLARS	——	——

(Beware of spurious specimens cast in base metal.)

MASSACHUSETTS AND CALIFORNIA COMPANY
San Francisco 1849

This company was believed to have been organized in Northampton, Mass. in May 1849.

	Fine	Proof
1849 FIVE D.	17,500	60,000

MINERS' BANK
San Francisco 1849

The institution of Wright & Co., exchange brokers located in Portsmouth Square, San Francisco, was known as the Miners' Bank.

A ten-dollar piece was issued in the autumn of 1849, but the coins were not readily accepted because they were worth less than face value. The firm dissolved January 14, 1850. Unlike most issues, the gold in these coins was alloyed with copper.

	V. Fine	E. Fine	Unc.
(1849) TEN. D.	$6,000	$9,000	$20,000

J. S. ORMSBY
Sacramento 1849

The initials J. S. O. which appear on certain issues of California privately coined gold pieces represent the firm of J. S. Ormsby & Co. They struck both five- and ten-dollar denominations, all undated.

	V. Fine
(1849) 5 DOLLS. *(Unique)*	—
(1849) 10 DOLLS.	$35,000

PACIFIC COMPANY
San Francisco 1849

The origin of the Pacific Co. is very uncertain. All data regarding the firm is based on conjecture.

Edgar H. Adams wrote that he believed that the coins bearing the stamp of the Pacific Company were produced by the coining firm of Broderick and Kohler. The coins were probably handstruck, with the aid of a sledgehammer.

PACIFIC COMPANY

1849 5 DOLLARS
 Gibson Sale, 1974
 Ex. Fine $90,000

1849 10 DOLLARS
 Waldorf Sale, 1964
 Ex. Fine $24,000

F. D. KOHLER
California State Assayer 1850

The State Assay Office was authorized April 12, 1850. Governor Burnett appointed F. D. Kohler that year who thereupon sold his assaying business to Baldwin & Co. He served at both San Francisco and Sacramento Offices. The State Assay Offices were discontinued at the time the U. S. Assay Office was established Feb. 1, 1851.

 Ingots issued ranged from $36.55 to $150.

	Fine
$36.55 Sacramento	——
$37.31 San Francisco	——
$40.07 San Francisco	——
Note: $40.07 stolen from the Mint Cabinet in 1858 and was never recovered.	
$41.68 San Francisco	——
$45.34 San Francisco	——
$50.00 San Francisco	——
$54.09 San Francisco	——

DUBOSQ & COMPANY
San Francisco 1850

Theodore Dubosq, a Philadelphia jeweler, took melting and coining machinery to San Francisco in 1849.

	V. Fine
1850 FIVE D............	$25,000
1850 TEN D.	35,000

BALDWIN & COMPANY
San Francisco 1850

George C. Baldwin and Thomas S. Holman were in the jewelry business in San Francisco and were known as Baldwin & Co. They were the successors to F. D. Kohler & Co., taking over their machinery and other equipment in May, 1850.

	Fine	V. Fine	E. Fine	Unc.
1850 FIVE DOL...........................	$1,500	$2,750	$4,500	$7,000
1850 TEN DOLLARS — Horseman type......	10,000	17,500	40,000	——

1851 TEN D............................	5,000	9,000	14,000	——

The Baldwin & Co. $20 piece was the first of that denomination issued in California.

Baldwin coins were believed to have contained about twenty-thousandths copper alloy.

1851 TWENTY D... —— ——
    Beware of spurious specimens cast in base metal.

SCHULTZ & COMPANY
San Francisco 1851

The firm located in back of Baldwin's establishment conducted a brass foundry beginning in 1851. Judge G. W. Schultz and William T. Garratt were partners in the enterprise.

	Fine
1851 FIVE D — Rio Rancho Sale 1974	$12,750

DUNBAR & COMPANY
San Francisco 1851

Edward E. Dunbar conducted the California Bank in San Francisco. Mr. Dunbar later returned to New York and organized the famous Continental Bank Note Co.

	E. Fine
1851 FIVE D — A.N.A. Sale 1973	$37,500

WASS, MOLITOR & COMPANY
San Francisco 1852-1855

The gold smelting and assaying plant of Wass, Molitor & Co. was composed of two Hungarian patriots Count S. C. Wass and A. P. Molitor. They maintained an excellent laboratory and compete apparatus for analysis and coinage of gold.

Large Head, Pointed Bust

	Fine	V. Fine	E. Fine	Unc.
1852 FIVE DOLLARS. Small head with rounded bust	$1,750	$2,500	$3,500	——
1852 FIVE DOLLARS. Large head with pointed bust	1,750	2,500	3,500	——

WASS, MOLITOR & COMPANY

The company struck five-, ten-, twenty- and fifty-dollar coins. In 1852 in addition to the five-dollar piece illustrated above they produced a ten-dollar piece similar in design to the five-dollar denomination. The difference is in the reverse legend which reads: S.M.V. (Standard Mint Value) CALIFORNIA GOLD TEN D.

| | Large Head | | | Small Head | Small Date |

	Fine	V. Fine	E. Fine	Unc.
1852 TEN D. Large head	$750.00	$1,250	$2,500	——
1852 TEN D. Small head	2,000	2,750	5,000	——
1852 TEN D. Small close date.............		*(Unique)*		

No pieces were coined in 1853 or 1854, but they brought out the twenty-dollar and fifty-dollar pieces in 1855. A considerable number of the fifty-dollar coins were made. There was a ten-dollar piece issued in 1855 also, with the Liberty head and small close date.

1855 TEN D..........................	2,500	4,500	7,000	12,000

| | Large Head | | Small Head |

1855 TWENTY DOL. Large head	——	——	——	——
1855 TWENTY DOL. Small head	3,000	5,000	10,000	——

WASS, MOLITOR & COMPANY

	Fine	V. Fine	E. Fine	Unc.
1855 50 DOLLARS........................	$7,500	$12,000	$17,500	——

KELLOGG & COMPANY
San Francisco 1854-1855

John G. Kellogg came to San Francisco October 12, 1849, from Auburn, New York. At first he was employed by Moffat and Company, and remained with that organization when control passed to Curtis, Perry and Ward. When the United States Assay Office was discontinued December 14, 1853, Mr. Kellogg became associated with G. F. Richter, who had been an assayer in the government assay office. These two set up business as Kellogg & Richter December 19, 1853.

When the U. S. Assay Office ceased operations a period ensued during which no private firm was striking gold. The new San Francisco branch mint did not produce coins for some months after Curtis & Perry took the contract for the government. The lack of coin was again keenly felt by businessmen who petitioned Kellogg & Richter to "supply the vacuum" by issuing private coin.

Their plea was soon answered, for on February 9, 1854, Kellogg & Co. placed their first twenty-dollar piece in circulation.

1854 TWENTY D........................	700.00	1,000	1,500	2,750

The 1855 twenty-dollar piece is similar to that dated 1854. The letters on the reverse side are larger and the arrows longer on one 1854 variety. There are several die varieties of both issues.

KELLOGG & COMPANY

	Fine	V. Fine	E. Fine	Unc.
1855 TWENTY D..........................	$750.00	$1,250	$1,750	$3,000

The firm dissolved late in 1854 and reorganized as Kellogg & Humbert. The latter partner was Augustus Humbert, for some time identified as U. S. Assayer.

Regardless of the fact that the branch mint was then producing coins, Kellogg & Humbert issued coins in 1855 in a quantity greater than before.

	Proof
1855 FIFTY DOLLS. — Beck Sale 1975....................................	$120,000

CALIFORNIA SMALL
DENOMINATION GOLD PIECES

California Gold quarters, halves and dollars were struck from 1852 to 1882, when the U. S. Government passed a law forbidding private coinage. The impetus of the gold rush created a shortage of "small change," and private companies supplied these coins for the 30-year period in direct proportion to the need.

Shapes were both octagonal and round, and the genuine coins bear one of the following — "cents," "Dol," "Doll" or "Dollar" on the reverse. Obverses are of three main types — Liberty Head, Indian Head and Washington Head. The reverses are also of three main types — Wreath, Beaded Circle and Eagle. Coins with the word "cents" or the Washington Head or the Eagle Reverse are more scarce and command premium prices of about twice regular values.

CALIFORNIA SMALL DENOMINATION GOLD PIECES

Values are only for genuine coins with the denomination on the reverse expressed as: CENTS, DOL., DOLL., *or* DOLLAR.

	V. Fine	Unc.	Proof*
25c Octagonal: Liberty head	65.00	95.00	120.00
Indian head	65.00	100.00	125.00
Washington head	225.00	350.00	400.00
25c Round: Liberty head	65.00	95.00	120.00
Indian head	65.00	100.00	125.00
Washington head	225.00	350.00	400.00
50c Octagonal: Liberty head	65.00	100.00	125.00
Indian head	65.00	100.00	130.00
Liberty head with eagle rev.	275.00	400.00	450.00
50c Round: Liberty head	65.00	100.00	125.00
Indian head	65.00	100.00	125.00
Liberty head with eagle rev.	275.00	400.00	450.00
Arms of California	275.00	400.00	450.00
$1.00 Octagonal: Liberty head	150.00	225.00	275.00
Indian head	150.00	225.00	275.00
Liberty head with eagle rev.	300.00	425.00	500.00
$1.00 Round: Liberty head	850.00	1,400	1,850
Indian head	850.00	1,400	1,850

*Not actually struck as proofs, but proof-like in appearance and quality.
See bibliography on page 219.

OREGON EXCHANGE COMPANY
Oregon City, 1849
THE BEAVER COINS OF OREGON

Upon the discovery of gold in California there was a great exodus of settlers who joined in the hunt for the precious metal. Soon returning gold seekers offered their gold dust, which became the accepted medium of exchange. As in other western areas of that time the uncertain qualities of the gold and weighing devices tended to irk the tradespeople and petitions were made to the legislature for a standard gold coin issue.

On February 16, 1849, the legislature passed an act providing for a mint and specified five- and ten-dollar gold coins without alloy. Oregon City, the largest city in the territory with a population of about 1000, was designated as the location for the mint. At the time this act was passed Oregon had been brought into the United States as a territory by act of Congress. When the new governor arrived March second, he declared the coinage act unconstitutional.

The public-spirited people, however, continued to work for a convenient medium of exchange and soon took matters into their own hands by starting a private mint. Eight men of affairs whose names were Kilborne, Magruder, Taylor, Abernethy, Willson, Rector, Campbell and Smith set up the Oregon Exchange Company.

OREGON EXCHANGE COMPANY

The coins struck were of virgin gold as specified in the original act. Ten-dollar dies were made later, and were of finer design and workmanship.

	Fine	V. Fine	E. Fine	Unc.
1849 5 D	$3,500	$6,500	$9,000	——

1849 TEN D	12,000	18,000	27,500	——

MORMON GOLD PIECES
Salt Lake City, Utah 1849-1860

The first name given to the organized Mormon Territory was the "State of Deseret," the last word meaning "honey bee." The beehive, which is shown on the reverse of the five-dollar 1860 piece, was a favorite device of the followers of Joseph Smith and Brigham Young. The clasped hands appear on most Mormon coins and exemplify strength in unity. "Holiness to the Lord" was an inscription frequently used.

Brigham Young was the instigator of the coinage system and personally supervised the mint which was housed in a little adobe building in Salt Lake City.

The mint was inaugurated late in 1849 as a public convenience.

	Fine	V. Fine	E. Fine	Unc.
1849 TWO AND HALF DO...................	$1,100	$1,850	$2,700	$4,000
1849 FIVE DOLLARS	900.00	1,700	2,500	3,750

MORMON GOLD PIECES

1849 TEN DOLLARS.. *Fine*
$32,500

1849 TWENTY DOLLARS... *V. Fine*
$17,500

The Mormon twenty-dollar piece was the first of that denomination to be coined in this country.

1850 FIVE DOLLARS

Fine	$850.00
V. Fine....................	1,250
Ex. Fine....................	2,500
Unc.	——

1860 5D

V. Fine	$3,000
Ex. Fine	5,000
Unc......................	9,000

COLORADO GOLD PIECES
Clark, Gruber & Co. — Denver 1860-1861

Clark, Gruber and Co. was a well-known private minting firm in Denver, Colo. in the early sixties.

COLORADO GOLD PIECES
CLARK, GRUBER & CO. 1860-1861

	Fine	V. Fine	E. Fine	Unc.
1860 2½ D	$450.00	$650.00	$1,000	$2,000
1860 5D	600.00	900.00	1,500	3,250

1860 TEN D	1,000	2,000	3,250	7,000
1860 TWENTY D	9,000	15,000	20,000	——

The $2.50 and five-dollar pieces of 1861 follow closely the designs of the 1860 issues. The main difference is found in the legends. The reverse side now has CLARK GRUBER & CO. DENVER. PIKES PEAK is on the coronet of Liberty.

1861 2½ D	475.00	650.00	900.00	1,800
1861 FIVE D	600.00	1,000	1,750	2,200
1861 TEN D	800.00	1,200	2,200	3,600

1861 TWENTY D	3,000	5,000	15,000	——

JOHN PARSONS & COMPANY
Tarryall Mines — Colorado 1861

Very little is known regarding the mint of John Parsons and Co., although it is reasonably certain that it operated in the South Park of Colorado, near Tarryall, in the summer of 1861.

PIKES PEAK GOLD

		E. Fine
(1861)	Undated 2½ D.	$22,500
(1861)	Undated FIVE D.	35,000

J. J. CONWAY & COMPANY
Georgia Gulch, Colorado, 1861

Records show that the Conway Mint operated for a short while in 1861. As in all gold mining areas the value of gold dust caused disagreement among the merchants and the miners. The firm of J. J. Conway & Co. solved this difficulty by bringing out their gold pieces in August, 1861.

(1861)	Undated 2½ DOLL'S — Gibson Sale, 1974	39,000
(1861)	Undated FIVE DOLLARS	45,000
(1861)	Undated FIVE DOLLARS, Similar.	
	Variety without numeral 5 on reverse — Marks Sale, 1972	36,000

(1861) Undated
    TEN DOLLARS . . . . . .   ——

THE IMPORTANCE OF COIN GRADING TODAY

This edition of the Guide Book takes one more step toward a stronger, simpler pattern for rating the condition of United States coins. The familiar terms used in the Red Book since the 16th Edition (1963) are still basically unchanged throughout this catalog, but we have updated grade references by adding designation numbers corresponding to the *Official A.N.A. Grading Standards for United States Coins.* Some clarifying changes of language have also been made to give readers a sharper grading tool.

Several years ago the American Numismatic Association embarked on a program to produce a universally acceptable set of grading standards for the United States regular series of coinage. A committee of many experts was formed, and with their collective experience and knowledge they have now produced with a system of grading guides that goes far to eliminate vagueness and confusion. We have accepted that system and have incorporated fundamental elements into this catalog, though somewhat capsulized in keeping with space limitations. Our objective is the same as that of the A.N.A., namely, to achieve clear, understandable terms stated as precisely as possible to minimize misunderstanding between buyer and seller.

It is probably a good time to pause and review the progress of numismatic grading during the past half century or so to see how far we have come on the path to a perfect system, and, more important, why these refinements have become necessary.

The system we now embrace comprises a series of numbers, 1 to 70, planned with set number groupings for each grade and separation of the grades to eliminate overlapping. The emphasis is on clarity and increased accuracy without being complicated. There is no question that we are closer to perfection with this new system because of its freedom from ambiguity, which has the effect of sharpening our skill in appraising the condition of our coins. While some may say that we have farther to go to reach the top rung of full agreement among persons who buy and sell United States coins, this newly established set of grades is a great advance. It is probably true that numbers are more precise than adverbs, adjectives and prepositions. Yes, this step is a long one.

Our progress in coin grading comes into sharper focus when we glance back to an earlier coin market. The expansion of condition classifications was brought about by economics. Great and rapid increases in the value of coins, especially those older than 25 years, made narrower grade distinctions mandatory. Much has been written about the price lists of 40 or 50 years ago when the Fine grade was sufficient for describing a coin that was worn, or just less than Uncirculated. We lived with such a broad term because coin prices were then low and the difference between used and unused was often less than a dollar.

When, after several decades, such a coin came out of the cabinet and was held under a strong magnifier, it faced six or more standard grades that had come into being. It now was classified as Extremely Fine and worth perhaps 100 times its original cost. Moreover, if the seller were at all persuasive he might get the buyer to declare it About Uncirculated. For such agressiveness the coin might bring an extra $25.00 or so.

No matter what the actual grade of a piece, it would be normal and expected that a buyer downgrade, or a seller upgrade, any typical coin. That's a human reaction, of course. Look that sentence over again. Buyer could be collector or dealer; seller could be dealer or collector. Horse trading is a very old game.

There has been impressive progress in our science and hobby. Where there were only hundreds of numismatists and dozens of dealers among them, in a few short decades the ranks have swelled to millions. Standardization has improved gradually, but we have been somewhat clumsy in our attempts at describing the condition of our coins. You may find interest in the following recap of an article published in the April 1967 Whitman Numismatic Journal. The problem which then prompted the report was the multiplicity of grading terms being used in retail price lists that was giving the hobby the jitters. While some sanity has returned in the description of coins among dealers, the general awkwardness prevailing over ten years ago has not been greatly lessened.

During January 1967 we paged through several numismatic periodicals to see how coins were being graded by retail dealers for mail order sale. We checked and recorded 54 lists, confining the study to regular United States coin issues. Our compilation revealed that those 54 dealers used a total of 28 separate conditions of coin wear, from Uncirculated to Fair. We believe it would be interesting and useful to reprint the list used by the advertisers. We noted that the extreme example, the extravagant user of grade terms, was one that employed 23 grades and split grades. The conservative example showed use of only five. Here they are:

Fair	Very good plus	Very fine-plus
Fair-about good	Very good-fine	Very fine-Ex. fine
About good	About fine	About Ex. fine
About good-good	Fine-minus	Extra fine
Good	Fine	Extra fine-plus
Good-plus	Fine-plus	Extra fine-almost unc.
Good-very good	Fine-very fine	About unc.
About very good	About very fine	About Unc.-plus
Very good	Very fine	About unc.-unc.
		Unc.

The average number of grade terms used by the 54 dealers was 10.3, probably a manageable range for any list.

We went a step farther and became enchanted with the different terms used to describe "uncirculated." As we went through the 54 advertisements, one by one, we jotted down each variation or degree of this state of numismatic perfection. Brilliant Uncirculated then as now was the most-used label, together with its variants. While our list of 29 degrees of uncirculated contained no new term, the difficulty, which makes the point of this report, was how to place these terms in their order of quality. The following is an attempt, but hardly of official importance:

Uncirculated	Strong BU
Strictly Unc.	Nice Strike BU
Nice Unc.	Special BU
Brown Unc.	Choice BU
Choice Brown Unc.	Choice Full Strike BU
Red Unc.	BU Full Luster
Sharp Unc.	Sharp BU
Sharp Strike Unc.	Sharp Strike BU
Gem	Full Strike BU
Unc. Luster Gem Strike	Sharp Flawless BU
Choice Gem Unc.	Selected BU
BU Soft Strike	Gem BU
Brilliant Unc. (BU)	Proof-like Surface
Strict Brilliant Unc.	BU Proof Surface
Nice BU	

The new A.N.A. Standards are designed to eliminate the state of affairs described in the report above. The most useful segment of the system, we believe, is the MS-60 to 70 uncirculated range. With three cardinal check points: MS-60 Uncirculated Typical, MS-65 Uncirculated Choice, and MS-70 Uncirculated Perfect, we have a safe and sane framework all numismatists can live with. The lower grades, too, are similar in concept and are just as workable.

As a general rule, uncirculated coins over 40 years old are most prevalent in MS-60 (Typical Unc.) condition, and are so priced in the Guide Book. Occasionally MS-65 (Choice Unc.) coins are available, but these are valued considerably higher. MS-70 (Perfect Unc.) specimens of older coins are very rare and always command substantially higher premiums. Many types of early coins are unknown in this condition.

Unless otherwise noted, recent uncirculated coins are valued in MS-65 (Choice Unc.) condition in the Guide Book when this grade is commonly available.

Valuations for worn coins in the Guide Book are for those grades of condition most frequently encountered by collectors. In most instances this is the "typical" level within each grade. A "choice" coin (with more attractive surface, color, or fewer blemishes) would be valued somewhat higher. The precise numerical grade level for the coins listed are specified in the capsule grading notes preceding each series.

For a complete study of the A.N.A. grading system we strongly recommend that every collector acquire and use a copy of the "Official A.N.A. Grading Standards for United States Coins." With its universal acceptance and use, we can relax until modern technology produces an electronic scanner to end all grading controversy.

The following is an example of a typical section of the A.N.A. Official Grading Standards book.

SMALL CENTS—FLYING EAGLE 1856–1858

MINT STATE *Absolutely no trace of wear.*

MS-65 UNCIRCULATED *Choice*
No trace of wear; nearly as perfect as minted except for some small blemish. Has full mint luster but may be unevenly toned or lightly fingermarked. A few barely noticeable nicks or marks may be present. Any unusual die or planchet traits must be described.

MS-60 UNCIRCULATED *Typical*
A strictly Uncirculated coin with no trace of wear, but with blemishes more obvious than for MS-65. May lack full mint luster, and surface may be dull or spotted.
Check point for signs of wear: feathers on eagle's breast.

ABOUT UNCIRCULATED *Small trace of wear visible on highest points.*

AU-55 *Choice*
OBVERSE: Only a trace of wear shows on the breast and left wing tip.

REVERSE: A trace of wear shows on the bow. Three-quarters of the mint luster is still present.

AU-50 *Typical*
OBVERSE: Traces of wear show on the breast, left wing tip, and head.

REVERSE: Traces of wear show on the leaves and bow. Half of the mint luster is still present.

SMALL CENTS—FLYING EAGLE 1856–1858

EXTREMELY FINE *Very light wear on only the highest points.*

EF-45 *Choice*
OBVERSE: Wear shows on breast, wing tips and head. All feathers are very plain.

REVERSE: High points of the leaves and bow are lightly worn.

Traces of mint luster still show.

EF-40 *Typical*
OBVERSE: Feathers in wings and tail are plain. Wear shows on breast, wing tips, head and thigh.

REVERSE: High points of the leaves and bow are worn.

VERY FINE *Light to moderate even wear. All major features are sharp.*

VF-30 *Choice*
OBVERSE: Small flat spot of wear shows on breast and thigh. Feathers in wings still show nearly full details. Head worn but sharp.

REVERSE: Ends of leaves and bow worn almost smooth.

VF-20 *Typical*
OBVERSE: Breast shows considerable flatness. Over half of the details are visible in feathers of the wings. Head worn but bold. Thigh smooth, but feathers in tail are complete.

REVERSE: Ends of leaves and bow worn smooth.

FINE   *Moderate to heavy even wear. Entire design clear and bold.*

F-12   OBVERSE: Some details show at breast, head, and tail. Outlines of feathers in right wing and tail show with no ends missing.

REVERSE: Some details visible in the wreath. Bow is very smooth.

VERY GOOD   *Well worn. Design clear but flat and lacking details.*

VG-8   OBVERSE: Outline of feathers in right wing ends show but some are smooth. Legend and date are visible. The eye shows clearly.

REVERSE: Slight detail in wreath shows, but the top is worn smooth. Very little outline showing in the bow.

GOOD   *Heavily worn. Design and legend visible but faint in spots.*

G-4   OBVERSE: Entire design well worn with very little detail remaining. Legend and date are weak but visible.

REVERSE: Wreath is worn flat but completely outlined. Bow merges with wreath.

LESHER REFERENDUM DOLLARS

Coined by Joseph Lesher in 1900 and 1901 at Victor, Colorado. Used in trade to some extent, and stocked by various merchants who redeemed them in goods. Coins were numbered and a blank space left at bottom of 1901 issues, in which were stamped names of businessmen who bought them. All are quite rare, many varieties extremely rare. Composition is .950 fine silver alloyed with copper.

	V.F.	Unc.
1900 First Type, no business name	$300.00	$600.00
1900 A.B. Bumstead, with scrolls	250.00	500.00
1900 A.B. Bumstead, no scrolls	225.00	450.00
1900 Bank Type (5 known)	——	——
1901 Imprint Type, no name	275.00	550.00
1901 Imprint Type, various names	$225-$750	$400-$1,750

FEUCHTWANGER CENT 1837

Dr. Lewis Feuchtwanger produced a metal which was really a variety of German silver consisting of nickel, copper and some zinc. He suggested as early as 1837 to Congress that his metal be substituted for copper, and made one-cent and three-cent trial pieces.

Values: Cent....... Fine $18.50; Ex. Fine $65.00   Three-Cent piece .... V. Scarce

**HARD TIMES
TOKENS
1834-1844**

In addition to the coins issued by the United States government, numismatists include in their collections the Hard Times and Civil War tokens which circulated as money during two periods in this country's history when nearly all the minor coin was hoarded.

The Hard Times tokens were issued in the period 1834-1844 and are the size of the large U. S. cent. They were generally struck in copper and are of two general groups: political tokens whose theme centered around President Jackson's fight against the United States Bank, and those issued by merchants (tradesmen's cards). Many different varieties exist. The most common pieces are generally valued at $2.25 Good to $12.50 Ex. Fine.

CIVIL WAR TOKENS — 1861-1864

Civil War Tokens are generally divided into two groups: tradesmen's tokens, and anonymously issued pieces with political or patriotic themes. They came into existence only because of the scarcity of government coins and disappeared as soon as the bronze coins of 1864 met the public demand for small copper change.

From the outset of the Civil War, government cents were insufficient in number, widely hoarded and worth a premium over all other currencies. As a result of this scarcity of cent pieces, private copper coins were issued by many individuals. Their wide circulation was made possible by the scarcity of copper-nickel cents and the public dislike of fractional paper money.

The tradesmen's tokens were issued by various firms to provide change and advertise the dealers' wares. They usually bore an implied or an explicit promise of redemption in goods or money. The second type was simply unauthorized substitutes for government coins, produced at a profit by private manufacturers and put into general circulation through various agencies.

These tokens are of great variety in composition and design. A number were more or less faithful imitations of the copper-nickel cent. A few of this type have the word "NOT" in very small letters above the words "ONE CENT."

Many pieces, especially of the tradesmen token type, were individual in device and size, representing any caprice of design or slogan that appealed to the maker. Some were political or patriotic in character, carrying the likeness of some military leader such as McClellan or bearing such inscriptions as "Millions for contractors, not one cent for the widows." An estimated 50,000,000 or more of these pieces were issued. Approximately 10,000 different varieties have been recorded.

The legal status of the Civil War Tokens was uncertain. Mint Director Pollock thought they were illegal; however, there was no law prohibiting the issue of tradesmen's tokens or of private coins not in imitation of United States coins. A law was passed on April 22, 1864 prohibiting the issue of any one or two-cent coins, tokens, or devices for use as money, and on June 8 another law was passed when abolished private coinage of every kind.

	Fine	V. Fine	Unc.
Copper or Brass Tokens	1.50	3.00	6.00
Nickel or German Silver Tokens	10.00	20.00	40.00
White Metal Tokens	10.00	20.00	35.00
Copper-Nickel Tokens	15.00	25.00	45.00
Silver Tokens	25.00	35.00	50.00

CONFEDERATE STATES OF AMERICA
CONFEDERATE 1861 HALF DOLLAR

The half dollar struck by the Confederacy was unknown to collectors until 1879. A specimen of the coin and both dies were found in the possession of Dr. B. F. Taylor of New Orleans, Mr. E. Mason, Jr. of Philadelphia purchased Dr. Taylor's specimen and the reverse die and later sold them to J. W. Scott and Company of New York.

CONFEDERATE STATES OF AMERICA — 1861

Five hundred genuine 1861 half dollars from the New Orleans mint were acquired by J. W. Scott and Company. The reverses were planed off and then restamped with the Confederate die. These are known as restrikes. The restrikes have flattened obverses.

According to records only four originals were struck. These were made on a hand press. Original silver half dollar planchets were used, as well as the original obverse die. One of the coins was given to the Secretary of the Confederacy Memminger who passed it on to President Jefferson Davis for his approval. Another was given to Prof. F. L. Riddell of the University of Louisiana. Dr. E. Ames of New Orleans received a third specimen, the last being kept by Chief Coiner B. F. Taylor, who sold it later as mentioned above.

Lack of bullion prevented the Confederate government from proceeding with any coinage plans that might have been made.

J. W. Scott struck some tokens in white metal using the Confederate reverse die and a special die bearing the inscription

4 ORIGINALS STRUCK BY ORDER OF C. S. A. IN NEW ORLEANS 1861 ******* REV. SAME AS U.S. (FROM ORIGINAL DIE SCOTT)

Confederate Reverse   Scott Obverse

	Quan. Minted	V. Fine	Unc.
1861 HALF DOL. (Ex. Rare)	4		
1861 HALF DOL. Restrike	500	$475.00	$900.00
1861 Scott Token, obverse. Confederate reverse	500	90.00	225.00

THE CONFEDERATE CENT

An order to make cents for the Confederacy was placed with Mr. Robert Lovett Jr., an engraver and die-sinker of Philadelphia, through a jewelry firm of that city. Fearing arrest by the United States government for giving assistance to the enemy, Mr. Lovett decided against delivering the coins to the Confederate government and hid the coins and dies in his cellar.

The original dies were later purchased by Capt. John W. Haseltine who made restrikes from the dies.

		Proof
1861 Cent Original (copper-nickel)	12	$3,500
1861 Cent Restrike (copper)	55	1,750
1861 Cent Restrike (gold)	7	4,500
1861 Cent Restrike (silver)	12	2,250

COINS AND TOKENS OF HAWAII

The first official coins of Hawaii were the copper cents of 1847 issued by King Kamehameha III. The five cent piece of 1881 and the eighth dollar piece of 1883 are patterns. In 1883 Kalakaua I issued silver dimes, quarters, halves and dollars bearing his bust and showing the Hawaiian coat of arms on the reverse. By 1937 most of these silver coins had been withdrawn and melted. The plantation tokens listed here were all used as small change on the Islands.

Ten Cents 1883

One Cent 1847

	Quan. Minted	Fine	V. Fine	E. Fine	Unc.	Proof
1847 Cent	100,000	$150.00	$175.00	$225.00	$575.00	
1881 Five Cents		800.00	1,200	2,250	3,300	$4,000
1883 Ten Cents	250,000	20.00	37.50	130.00	700.00	3,000
1883 Eighth Dollar (12½¢)						10,000
1883 Quarter Dollar	500,000	22.00	30.00	45.00	150.00	2,700
1883 Half Dollar	700,000	45.00	60.00	110.00	600.00	3,500
1883 Dollar	500,000	150.00	190.00	325.00	2,500	5,000

HAWAIIAN TOKENS

Thomas Hobron Token 1879

Haiku Plantation 1882

Wailuku Plantation 1871

Wailuku Plantation 1880

	Fine	V.F.	E.F.
Waterhouse Token 1862. Bust of Kamehameha IV	100.00	175.00	475.00
Wailuku Plantation Token 1871	60.00	90.00	150.00
Wailuku Plantation Token 1880	60.00	80.00	140.00
Wailuku Plantation Token, Half Real 1880	90.00	125.00	175.00
Thomas Hobron Token 1879	35.00	50.00	100.00
Haiku Plantation Token	45.00	75.00	110.00
Grove Ranch Plantation Token 1886	90.00	125.00	175.00
Grove Ranch Plantation Token 1887	125.00	150.00	225.00

ALASKA RURAL REHABILITATION CORPORATION
TOKENS OF 1935

These tokens were issued by the U. S. Government for the use of the colonists of the Matanuska Valley Colonization Project to supply them with much needed Federal aid. They were redeemable only at the ARRC stores. The "Bingles," as they were called, were in use only about six months during 1935-1936 after which they were redeemed for regular U. S. money and destroyed. They were issued on a basis of family dependents. Each token is the size of the corresponding U. S. coin with the exception of the one cent piece which is octagonal. The design is the same on both sides of each denomination.

Aluminum				Quan. Mtd.	V. Fine	Unc.
	Quan. Mtd.	V. Fine	Unc.	50¢ 2,500	$30.00	$50.00
1¢ 5,000	$12.50	$25.00	$1.00 2,500	40.00	75.00
5¢ 5,000	12.50	25.00	**Brass**		
10¢ 5,000	12.50	25.00	$5.00 1,000	65.00	100.00
25¢ 3,000	17.50	35.00	$10.00 1,000	75.00	125.00

PHILIPPINES UNDER SOVEREIGNTY OF THE U.S.

The 1903-19 issues were struck at Philadelphia and San Francisco. 1920 and after were struck at Manila. Because of World War II the 1944-45 coins were minted at Philadelphia, Denver and San Francisco.

Bronze

	E.F.	Unc.
½ Centavo 1903-08	$1.50	$5.00
1 Centavo 1903-36	1.50	5.00

PHILIPPINES UNDER SOVEREIGNTY OF THE U.S.

Copper-Nickel

	E.F.	Unc.
5 Centavos 1903-28	$1.75	$6.00
5 Centavos 1918		
Rev. of 20 Centavos		
(Mule) Fine $75.00	200.00	——

Reduced Size

5 Centavos 1930-35	4.00	11.00

Silver

10 Centavos 1903-06 ...	3.00	9.00
20 Centavos 1903-06 ...	3.50	10.00
50 Centavos 1903-06 ...	9.00	22.50
1 Peso 1903-06........	11.00	27.50

Size Reduced

10 Centavos 1907-35 ...	2.00	7.00
20 Centavos 1907-29 ...	3.00	10.00
20 Centavos 1928		
Rev. of 5 Centavos		
(Mule)	15.00	100.00
50 Centavos 1907-21 ...	3.00	11.00
1 Peso 1907-12........	6.00	17.50

COMMONWEALTH ISSUES

Bronze

1 Centavo 1937-44	.15	.40

Copper-Nickel

	E.F.	Unc.
5 Centavos 1937-41 ...	$2.50	$6.00

Copper-Nickel-Zinc
Same Type as Cop.-Nic.

5 Centavos 1944-45 ...	.20	.50

Silver

10 Centavos 1937-45 ..	.30	.60
20 Centavos 1937-45 ..	.55	.80
50 Centavos 1944-45 ..	1.25	1.75

COMMEMORATIVE ISSUES

Establishment of the
Commonwealth 1935

Gov. Gen. Murphy and Quezon

50 Centavos 1936.....	35.00	55.00
1 Peso 1936	55.00	110.00

Roosevelt and Quezon

1 Peso 1936	55.00	110.00

INDEX

INDEX — *Continued*

The following numismatic magazines are obtainable by subscription. They are published monthly or as indicated below. Information or sample copies may be obtained by writing to the individual publisher.

The Numismatist
Published by the American
Numismatic Association
P.O. Box 2366
Colorado Springs, Colo.   80901

Hobbies Magazine
1106 S. Michigan Ave.
Chicago, Ill.   60605
(Has a coin section)

Numismatic News Weekly
Iola, Wisconsin   54945

COINage Magazine
16250 Ventura Blvd.
Encino, California   91316

Coin World (Weekly)
P.O. Box 150
Sidney, Ohio   45365

Coins Magazine
Iola, Wiconsin   54945

The Canadian Numismatic Journal
Published by the Canadian
Numismatic Association
P.O. Box 226
Barrie, Ontario, Canada

The Forecaster
(Weekly economic newsletter)
19623 Ventura Blvd.
Tarzana, Calif.   91356

ARE YOUR COINS GENUINE . . .

Coin authentication and certification service is available at a fee through the American Numismatic Association. Coins must not be submitted without first requesting mailing instructions and a schedule of fees charged for this service. Inquiries about coin authentication should be accompanied by a self-addressed stamped envelope and sent to:

A.N.A. Certification Service
818 N. Cascade
Colorado Springs, Colorado   80903